INTERNATIONAL BEST-SE

JOZEF BAN

STOP DUBČEK!

THE STORY OF A MAN WHO DEFIED POWER

GLOBAL SLOVAKIA

Jozef Banáš
STOP DUBČEK!
The Story of a Man who Defied Power
(Documentary Novel)

Jozef Banáš
ZASTAVTE DUBČEKA!

Text © 2009 by Jozef Banáš
Slovak edition © 2009 by Ikar
Translation © 2019 by James Sutherland-Smith
Foreword © 2020 by Michal J. Kopanic, John Palka, Josette Baer
Jacket design © 2020 by Klára Štefanovičová and Mária Škuléty
Cover photograph © 2020 by Jan Lorincz
English edition © 2020 published by Hybrid Global Publishing, 301 E 57th Street, 4th Fl, New
York , NY 10022 USA and co-published by Global Slovakia, Bratislava Slovakia

Library of congress cataloging-in-publication data available upon request.

Paperback: 978-1-951943-24-0
Ebook: 978-1-951943-25-7

WWW.GLOBALSLOVAKIA.COM

OUR FUTURE IS GREATER THAN OUR PAST

Jozef Banáš
STOP DUBČEK!
The Story of a Man who Defied Power
(Documentary Novel)

Translated by James Sutherland-Smith

Motto: "Sparrows fly in a flock, the eagle flies alone."

The wing of a butterfly

"From my world, my friend Sášenka Dubcek left ... When they asked me what I would say about Gorbachev's election, I said he would have the same fate as him ... He is just as young as Sašenka when he gained power, but that they both have the same eyes as Christ had when he prayed on the Mount of Olives ... He once looked for me in U Tygra, but I was not there. If I had talked to him then, the conversation would have been a butterfly wing that would have changed his whole destiny and he would still be among us ... We met in the Castle during the Prague Spring. When he came through the wallpapered door, I was blind because there was a glow around the figure of Sášenka Dubček ... He is the first noble communist who also rules in the Christian heavens ... My guardian angel, cared for not only my soul, but also the soul of Saint Sášenka ... He was a hero and drank his cup of bitterness to the bottom ..."

Bohumil Hrabal

WHAT THEY SAID ABOUT DUBČEK

"The sun showed us its face to us for a moment. It was the Prague Spring, in which Mr. Dubček played such an important role before hope was so brutally destroyed. The expressions of this courageous attempt are indelibly embedded in our memory, and our inability to help you constantly weighs on the conscience of the free world."
Margaret Thatcher, Prime Minister of the UK Government

"I bow in deep respect to Mr Dubček's character and activities. I remember the Prague Spring until they violently broke it. We loved and admired those of you who over the long years refused to have their conscience silenced."
Francois Mitterand, President of the French Republic

"The death of Alexander Dubček has grieved me, but on the other hand, I am glad that one of the leading figures of the Prague Spring has experienced the moment to see with his own eyes how democracy spreads in Eastern Europe."
Bill Clinton, President of the United States

"Europe could have gone much further if Alexander Dubček had been allowed to continue his politics after 1968."
Willy Brandt, Chancellor of the German Federal Republic

"I am convinced that the breath of freedom that the Czechs and Slovaks enjoyed when led by Alexander Dubček became the prologue to the bloodless revolutions in Eastern Europe and in the Czecho - Slovakia itself. Again, they gave us an example, again their enemies took fright."
Andrej Sakharov, Nobel Peace Prize winner

"I feel respect for this man and bow before him. If we had all followed the journey the Czecho – Slovak Republic had begun, a journey of avoiding twists and extremes, I think we would be different, the world would be different. I value highly the dedication of the creators of the Prague Spring to democratic and humanistic values and their courage to end with fossilized stereotypes."
Mikhail Gorbachev, President of the USSR

"Why do I have on my helmet A.D. and 1968? My grandmother talked a lot about 1968, about what it meant for her, and about Mr. Dubček, whom she honoured very much. I really honoured my grandmother very much, too, and I believed her. That's the reason for Dubček's initials and that year."
Jaromir Jagr, ice hockey player

FOREWORD
Dubček --- The Smiling Idealist with a Dream

No Slovak is more well-known in world history than Alexander Dubček. He spear-headed the Prague Spring which attempted to "build socialism with a human face." In the short-run, his experiment failed because of the Soviet-led invasion in August 1968. But in the long run, Dubček challenged the world by attempting to show that a communist-led government could attempt to become a genuinely popular ruling party.

In this historical novel, Jozef Banáš aims to reintroduce Slovakia's famous histori-cal figure. *Stop Dubček!* is an introduction to the politician **and the person**. Originally published in Slovak in 2009, James Sutherland-Smith has translated the original book into very readable English so that a larger audience would become more acquainted with the Dubček story.

In a little more than a decade, Banáš, a former journalist, manager, diplomat, and politician turned novelist, has become one of Slovakia's most popular writers. And for good reason, for he has a flare for relating a story with compelling and lively prose. Using extensive research and interviews, the author combines his talent for writing with a vivid portrait of his characters. His fictional re-creation of conversations that might have taken place help liven the story, even though Banáš uses these dialogues to insert his own views about hypothetical situations.

In creating his portrait of Dubček, Banáš utilized scholarly studies as well the testi-monies, memories of Dubček's co-workers, friends, neighbors and people who came in contact with the former Slovak leader. He also provided a context by explaining essential historical background for readers, and included a useful bibliography of Slovak sources. While using the liberties of fiction in writing, he still managed to present a close-up picture of the personality of Alexander Dubček and his family life.

In order to understand Dubček and what he was trying to achieve, it is necessary to understand the man himself. While I was in Bratislava in May 1990, I enjoyed the rare pleasure and privilege of meeting Mr. Dubček, one of the great personalities of world his-tory. As an historian, it was awe-inspiring to meet someone of such stature and character. I walked right up to Dubček and introduced myself as an American historian of Slovak ethnicity. He greeted me and graced me with one of his famous Dubček smiles, and we began a conversation. What immediately struck me was his openness and candor, his genuine kindness, his easy and relaxed manner, and his eagerness to listen to others. I could sense that he cared about people, and he cared about me and my ideas. He made me feel important in those short few minutes, and I could better understand how he gen-erated a feeling of hope among Slovaks, Rusyns, and Czechs during those memorable days of 1968 and 1989.

This is what made Alexander Dubček great – his human side. His faith in the basic goodness of people lay at the heart of his vision of creating a better society. Dubček truly believed that socialism could work, but he also believed that democracy and socialism went hand in hand. And he thought that governing was about serving the people, and not the system serving just the communist elites. People knew that, especially Slovaks.

Dubček was a man whom anyone could approach, talk to, and most importantly, **he listened**. That is something lacking in many politicians, especially former communist leaders. Slovaks can surely take pride in having a leader of his quality as part of their history. And Banáš wants to share his story with the world.

The book begins with the life of Alexander's father Štefan in America, and over-views the family's dedication to socialism. It ends with the tragic death of Alexander Dubček after a car crash in 1992. Banáš disagrees with the official investigations and remains skeptical of the findings, but he has no solid evidence to back that up aside from references to Soviet communists fearing for losing their Swiss bank accounts and the deaths of others who were to attend the to present evidence of corruption at a Constitutional Court in Moscow. Similar to the rumors surrounding Milan R. Štefánik's death in 1919, conspiratorial theories about a sinister plot may continue to haunt the death of another famous Slovak leader.

No doubt, like Štefánik's passing, Dubček's premature death cost Slovakia a valuable and popular leader in the transition from communism. Since Dubček was the most well known of all Slovaks in world history, he would have been a prime candidate for President of the Slovak Republic. His reputation would also have gained Slovakia more favorable recognition internationally - perhaps even some empathy for the lesser known part of the country that split with the Czechs in the Velvet Divorce. With Dubček out of the way, it cleared the path for politicians such as Vladimír Mečiar, who tarnished Slovakia image in the 1990s. Mečiar would pursue more abrasive foreign policy toward Slovakia's neighbors and his administration became rife with corruption.

With his death, Dubček never had the chance to play a role in shaping a newly independent Slovakia. While the Czech Republic would have President Havel's notoriety to lean on, Slovakia lacked another personality with the worldwide stature of Dubček. In 1993, the new Slovak Republic would begin with a disadvantage on the international stage.

How will Dubček go down in history? Despite his failings and events that ended the Prague Spring and its ambitious reforms, he will always be remembered in a positive light, as an idealist who firmly believed in making a state of Czechs and Slovaks work. In this sense, he was increasingly out of touch with events of the 1990s that led to the parting of paths between Czechs and Slovaks. His death also symbolized the passing of the Czechoslovak idea and the birth of an independent Slovak state.

Some portray him as communism's chance to humanize a system that wreaked havoc with individual lives and abused power, yet at the same time, Dubček's experiment aimed to open up the discussion of how to best organize society, but ended before it ever had a chance to freely evolve and so there will always be speculation that he had been allowed to proceed, the course of history might have changed. Then again, the experiment might have collapsed as it did in the Soviet Union when Gorbachev tried to reform communism. It is very possible that Dubček's reforms might have been nothing more than a slower path to a capitalist system, the very system that communist despised.

Dubček will never be remembered as an original thinker, but rather a publicist and a man of the people. Over a half a century after Czechoslovakia's Prague Spring of 1968, we remember a man whose death touched not only Slovakia and the Czech Republic, but all people who profess to work for truth and justice throughout the world.

From the time of his failed attempt to mold "socialism with a human face," people throughout Slovakia loved Dubček and saw him as one of their own who had risen despite the terrors of Stalinist style communism. He will always be remembered as a warm man, with a cheerful smile and a firm belief in the basic goodness of the people. At the same time, he also retained a certain naivité about the possibilities of genuinely reforming communism into a humane system, if only given the chance. As Dubček himself pointed out in his autobiography, "Dreams rarely match reality. They tend rather to the ominous or the optimistic" (Dubček, *Hope Dies Last*, 15).

Whatever one's view of Dubček, one cannot deny his major historical role. No can one deny the genuine love he inspired among people and the hope he gave them for a brighter future.

A short anecdote helps illustrate this admiration. In 1982-83, during the heyday of the post-1968 "normalization," I lived in Bratislava as a young graduate student working on my dissertation. I used to frequent a small shop near the university library which sold tobacco and a number of other odds and ends. The saleslady gradually came to know me, trust me, and found out that I was an American studying Slovak history. One day she opened her locket, gave me a big smile, and showed me a picture of Alexander Dubček. That says it all. Dubček touched her and others, and gave them hope. And he himself never gave up hope, hope for a better future. This remains an important message to this day as Slovakia treads the difficult and twisted path from communism and continues to build a tradition of democratic evolution with an open society and a free market.

Professor Michael Kopanic, Jr.
University of Maryland Global Campus

FOREWORD
Dubček --- A Touch of Spring in a Czechoslovak Winter

Alexander Dubček was a remarkable man who rose from humble origins to head the Communist Party of Czechoslovakia. That alone would have been a significant accomplishment. However, Dubček's place in history far exceeds his stature within his own country. He was a key figure in the internal changes within the Communist world that ultimately led to the fall of the Iron Curtain, the end of the Cold War, the end of the East-West partitioning of Europe, and a realignment of geopolitical forces around the globe.

Dubček didn't do all this himself, of course. But he led Czechoslovakia during the time of one of the most important single steps in the whole process, the Prague Spring. He arrived at this position of leadership by first rising through the ranks of the Communist Party of Slovakia. He was a reformist throughout his political career, so his success in the Slovak party reflects something important—discussing reform at that time was permissible in Slovakia, more so than it was in the Czech lands. In fact, the 1960s was a period when Czech intellectuals, traditionally the leaders of intellectual life for the whole of Czechoslovakia, started to publish in Slovak periodicals because new thinking was more acceptable there than it was in Prague. In this sense, the Prague Spring as a movement within Communist society spoke with a rather Slovak accent! More than one historian has suggested that the term "Prague Spring" is a misnomer, and that identifying the whole thrust toward reform as the "Czechoslovak Spring" would be more appropriate.

Irrespective of what designation is most appropriate, this time of political liberalization had international ramifications. It culminated in one of the most dramatic moments in the history of the entire Communist period. In 1968, on the night of August 20, a quarter of a million troops from the Soviet Union, Poland, Hungary and Bulgaria (the so-called Warsaw Pact, though lacking members Romania and Albania) invaded Czechoslovakia, crossing the border at a multiplicity of points. They expected to fight for four days before subduing the country. Instead, Czechoslovaks offered only passive resistance, but this resistance lasted for eight months. Dubček was thrown out of office. He was not jailed, but he was pushed aside to a minor post dealing with forestry. The country entered a period referred to by the Communist Party as "Normalization," which is to say a period when party control was reasserted and the relative freedom of thought and speech implemented by Dubček was vigorously suppressed. Nevertheless, the memory of ideological resistance persisted in Czechoslovakia and formed the underpinning of the Velvet Revolution that finally brought down Communism twenty years later in 1989.

During the dramatic night of the invasion, I was attending a meeting of the Society for Neuroscience in Washington, D.C. This was a large and highly international gathering at which scientists from the Soviet Union were also present. The next day I rode with a few of them in an elevator, listening to them speak in Russian. It felt like they were the embodiment of what had just happened, the violent trampling of the legitimate aspirations of my own people.

One of the sessions I attended included Sir John Eccles, a Nobel Prize winner from Australia. Instead of sticking to science, he stood to ask that the Society issue a formal condemnation of the Soviet action. The chair of the session declined to act on this request on the grounds that the Society was a scientific, not a political, organization and that it was important to maintain good working relations with colleagues around the world in spite of political differences. He was probably right, but I found it moving to hear Eccles speak. The issue was a closely personal one for him, because he had recently married a colleague from Prague whose family was living through the invasion.

8

It was also very personal to my family. My mother's father Milan Hodža, like Dubček a Slovak, had been the prime minister of Czechoslovakia during the years 1935 to 1938 and was staunchly anti-Communist. This was one of several important points on which he broke with the country's president, Edvard Beneš, who had considerable admiration for the Soviet Union and even for Stalin. Milan Hodža's son, my uncle Fedor Hodža, was one of the leaders of the post-war Democratic Party of Slovakia and also a vigorous anti-Communist. In Czechoslovakia's first post-war election in 1946, the Democratic Party swept to victory in Slovakia with about two thirds of the popular vote, while the Communist Party received only one third. The Communists and their allies, however, gained a majority in the Czech lands and thereby in the whole of Czechoslovakia. This enabled them to secure several of the most important ministries in the resulting coalition government, including the Defense Ministry and the Interior Ministry which had control over the secret police. In a very direct way, this led to the Communist coup in February of 1948. As a prominent leader of democratic forces, Fedor Hodža felt he had to flee the country else his life would be in danger. In exile he devoted himself to anti-Communist political action within the émigré community, first in Paris and later in New York.

On the night of the invasion, he lay in a hospital in New York dying of lung cancer. My mother wrote about her brother's final days to the family in Slovakia in the following words:

He was probably never fully aware of the events of August 20, even though in July he was still following the events in Czechoslovakia very closely. . . I remember August 20 especially well, because that evening when I returned from visiting him, I was shaken by his condition. Later that night came the news about the invasion. . . Later, when I sometimes asked whether I should tell him what's new at home, he always just shook his head. You know, he was one of those who believed that a gradual relaxation would take place and he was extremely interested in domestic developments. . . He remained just as you remember him, gay, witty, content. He was truly a unifying force among our exiles.

So here was a life-long, politically sophisticated anti-Communist, who'd had to flee his home country to avoid arrest if not worse, believing literally to his dying day that just the sort of change introduced by Alexander Dubček would eventually come about in Czechoslovakia.

It is important to remember that history does not consist of disconnected events associated with the names of disembodied people. History is an uninterrupted stream, and it is lived and led by real people with visions and feelings, with flaws but also often with real nobility. The story of Alexander Dubček is a great example of this truth. How appropriate to have it told in this vivid book by Jozef Banáš, *Stop Dubček*.

Professor John Palka,
University of Washington,
Grandson of Czechoslovak Prime Minister Milan Hodza

FOREWORD
Dubček --- A Decent Human Being

Alexander Dubček (1921 – 1992) needs no introduction. He is known to the entire world, or so one might think. Jozef Banáš's novel *Stop Dubček!* begs to differ.

Already in the first few pages the reader is surprised to learn that little Shanjo (Alexander) was born in the house in Uhrovec where Ľudovít Štúr (1815–1856), the father of the Slovak written language, had lived as a child. Alexander was the second son of Slovak Communists who had returned from the USA to Slovakia in 1921, when the First Czechoslovak Republic (1918–1938) promised the returning emigrants democracy, the end of Magyar oppression, and jobs at home. The government was able to fulfil the first two promises, but not the last one. That's why the Dubčeks, soon to be disappointed by the dire economic situation in Slovakia, decided to move again. Together with friends and acquaintances, they founded the Czechoslovak Communist Co-operative Interhelpo and moved to Kirghizia, today's Republic of Kyrgyzstan, in 1922.

Many academic studies have analysed the reforms of the Prague Spring of 1968, focusing on the eight months of comparative liberty, the end of censorship, the opening of the borders and political debates that questioned the Communist Party's monopoly of power. Many studies have scrutinized the Soviet-led invasion of 21 August 1968 and the neo-Stalinist course, euphemistically referred to as Normalization (1969–1989), which the Soviet Union pressed upon the Slovaks and Czechs. *Stop Dubček!* is neither a work of fiction nor a scholarly analysis or political biography, but something in-between, a compelling account of the life of a Communist leader, who, unlike any other prominent European Communist, was loved by the citizens and became the embodiment and then the symbol of the Czechoslovak Spring of 1968.

Banáš's literary talent enables him to present the story of Dubček's life in a gripping fashion. The tempo of the narrative, the careful presentation of the historical events, the clear distinction between the realms of fact and interpretation make this novel a welcome new contribution, accessible to the English-reading public. *Stop Dubček!* is an 'unputdownable' account of Czechoslovakia under Communist rule, which will appeal to a wide readership. Its depiction of everyday life tells the social history of the period, against a backdrop of economic problems and internal Party power struggles, brought to life as if in a movie, with Alexander Dubček playing the male lead.

Banáš thoroughly researched every aspect of Dubček's life: the origins of his family; Alexander's membership of the Communist Party, which he joined when he was only eighteen years old; his participation in the Slovak National Uprising (SNP) of 1944, fighting the Nazis as a teenager; the painful death of his beloved elder brother Július; and Alexander's rise to power in the Slovak Communist Party KSS, which he would steer towards a path of reform in the 1960s. The process of reform began within the KSS and soon became a threat to the Stalinists in the Czechoslovak Communist Party KSČ in Prague.

Banáš's Dubček is a human being with positive features, but also failings, who experiences normal human joys as well as fears and doubts, who is prone to naivety and makes political mistakes.

Jozef Banáš became known to the Slovak and Czech public in the 1980s. He served as a Czechoslovak diplomat and was posted to East Berlin in the GDR during the regime under Erich

Honecker. In November 1989, still a member of the KSS, he gave a public speech in Bratislava, advocating regime change, expressing his support for the Velvet Revolution and Public Against Violence, the political movement that was the Slovak counterpart of the Czech Civic Forum. In those crucial moments, more powerful party members hid at home, watching TV in the company of home-made slivovitz.

In today's Slovakia, thirty years after the regime change, there are still those who despise Jozef Banáš as a long-serving member of the communist hierarchy or a cynical turncoat. Unlike other Slovaks in high politics or international business, Banáš has never denied his KSS membership. As a Party member in diplomatic services, he was automatically part of the *nomenklatura*. As for cynical turncoat: how would such a person have behaved after the regime change of 1989?

I can imagine two ways. First, he would have kept his head down, under the radar of the newly free press, and used all his contacts to network and make as much money as possible in privatization schemes of state-owned companies. Privatization of Communist national property in the early 1990s in Central Europe was a judicial grey zone, it was basically the Wild East. Everything was possible with the right connections.

Second, a cynical turncoat might also have stepped into the public arena, denouncing former Party members and styling himself as a concealed democrat, biding his time since 1968, as someone who had to toe the Party line to save himself, his family and friends from the scrutiny of State Security .

What a cynical turncoat definitely would not have done is get up every day at 5 am to write books that may or may not be successful.

That's why this novel is worth reading, an honest and truthful work, composed by an honest person who has nothing to hide about his past in Communist Czechoslovakia.

Professor Josette Baer
University of Zurich, Switzerland

I dedicate this to those who seek the truth.

Acknowledgements

I thank with all my heart all those who helped me in the creation of this book. If I have forgotten someone, I apologize. They are:
Anton Baláž, Teodor Baník, Jozef Brinzík, Ján Budaj, Valéria Csontosová, Dušan Čabrák, Martin Čukan, Milan Dubček, Pavol Dubček, Peter Dubček, František Dvorský, Igor Gallo, Alena Greppelová, Bohumil Hanzel, Róbert Harenčár, Jaroslav Hlinický, Dušan Hudec, Peter Ilčík, Michal Kováč, Jozef Križanovič, Drahoslav Machala, Pavel Pollák, Rudolf Schuster, Tatiana Šimková, Ladislav Ťažký, Michal Vojtuš, Jaroslav Volf.

Reviewed by: **Professor. Mgr. Ivan Laluha, CSc**
                                  Mgr. Stanislav Sikora, CSc

The publication of the book has been supported by the Literary Fund

Lest We Forget

I talked to Bohuš Hanzel, one of the close friends of Alexander Dubček, about my experience with him in the 1990s. In the Hofburg in Vienna, I apologized to Dubček in a friendly discussion about the year 1968. It was because I did not find more courage and strength at that time to defend him, together with other citizens of Czechoslovakia after the Soviet occupation, that I ate humble pie in public. Bohuš listened to me carefully. "I know how he reacted. He said nothing, just grasped your hand." It was exactly like that. Alexander Dubček gave me a firm handshake. I was a little embarrassed and consoled myself with the fact that there another fifteen million like me. Then, as if he knew what I meant, he added, "We have nothing to be ashamed of. Let them be ashamed." We Slovaks are a small nation and every small nation is made visible by outstanding individuals who have done something that crosses the boundaries of national limits. Alexander Dubček is undoubtedly the Slovak, of whom they know the most in the world. During my meetings with young people in Slovakia, I unfortunately found out that they know little of Dubček. This is why I wrote this book. I believe it will help us not to forget the man who brought us hope.

Jozef Banáš, summer 2009

TRANSLATOR'S NOTE

I'm grateful to my daughter, Katarína Šoltisová, for her corrections to my translation and for proof-reading the second and third drafts.

Below is a list of acronyms used in the text. I decided to retain the original Slovak acronyms rather than trying to create equivalents in English except, for example the USSR, which is now in the English language. Using acronyms means the reader doesn't have to read the sometimes cumbersome Communist titles for various party organs over and over again and thus have their patience tested.

BOI – Bureau of investigation founded in 1908 by Charles Bonaparte, a descendant of Napoleon's youngest brother and President Theodore Roosevelt's Attorney General. The predecessor of the FBI, it came into its own during the Red Scare of 1917.

JRD - Jednotné roľnícke družstvo – United Smallholders' Cooperative. The organisations throughout Czechoslovakia between 1949 and 1990 that collectivized and ran agricultural production.

KSC – (KSČ) Komunistická strana Československa – Communist Party of Czechoslovakia

KSS - Komunistická strana Slovenska – Communist Party of Slovakia

KSSZ - Komunistická strana Sovietskeho zväzu – Communist Party of the Soviet Union

Ludak – nickname of a member of the Hlinkova slovenská ľudová strana, the Hlinka Slovak People's Party from whose ranks the Slovak puppet clerical fascist government of 1938 to 1945 was formed.

NKVD - Narodnyi komissariat vnutrennikh del (Russian) – the People's Commissariat for Internal Affairs formed in 1918 to control such bodies as the police and fire service, it quickly became associated with the secret police in the USSR and was the forerunner of the KGB.

PRZR - Polska Zjednoczona Partia Robotnicza, Polish United Workers' Party – the Communist Party of Poland

StB - Štátna bezpečnosť – the plainclothes secret police in Czechoslovakia from 1945 to 1990

UV KSC - Ústredný výbor komunistická strana Československa – Central committee of the Communist Party of Czechoslovakia

UV KSS - Ústredný výbor komunistická strana Slovenska - Central committee of the Communist Party of Slovakia

VB - Verejná bezpečnosť – Public security – the regular police force in Slovakia.

Contents

PART 1

CHAPTER 1

THEY WEREN'T ON THE TITANIC

If Michal and Štefan Dubček had been richer, they might never have gone to America. Perhaps they'd have travelled on the new, super-modern liner, the Titanic, which struck a glacier on its first voyage from Europe to America on April 1912 and sank. In the same year, about forty thousand Slovak emigrants, including the Dubčeks, arrived in the dreamed of land on significantly cheaper ships. America was a republic, which was very tempting for Europeans, still under the thumb of kings and emperors.

Štefan went to America directly from Budapest, where he'd lost his job because he'd joined the Workers' Party. Michal had gone back to Uhrovec from Budapest, but soon he left with Peter Tomášek after his brother. Then Dubčeks settled in the northern part of Chicago, where there was a strong Slovak community. At first he worked on different construction sites as a carpenter, but in 1915, when he was twenty-four, he found a better paid place in the musical instrument factory. Most of the workers were Hungarians, whose speech was dominated by the effects of living in Budapest. In addition to his work, he also worked in the Workers' Party centre, attending a lessons in rhetoric and an English course.

Early in November 1917, Dubček and his friend, Griger, were caught by the police of New Mexico. Along with Quakers and many other opponents of war, they tried to illegally cross the border at Laredo to Mexico, where they wanted conscientious objectors not to go to war. The court imposed a fine of one thousand dollars or eighteen months imprisonment. Earlier, however, the judge had proposed to Dubček the suspension of this punishment provided he entered the army. However, Dubček said that he might be shooting at his Slovak and Czech brothers. He didn't have the fine and so he went to prison from which he was released shortly after the end of the war. He returned to Chicago and back to his original job in the musical instruments factory on Webster Street, north of North Avenue. He used to board with a widow with four children in an inconvenient room without a shower or toilet. But he didn't want to leave it because the rent was her only income.

In the Slovak Workers' centre he met the blue-eyed Pavlína, who, although five years younger than him, had been in America longer. She'd come to the United States with her brother, Michal, and her sisters Katarina and Antonia in 1909. She came from Bánovce nad Bebravou, from the same region as the Dubčeks and so they became closer in America. She worked as a cook and a maid in the house of a wealthy Jewish merchant and took part in the activities of the Slovak section of the Socialist Party. With Štefan, she acted in the amateur theatre in the Slovak Workers' Centre, singing in the Spevokol workers' club. The young people fell in love with each other and shortly after the end of the First World War they married in Chicago.

In the midst of post-war confusion little Július was born in December 1919.

In distant Russia on 15th March, 1917, Nicholas II abdicated. His throne and his power were taken over by the provisional government. Their work was ceaselessly undermined by the Petrograd Soviet military and smallholder representatives. Anarchy took hold of the country and this was used by the professional revolutionary, Lenin. The German government offered the Russian Socialists money and a safe passage from Switzerland to Russia with the aim of establishing a new government that would conclude a separate peace with Germany and release the German, Austrian and Hungarian forces from the Eastern Front. Leninist and Trotskyite Bolsheviks used the dissatisfaction of the smallholders, who made up most of the Czarist troops and instigated a state coup on 25th October, 1917, precisely on the birthday of the chairman of the Leningrad Soviet, Leon Trotsky. The provisional government was replaced by a Bolshevik government with Lenin at the head. Trotsky, the Foreign Affairs Commissioner signed a separate peace in March 1918 in Brest-Litovsk with the Germans. The German aim on the Eastern Front was successful. The Bolsheviks began the greatest social and political experiment in the history of humanity - the dictatorship of the proletariat.

On November 11, at 11 minutes past 11 in the morning, Germany signed a ceasefire in Compiègne Forest, which ended the First World War. In Germany, the Reich fell and the Weimar republic emerged. New countries had already emerged in Europe - Finland, Estonia, Latvia, Lithuania, Poland and on 28th October, 1918, also the Czechoslovak Republic.

CHAPTER 2.

ŠTEFAN, I'M STARTING TO WORRY

It was after the war, but the economic situation in the in the USA had not improved. Prices had increased two and half times compared with before the war. While the rich grew richer, the situation of the workers rapidly deteriorated. In order to escape this tough reality many people began to drink. The government responded to the break out of alcoholism by introducing total prohibition. It was a direct incentive to an emerging mafia to embark on the wholescale smuggling of alcohol into the country. Life in Chicago became dangerous. Strikes broke out and there was fighting in the streets. In July 1919, a US Communist Party emerged in Chicago which shortly after its inauguration Pavlína and Štefan joined.

The government of the United States began to fear that the example of the Russian Bolsheviks would incite its own proletariat. Members of socialist, communist and anarchist organizations became exposed to persecution. The United States lived in a period of what was known as the Red Scare.

"What do you say to this?" Pavlína entered the kitchen in a dress that Štefan hadn't yet seen on her. "Klara sold it to me. She tried it on and wasn't going to get into it. Isn't it nice?" the young mother asked, seeking praise from her husband, who had dismantled a neighbour's cupboard on the kitchen table and was reinforcing it. The kitchen stank of glue, but the wife did not object. Štefan occasionally repaired furniture and earned dollars to improve the family's poor financial situation. Two-year-old Julko sat on the floor and messed about with his father.

"You said you were going to the meeting of the Marxist circle."

"So I was. Klara brought me a dress. Don't you like it? "

"Even though you're beautiful in it, I just don't know if we've got the money for such things ..."

"Števko, I know we can't throw money away, but Klarika was giving them away almost free of charge and ... Well, I would like to look a little bit fashionable. I'm looking forward to trying that new dance. The Charleston. This is how it goes."

Pavla twirled on the kitchen floor for a moment. Then she went over to her brooding husband and caressed him. "I know the times are hard, but we only live once and ...". She sat down silently, her husband looking intently at her.

"Something happened?"

"Nothing. Nothing very serious."

"You're hiding something," Štefan murmured.

"You will have the opportunity to honour Štefánik ..." Stefan observed her without comprehension.

"You said the second son would be Milan ... Well, I'm in the family way ... Julko will have a brother ... or a sister."

She watched her husband cautiously as he had not shown any signs of enthusiasm. "Aren't you happy?"

"Indeed, I am. I'm looking forward to this," he stood up, hugged her and kissed her hair. ""It's just, I guess ... You know what's going on ... Read the Herald. There are powerful voices for Sacco and Vanzetti to get the death penalty. For what? They accuse them of murder, which no one has ever been able to prove! " Štefan snorted. "The real reason for this is different. The reason is that they're fighting against exploitation ... " Then he added softly. "Did you know that there are signs that my work is in danger through my membership of the Communist Party? Just think, Hughes called me."

"The owner himself?"

"Yes. Even though I've been doing it for six years now, with a break when I was in jail, he knew me as well as his own socks and he was always happy with my work, and we had a strange conversation. That I was punished for refusing military service, that I was in the Communist Party ... And then it came out of. He showed me a list of anarchists. We're both on it."

"Me an anarchist? My landlord, Mr Herzl, is very happy with me and has never complained about anything. On the contrary, you know very well that where it's possible he gives me a little extra money."

"Since the adoption by Congress of the Sedition Act, it is getting worse," Dubček said.

"I didn't want to talk to you, but ... in the evening, when you were at the club, there was a BOI guy ..."

"What! From the Bureau of Investigation? So, the cops are already coming to our home! Both Jánoš and Lojzo Kupka told me that they also came to them. What did he want?"

"He was quite decent, he asked who you do you meet in general, what you read, and so on..." Pavlina sighed. At that moment, Julko cried, his fingers stuck to paper that was sticky with glue so he couldn't tear them away. His mother took his hands and bathed them in warm water so the newspaper came away from his fingers.

"I'm starting to worry, Štefan. They have jailed over ten thousand people for their political views last year ... The newspapers are full of harassment against trade unionists and communists. They're calling for strict punishments and the liquidation of all anarchists. Števko, I ... I wanted to tell you that I was thinking about ... going back ... home ... This endless fear that they could put you back in jail ... Mama writes that in Bánovce things have improved ... " As she spoke she looked at her husband for his reaction. Štefan laughed.

"Well, I confess that I've been thinking about it, too, even though things don't look rosy at home. Many are leaving their homes. Today every fourth Slovak lives in America. "

"You're a carpenter and cabinet maker. You know English and Hungarian, you can find work at home. And I, too, will be able to do everything for us to live, "said Pavlína.

"The American Slovak writes that in Krompachy there was a riot against the reduction in flour available. Four workers killed and fourteen injured. It does not seem to be easy at home. God, my home ... Uhrovec," said Stefan. "I mean, I think of our house next to the gendarmerie station at Závodská. I dream about it. It's in the courtyard with a number of one-room houses whose shingle roofs are connected. The first belongs to Gylko's widow with her boys Jánko, Ondrej, Miško and Palo. What didn't we used to do with them as children. The second is Barták's, the third belongs to the Pavel family, but they've already built a new house at the end of the row. And then our house with a room and kitchen. In it Mum with me, sister Zuzka and brother Mišo. Um ... I remember how Rohlík, who was a nightwatchman and a gravedigger, was constantly driving us away from his apple tree... The last house belongs to Sečansky. At the end of the row a timber stack, a backyard, garden and our lumpy hill ... It tugs at my heart when I think of our valley ... Mama worked in the glassworks at the beginning, but when my father died, she went to work in the lacemakers'. And lord, the parish priest, Riesz, with whom I was under instruction ... " Štefan remembered and his eyes wrinkled up. His wife listened to him in silence, then added somewhat sadly, "I'm still crying for Banovce."

Štefan's dreaming continued. "Miško was under instruction to Rector Knepp. We were both able to ring the church bell, but I was brave enough to work the bellows on the organ ... All the boys were jealous ... Even the apprentice years with Master Hudec were good. Hey, no one in the whole neighborhood did better than him ... Lord knows how our house looks. My godfather, Trančík, writes that his roof has already gone ... "

"And perhaps not a single carpenter knowing how to put a house in order?"

"You're right. Roses won't bloom here. I have already talked about this to Michal. He also thinks that things are going to get hot here." Then Štefan stood up and resolutely gesturing as was his habit, he declared. "Okay, we'll go home."

He went over to his wife and gazed at her. He didn't realize that he was covered with wood shavings, many of which fell on Pavlínka's beautiful dress. "And when can we expect our Milan?"

"In November. And what if it's Pavlínka? "

"So she will be Pavlínka, but she will be born at home. But you're still dancing in those new clothes in America! Pavlínka, when I think that we're going home. We left Hungary and will return to a free Czechoslovakia ... " Štefan looked into the distance and a strange glint came into his eyes.

The Dubčeks returned to Uhrovec at the end of summer 1921. Miško found an apartment at Stážovec, Štefan found for Pavla and little Julko at the upper end by the Ondruškovs. Miško's Mariška was happy with her apartment but Pavlína did not like hers so Alexander Trančík prepared his cantor's apartment in the old Evangelical school. He did not live there as he had an apartment in a state school that was enough for a wife and one child. At the time no one knew that a man would be born in this house, the most famous Slovak in the world.

CHAPTER 3

THE BIRTH OF A LEGEND

On 25ᵗʰ September, 1921, the smoke in the Uhrovec Workers' Centre was cut through by fresh air. The dense fumes of smoke muffled the eternal smell of kerosene that had impregnated the planks of the floor. Jáno Zajac, a member of the mayoral council, amiably greeted lads who came from from Radiša, Miezgoviec, Omastina and even distant Kšinna. Due to the industrial companies created by the Zaivs, there were a lot of workers in the village. Next to the door, on the way to the latrine, a kite with amateurishly-painted hammer and sickle hung on the wall. The hall was suddenly buzzing. "It's them. The Americans. The Dubčeks". Štefan and Michal, accompanied by a socialist official from Bánovce called Balaśtiak, came into the room. They sat down behind the chairman's table.

"Comrades, citizens and friends. I see many faces familiar and unfamiliar to me. I hear you came from Radišá, Omastiná and Miezgoviec and even from Kšinná. My name is Balaštiak. Ján. This is comrade Dubček. Štefan and his brother, Michal. They've come back after some time in America. From Chicago. I now give the floor to Štefan Dubček."

"Good evening," said Štefan. "It's good to see that so many have turned up. It demonstrates not only our interest in public affairs, but also our worker and peasant strength. We've come to establish a branch of the Communist Party in Uhrovec in the Uhrovka Valley!" He sipped a soda water and watched the people in the hall. The view was blurred, but people nodded. Silently he thanked his wife, Pavlína, who'd told him in Chicago to join classes in public speaking. He smiled his irresistible smile, and people responded intensely to his glamour. "I and my brother, Michal, lived in Chicago for nine years. Many ask why we came back when so many others are leaving. Well, we were hungry. It's possible to earn more than here, but you are only a slave to the power of the wages and your only right is to keep moving on the treadmill."

"And is it different here?" exclaimed Paľo Kalač.

"That's what we're doing to change it! As you know, in Prague this year in May the stage was set for the Communist Party of Czechoslovakia, into which the Czech and Slovak left-wing social-democratic parties merged. In November the German, Polish and Jewish Communists will join us! "

"Bravo, fine, that's it!" shouts rang out.

"There is strength in unity," said Dubček. "A load of our men have chosen me as chairman of the Preliminary Committee of the Uhrovec Communist Party. If you agree to me being a proper chairman, get your hands up. If you disagree, please suggest some one else!"

"We agree!" sounded almost as if from one mouth and the raised hands confirmed Dubček as chairman. They then signed a charter as members of the Communist Party, Ján Zajac, Jozef Zelenčík, Michal Chúťka, Katarína Chúťková, Michal Dubček, Štefan Guričan, Ondrej Plagan, Jozef Jamrich, Ondrej Sokolík, Ján Repka, Pavel Kalač, Eduard Kahúň, Mária Turková, Július Turek, Ján Šimko, Pavel Barták and others. Some others shook their heads, thinking that this was something they had to think over. Dubček was pleased. He'd got more members than he expected. "The gendarmerie is coming, let's go! They're here!" Suddenly panicky voices called out from the street. The gendarmes, tipped off by some members of the local council of Bánovce, invaded the chamber. People fled. The Dubček brothers and Balaštiak couldn't even look up before their hands were in handcuffs. "You come with us!" The commander laconically ordered and took them out to where a police vehicle was waiting.

"What have we done?" Dubček asked.

"Under Law 134 of the Collective and Assembly Laws of the Imperial Criminal Code, this assembly is unlawful and illegal! You will be heard by a judge and he will decide what to do with you."

"Where are we going?"

"To Bánovce. Go!, Go! "It was the first time that Štefan Dubček had been arrested in free Czechslovakia The judge in Bánovce condemned him to three months unconditionally for disturbing the peace. However, the district notary Anton Barančík, a friend of the Dubček family, challenged his sentence and got it reduced to two months.

On November 27, 1921, he was released. He went straight to Mišo Konský, whom he chose to be the vice-chairman of the organization of the Communist Party. Also Jáno Zajac came on board as treasurer. As soon as they began to talk about to organizing the unity of the proletariat, the mayor, Gusto Trančík intervened without a fuss. Although he had no love for the Communists, he did not hinder their activities. They organized youth into a theatre association, a choral circle, and when necessary, they were always able to talk to both the local Catholic and the Evangelical priests. That is why the Communists also respected him.

"Štefan you're hardly out of jail and you're meeting! You should be home. Pavlína is giving birth" the mayor amiably reminded him.

"How's she giving birth. She isn't due yet. "

"Then your son was born at the wrong time," the mayor smiled and congratulated him. Štefan stammered a little, put on his lambswool jacket and dashed home.

His neighbour, Beta, and the midwife, Pavlová, flitted about the rooms, in and out of where Pavlína was giving birth. They knew in the house that Štefan had come out of the prison in Trenčin and was angry that the first thing he'd done was go to a Communist meeting. That was just like him. He always put others before his family. Alexander Trančík brought fresh water to the kitchen stove,

26

pouring it from a bucket on the clay floor, boiling it for the woman. At the same time, he was dealing with little Julko, who was yawning between his legs. "Give it a rest. Right now, he has to be at a meeting ... ", he mumbled under his breath.

"It's a son. Run for Štefan and get him home," Beta emerged from the room, smiling. "Tell him he has an Alexander! Give me a coin to put it in the bath for the little one. So he won't be short of money in his life. "

"Why Alexander?" Trančík wondered. "They said he would be Milan. After Štefaník ".

"Pavlína says they have talked to Štefan that he'll be Alexander. After you. By way of thanks". Trančík pulled out a twenty-haliero coin from a handful and handed it to Beta. Inconspicuously she put it into the warm water in which the new born was washed together with a pen so that the child could learn well. Trančík thought things over, at first wanting to object, but it was quite flattering for him that Dubček's second son would be named after him. "So you have a brother," he said, putting down little Julko and starting to whirl him round in the kitchen.

"Oh, his voice is powerful. He's going to be a good guy," Trančík observed with admiration to Štefan, who had just walked into the kitchen. The wooden walls of this house were the second witnesses to the birth of a man who was to be part of the history of his nation. On Sunday 10th December, 1921, little Alexander was baptized in the evangelical church of the Zaiov chateau by a dignified Pastor Karol Riesz. He did not know that he was baptizing a man who would outgrow Štur's glory, who was baptized in this same place by Štefan Šimko a hundred and six years before. Alexander's father and his godfather, Trančík, were a little bit merry, the stairway from the chateau to their house being frozen, so little Alexander was carried by the midwife, Pavlová. In the old Evangelical school there was a cheerful christening with the participation of family and close friends. His grandmother Dubček came as did Trančíkova, Štefan, Bela Trančíks and Paľo Trančík, who happened to be in Uhrovec. Unfortunately, his father did not stay for long after the christening and left with his brother Michal to Nové Mesto, where he founded a wheelright's collective. The families of the two brothers remained in Uhrovec. Little Alexander didn't know then that he wouldn't see much of his father.

CHAPTER 4

LENIN A MODEL FOR HITLER

On the 22nd January, 1924, in the huge auditorium of the Bolshoi Theatre in Moscow, the deputies of the Supreme Soviet assembled in solemn, formal dress. The auditorium was packed to the last place. The Chairman of the Central Executive Committee, Kalinin, sat in his usual peasant's cloak behind a huge presidential table draped with red cloth. The deputies knew what Kalinin wanted to say when he stood up slowly and invited people to stand. He could hardly articulate his words, his voice broke and he began to sigh in tears. Those present understood. There was a wail, sobbing and crying with some smallholders showing their sadness with a traditional, loud lament. Mass hysteria broke out in the theatre. Yesterday the father of the revolution, Vladimir Ilyich Lenin, died. Just a year ago in his testament he'd written, "Stalin is rough. I propose comrades that Stalin is recalled from his position as Secretary General of the Party and replaced by someone who differs in all respects from Stalin, who will be more tolerant, loyal, better behaved to his comrades and less moody. "

Stalin, however, had already ensured of his position when he seized Lenin's testament, reading it personally in the Central Committee and making maximum use of the fact that he criticized other members as well. He offered his resignation, which the committee refused. It was even rejected by his biggest opponents, who were at their maximum strength, but they hated each other so much that the temporary retention of Stalin was a reasonable solution. They threw away a final chance of ditching Stalin and saving their lives. The once Georgian Jesuit seminarist became the unlimited lord of the Soviet Union. He was a scrawny individual, a hundred and sixty centimetres, with a face pock-marked from childhood by small pox. His earnest wish was to have strong arms. But as a result of an accident in childhood, his left elbow had thickened, his right arm was shorter and his left was visibly thicker than his right. That's why he deliberately hid his right arm behind his back or slipped it into his jacket or uniform. *The second and third toes on his left leg were fused. In May 1924, Stalin politically ousted his greatest rival, Trotsky, whom he had assassinated in Mexico in less than two decades. He ruled the Soviets for almost thirty years.*

At the other side of Europe, on 20 December in the same year Adolf Hitler, a former unsuccessful painter was released from Munich Prison. He had been imprisoned for an attempted bloody coup against the Bavarian government. Previously, he had taken over a small proletarian group called the Deutsche Arbeiterpartei - a German workers' party. He added to it the attributes of national-socialism and founded the NSDAP. A year and a half after Lenin had renamed the Bolshevik Party as the Communist Party of Russia, Hitler founded his NSDAP. Lenin's model set out to build a mass-working party and take power. In these most important aspects, Lenin was Hitler's model. He wrote Mein Kampf in prison in Munich where in chapter four, in praise of the United States, Italy, France and the United Kingdom, he called for a struggle for living space at the expense of Russia.

In Germany, the gradual rise of fascism began in the name of German workers. Communism entered the Soviet Union in the name of Soviet peasants. In Germany, a hammer, in the Soviet Union a sickle, in Germany the NSDAP, in the Soviet Union the KSSZ, in Germany Schickelgruber with the "artistic" name of Hitler, in the Soviet Union Djugasvili, with the "artificial" name of Stalin. And between them Czechoslovakia.

CHAPTER 5

A HAPPY FUTURE

In the social hall of the Trenčín Workers Centre, Rudolf Mareček was trying to calm the exasperated voices of those present. He was the chairman of Interhelp-Czechoslovakia, a branch of the International Worker's Assistance, which had been established in Berlin on the after Lenin's call for help for famine victims in Russia. Štefan Dubček had read about Interhelp in an article in Pravda on Poverty in 24th January edition. Since then, thoughts about helping the young Soviet country had bored into his head. Rudolf Mareček had experienced the Bolshevik Revolution and the subsequent civil war in Soviet Central Asia, and from this, the idea of helping the young state, where it was the most difficult, had grown. Kyrgyzstan, for which members of Czechoslovak Interhelp were being prepared, was one of the most unfortunate parts of the Soviet Union. He'd come to Trencin with his lecture on 9th October 1924, the day after the shooting of striking manual workers in a textile factory belonging to the French Tiberghien group. "They killed one of the workers and injured four. They have no shame," said Štefan Škultéty, Dubček's neighbor, who had come along with him to the lecture from Uhrovec. "We do not even have money to buy bread," cried Baraník, one of two hundred and seventy workers sacked by Tiberghien. "Forty-eight hours of piece work gets us two crowns! And if somebody makes a tiny mistake, he's fined forty crowns. We lose more than what we earn! "

"Truly roses don't bloom for the poor ..." somebody sighed.

"This all the more reason to go to our Slavonic Russian brothers to help build a just society," Mareček continued with his peroration interrupted several times. "If you want to make things better in our country, you must first build socialism in the Soviet Union and from there it will come to us. In the Soviet Union shooting at workmen as here in Trenčín couldn't have happened!" Mareček declared hot-headedly. "Here, look at Soviet Central Asia. I myself shot these images," he projected his photographic plates on to a white wall. In wonder people admired the images of endless furrows of fertile soil, dense forests, long rows of orchards laden with apples and peaches, vineyards with ripe grapes and exotic caravan trails. Dubček looked at pictures that in his romantic and adventurous soul, created an irresistible longing to see this remote landscape and help build a new social order. Many had similar thoughts.

"I personally negotiated with senators of the Upper House of the Czechoslovak parliament, with comrade Václav Chlumecký, in Moscow with the Soviet government. With the Council of People's Commissars in Turkestan, I signed an agreement to send a Czechoslovak group Interhelp to Piškek. It's a city at the foot of Mount Pamir and a new railroad runs there. Our brothers are looking forward to seeing us! "

"Who pays the way?" someone asked.

"As yet we can't ask the Soviet side to pay us anything. We're coming to them on a voluntary basis. Help them and at the same time find a place for a happy future. "

"How much will it cost?"

"A stake in the collective is three thousand crowns," Mareček said more cautiously. There was a buzz in the hall.

"That means my cottage as it stands with both the shed and the barn," said some.

"Yes, friends, you have to decide. All those who go there have to decide once and for all. Sell your house, bring all your tools and useful equipment. From the money you put in, we'll buy building materials, machines, complex machine equipment, a locomotive, generator, tractor, machines, lathes, saws for woodworking and a metalworking workshop, equipment for making bricks, textile machines, tannery machines. We have calculated that the transport of all this material to our destination will require a dozen railway wagons. That's without taking into account the people who'll travel there." Mareček paused for a moment and turned a questioning gaze on the chamber before him. People were shaking their heads, considering, debating in groups, hesitating, making up their minds. "How have you decided?" he asked.

"I still need to talk to a woman and my sons," said some. "I'll go!" Dubček stood up suddenly, making his decision emphatic. "Indeed I'll go. I've been dragged down quite enough in my life, I want to live in dignity as a human being. A person counts there. Indeed I'll go!"

"We'll go, too. We have nothing to lose. We'll sell the cottage and we'll go. As we agreed!" said Štefan Škultéty.

"We'll go, too," said Baraník, as did Ondáš, Jamrich, Palinkáš, Páleník, Skalický, Gombár and others.

CHAPTER 6

AT THE END OF THE WORLD

Sunday, 25th March, 1925, was a gloomy, moody morning. A twenty-four wagon train stood ready to leave the station at Žilina. Numerous family members, acquaintances and the curious, had come to rejoice with the daredevils who were undertaking the first expedition of Interhelp, the "General Production and Consumer Cooperative in Zilina", and heading east. Three hundred and three men, women and children had no idea what was waiting for them. They didn't know that the information given to them by Mareček was nowhere near the truth. The group of lads, dominated by Štefan Dubček, was debating furiously. " There are as many of us those going to make the revolution," Ondaš laughed. "Three hundred people and fourteen wagons of machinery, including locomotives and tractors ..."

"And even a new, expensive Ford!" said the enthusiastic Baraník. "And that's what we bought from the collection we took."

The train meanwhile approached the Polish-Soviet border where it was necessary to transfer the entire cargo to Soviet railway wagons on a wider gauge. The transfer lasted one and a half days and then the train, which would become their home for the next three weeks, moved back into motion. The villages and towns that they crossed were mostly made of wood. Houses of manufactured brick were a rarity here, where there were houses of unfired clay. In Penza, a stop half way between Voronezh and Samara, local inhabitants recalled the Czechoslovak Legionnaires. The train crossed the Volga, continued under the southern foot of the Urals, the forests dwindled and instead a large steppe with strips of desert appeared. The Autonomous Republic of Kazakhstan began at Orenburg. Happy parents pointed out to their bored children caravans with camels moving behind the windows on the never ending desert. In Aralsk, a city on the northern shore of the Aral sea, they took a longer break. They went to the local market, their first encounter with an Oriental bazaar. A mass of yurts, large circular tents testified that Kazakhs still lived in the traditional nomadic way. Pavlína Dubček, who had been elected by the expedition as chairwoman of the women's committee, tasted millet kumis for the first time in the local bazaar. Beyond Aralsk, it seemed that the long section of sand and rocks, called the Hungry Desert, had no end, and a number began to voice their first disappointment. But then they came across the mighty Himalayan river, Syrdarja, which irrigated the valley through which it ran. Greenery returned, and with it optimism on the faces of people who had been on the train for twenty-two days.

At the dawn on the 24th April, the train arrived at the end of the railway line, which ended four kilometers before Pišpek.

"That's what the end of the world looks like," somebody said. Pišpek, which was to become new home for the Interhelpers, who looked timidly around was a stopping off point for itinerant nomads. It had been founded it less than fifty years ago as a Russian military fortress. Nowadays, with the name Bishkek, it's the capital of Kyrghizstan. There were about fifteen thousand inhabitants and it was located at an eight-hundred-foot altitude above sea level on the slopes of the Tian Shan mountains. Nearby and more distant tops of the mountains were covered over four thousand metres by a permanent layer of snow even in summer. With the help of a local soviet, of which Stefan Dubček soon became a member, all the human and material cargo was moved to the city. The arrival of Interhelp caused a real sensation among the inhabitants of Pišpek. Kyrgyzh and Tajik, who had never seen a car or a tractor, were very excited. As the car passed and the dust billowed up, the local people fled panic-stricken screaming "shaytan-arba" (four-wheeled devil). After a while, however, they became used to it and the relationship of Interhelp with the local population was very friendly.

The hard conditions they encountered on arrival forced the cooperative to work and live the first year as a commune. The first months did not pay a wage. There was a common canteen. They were living in partly demolished barracks built by Japanese prisoners from the Russo-Japanese War of 1904 and 1905. Holes in the roofs were leaking water, doors and windows were missing, the floor was completely rotten. Some decided to return. The primary task was the construction of family houses, workshops, planting and harvesting the first crop. Fortunately, Interhelp discovered water, which was lacking in the region. Since the brickworks was not yet complete, bricks were dried in the sun, strengthened with damp clay and straw. Lime or cement was absent. Everyone worked, even the children. There were four families in each family house. A family had their room, a kitchen and everything else was in common.

There was never enough food. A huge flock of sparrows fluttered around. They had nested in the ruined roofs of a nearby military camp. Their eggs were everywhere, so Czech and Slovak children improved their diet with sparrow eggs. These they ate raw, even in from the shell. Roasted sparrow meat became a treat for the ever-hungry children.

Julko and the little blonde Šanko with others helped feed the pigs as well. They rummaged through rubbish tips to collect food not meant for them . They were crawling with worms that stuck to the boys long after they'd left the rubbish tips. Most of the year they went barefoot. The skin on the soles of their feet became so tough that when some of them stood on a thistles, theye didn't feel it at all. Once, when the boys were helping their father to unload boards that had had come from Samaria at the station they saw wraith-like figures shaped like human beings emerging from a freight train. They were emaciated skin and bones. Many of them were carried out and directly piled in heaps for the wagons prepared for them. They were clearly not breathing. There were half-naked babies with their bellies distended.

"Dad, who are those people?" asked Šanko.

"They had nothing to eat and died from hunger."

"But they're fat," the boy said. His father was concentrating on loading timber. "Why did they die from hunger when they have big bellies?", he murmured.

"You do not understand yet. When you're bigger, I'll explain," Štefan said and was glad that the boy stopped questioning him. He had enough to worry about with his own thoughts in his heart and soul, looking at the heaps of carnage, which the wagonners, without batting an eyelash, cold-bloodedly, routinely, drove to common graves. He tried to say that according to official propaganda they were kulaks who'd refused to supply food to workers, but somehow he didn't want to believe it very much. He put up with the image of these unfortunates, but he could never rid himself of it.

34

The climate of Pišpek was very arduous. In summer it was 40 degrees Celsius during the day and dropped to minus ten at night. In the winter frosts were around minus twenty. Hygiene was weak, and there was no doctor in the expedition. An epidemic of malaria broke out in. On 20th June, 1925, the Interhelpist volunteers had their first death; nine-month-old Václav Pagáč. In the next three months, another twelve children died, by the end of the year, thirty. The gaunt horse, Golubka, who carried breakfast from lager to beamhouses and steppes, carried more and more coffins. Julko and Šanko luckily survived. After a fire in 1926, which destroyed some of the dwellings and workshops, many decided to go to other places or return to Czechoslovakia. Mareček also left them. Fortunately, another 600 member group came including two doctors and two teachers. One of them was the writer, Peter Jilemnický. But in 1928 a special arrival was the Ondris family from Chocholná near Trenčín. And with them came their thirteen-year-old daughter, the beautiful Anička. As soon as they arrived, they put Anička in the Archangel section, where for the first time in the history of Kyrghizstan sugar beet was planted by Czechs and Slovaks.

Eight-year-old Šanko, along with fifty other children, aged between seven and fifteen, romped through breaks in the school playground. The boys with Kirghiz and Tajik counterparts from a nearby school played football with a ball made from rags. They yelled at each other in Russian, Czech, Slovak, Hungarian, Tajik, Uyghur, Polish, Kirghiz, as they contested in skill. It was a strange Esperanto that was Only dominated by the Interhelp children and their friends from home. Once a six-year-old Kirghiz, Kurman, came in to the football players' attention crying unhappily and showed that somebody had placed a piece of bacon into his rags. "What is this? What is this? It's meat. And we don't eat meat. Meat is sin, meat is unclean. Who gave me this? ... What shall I do now ?! Allah will not forgive me ... "

The boys stopped playing and Šaňko with the older Julo went over to one of their Slovak classmates. "Kulifaj ... did you give him this?" Julo demanded. Kulifaj stood in silence and shrugged his shoulders, nodding. Julo took the piece of bacon from the Kirghiz boy and said to him in Russian, "Don't worry, Kurman, when we put the bacon down the back of his neck, your sin is gone!" He stuck the bacon down the back of Kulifaj's neck. The boys began to giggle, Kurman laughing. Kulifaj stood embarrassed then began to wail.

"When I ... I ... saw he was hungry ... so I brought him ... bacon." 14-year-old Anička, who had been watching the scene with the girls, came to Julo and Šano. The boys parted before them in respect.

"You should be ashamed of yourselves!" She looked at them both narrowly.

"But I ... I thought Kulifaj wanted to tease ..." objected Julko. Anička shook her head and went back to her classmates. Little Šaňko started after her and tried to grab her hand. "Anička ... Anicka, wait ..." She, however, walked sternly away, and Šaňko looked sadly at her. He whimpered. "Boys, boys ... kiš, kiš, shame ..." they taunted the boys, who in the meantime had gone back to their football. Anička looked over at him and smiled a little. He wasn't to know that in a few years her smile would belong only to him.

CHAPTER 7

A TENDER GENIUS

"We lag behind the advanced countries at about fifty to a hundred years. This difference must be eliminated in ten years. We should do it or be crushed," Stalin contradicted his previous views on the need to slow down the headlong pace of building socialism. "We are under imperialist siege and we have to be able to defend ourselves. The imperialists are preparing for a new war. The capitalist countries do not want lend us money, we have to find our own resources." The only resource was human labour. But there was nothing to pay for it. So the Bolsheviks invented a plan of genius. Collectivization. They forced peasants to the kolkhoz and sovakov and those who refused were declared to be kulaks. In the worst case, they died of hunger, in a better case they became wage and slave labour in one of the many labour concentration camps that grew in the

country at an unprecedented rate. Conditions were such that for people to work for free they had to be afraid. If they had known that only those who had actually committed a crime were in the forced labor camps, no one would have been afraid. Fear was a prerequisite for working without complaint. Collectivized farmers received a minimum wage in grain and money. The hardest working kolkhoznik received 247 roubles a year with which he could buy a pair of shoes. Slaves built one of the largest hydropower stations in the world at Dneproges, the giant White Sea Canal, the Turkestan - Siberian Railways, the Moscow Metro and industrial areas in Krivo Roga, Ukraine. In the Urals they built the Uralmašstroj, Berznikovsky and Solikamsky chemical factories. They built the Magnitogorsk mining plant, opened the Kuzbas basin, the oil fields in Baku, built the Kramator and Gorlov plant in Donbass, reconstructed the Luganský works for the production of locomotives, automobile plants in Moscow and in Gorky. At Stalingrad, a huge tractor plant was constructed in eleven months, a gigantic plant for the production of agricultural machinery was built in Rostov-on-Don. The Soviet Union turned into a huge construction site. Bolsheviks drove the country to performances it could never have achieved.

Stalin never went among the people, as he was afraid of them and only knew of their lives from bulletins bellowed from heated podiums,, "Work had become the duty of slaves under capitalism, but is a matter of honour, a matter of glory, a matter of courage and heroism." Slaves working in the Gulags (Gosudarstvennoje upravlenie lagerej) became an organic part of the Soviet national economy. Repression and violence, especially of the peasants, became a matter of course. In the country there were peasant uprisings that were mercilessly suppressed. In 1929 there were 1307 uprisings in the country with some 300,000 insurgents and in 1930 the secret police counted about 2,700 rebellions with a million dissatisfied peasants. Bolshevik punishment sorties spread horror and death whenever they appeared. The repressions had no ending. In December 1932 just from thirteen districts in the Kuban region more than eighteen million farmers were deported to northern Kazakhstan. After a long interval national partisans – basmachi - appeared in Kyrgzystan. After nightfall they attacked Soviet agents, army units and militia. Their victims swung from trees and telegraph poles. Similarly Red Army soldiers and Chekas hanged basmachi suspended from the same poles. The suppression of the resistance of nomad Kazakhs in Central Asia was even more brutal, in which a third of the Kazakh population perished. Naturally, as peasants were brutally persecuted and killed not in more ethnic Stalin areas, but in the more fertile lands the famine of 1932-1933 broke out, with about six million people perishing. The state systematically liquidated the church. While there were 130 bishops in the country of Czarist Russia, the Orthodox Church, at the end of the thirties, there 28 all cooperating with the state. In Moscow, from the original 800 churches, there were less than twenty in operation. They knocked down the ancient Church of Christ the Saviour and built an open swimming pool in its place.

Official propaganda worked at full stretch. Many world figures were affected. The Soviet Union was visited by writers such as Johannes R.Becher, H.G.Wells, Emil Ludwig, and Pablo Neruda. Wells wrote on his meeting with Stalin, "I have never met a juster, more sincere and honourable man ... No one is afraid of him and everyone trusts him." The dean of Canterbury cathedral, Hewlett Johnson, said he "leads his people into new and unknown roadss of democracy." The American Ambassador to the USSR, Joseph E.Davies, wrote about Stalin, "He is urging the liberalization of the constitution. His brown eyes are immensely wise and loving. Every child would like to sit on his lap." A well-known author of biographies of the famous, Emil Ludwig, wrote that he was a man "to whom I would entrust the education of my children without hesitation." Poet Pablo Neruda added, "He is a good-hearted and affectionate man, a tender genius."

CHAPTER 8

A REIGN OF TERROR AND ENTHUSIASM

By 1932, three more transports had arrived. On one of them was the editor of Rudé Pravo, Julius Fučík. 1,078 Czechoslovakia, Slovaks, Germans, Hungarians, Ruthenians created a whole range of activities out of the blue in Kyrgyzstan. The Interhelp team had been declared the best team in the Soviet Union in the year of their arrival. In their first year they built the first power plant in Kyrgyzstan, a textile factory in a year, then a smelting works, a factory for furniture, hospitals, they provided technical assistance for the construction of the Turkestan-Siberian railroad and built the Čustro dam. In the capital of Pišpek, renamed Frunze in 1926, they built a government building and a state bank and even a race course for a thousand spectators. In 1924, Interhelp contributed one fifth to Kyrgyz industrial production. Štefan and Pavlína Dubcek were also co-founders of the amateur theater ensemble, with which they studied comedy, Kubo of Jozef Hollý.

After the invasion of the Soviet Union by Germany, part of the team went back home, part remained in the USSR. Fifty of them fought in the ranks of the 1st Czechoslovak Army Corps. In December 1943, Interhelp was liquidated. The members were persecuted by Stalinism and sixteen of them executed as enemies of the USSR. Factories and plants were taken over by the Kyrghiz Ministry of Agriculture.

"I just don't understand. Asherbei was the best wine and fruit farmer in the whole region. He supplied the whole of the Pishpek Soviet with the best wine. But they will punish him, is he out of his mind?" Pavlína Dubček lamented and shook her head.

"They've already punished him. And because they punished him, he did what he did.. They imposed a new tax they could not pay. It simply couldn't be done. It was inconsiderately high. In order not to close them, they stopped farming. They sowed seed and grubbed up the vineyards ... " Štefan sighed and looked away. "Someone's going to get fed up here. This collectivization is madness. It'll bring the country to destruction."

"There is practically nothing to get at the marketplace. Not even basic stuff for our workers' canteen. I think I'll give up this work. I just don't like to go almost every day to beg for flour or potatoes. When we came here, farmers had all sorts of goods from the world. Now the market is empty. Everyone is hoarding for themselves. Julko has chicken pox and if the neigbour hadn't got some sympathy I wouldn't have the kumis which I apply to his face. Sometimes he'll give me whey for the boy, but eggs no. She says he hasn't got any. But I know she has, she's just afraid. I could make an yolk oil and apply it to his scabs.. The boy will be scarred for life... What are we going to do?" she sighed.

"During that training in Moscow they asked if I knew English. Well, how could I not know as I lived in America."

"You admitted you know English? Are you crazy? Why they'll denounce you as a spy ?! My God, Števko, have you lost your mind?"

"Wait, don't wail. Fortunately, I have not lost my mind. American Ford has introduced new lines in the Gorky car factory and needs someone to interpret for Americans who come to train Russian engineers. They offered me the opportunity to join the production line for the preparation of car interior that are made of wood and need carpenters and cabinet makers. I know how to upholster. And they offered a decent salary. So, what do you say to that?"

"What? What do I think of that? Are you going to ask again? Let's get out of this end of the world right now. You're not having me on, are you?"

"I don't joke about such matters."

"When can you start?"

"Right away."

"Let's fix the formalities and go. I don't want to stay here a moment longer. Štefko, if we stay any longer, I might go mad. Thank God to have such luck. Gorky, which is Nizhny Novgorod, the old capital of Russia with an ancient university. The boys will be able to study there ... God, such luck ... "

The Dubčeks moved at the end of spring in nineteen thirty-three to a rented house in the Ruttenberg district in Gorky. Ruttenberg, was inhabited exclusively by American carmakers. Churches had been built by Presbyterians and Episcopalians. Pavlína Dubček didn't go to work, she looked after the household. "We've got everything we need for a decent life," she happily declared on arrival. "If we're lucky enough to even get on the waiting list for a couch, it would be amazing. I don't know why, but all my life I've dreamed about a three-piece suite. I guess that dream could come true." The little Šaňko listened carefully to his mother and thought that when he was grown-up, her dream would be fulfilled.

Štefan got into car body interior section as promised. The boys, Alexander and Július began attending a secondary school over which the local Soviets had supervision. Schools attended by children of foreigners were at a higher level than others. They even learned the basics of English. Julo and Saša, as their friends called him, went to school together. As both of them excelled in sports, they soon became friendly with many Russian boys and girls. GAZ, the car producer, supported sports clubs. Alexander played water polo and football at the youth club and raced on the Volga and Oka rivers that flowed together through the city. In winter they froze and turned into a giant surface of ice on which boys and girls used to skate.

In Germany Hitler came to power and the boys' parents watched with concern the growing influence of fascism in Germany and in other European countries. Newspapers and radio constantly reported on Kristallnacht and other pogroms in Germany while broadcasting superlatives on the successes in building socialism in the Soviet Union. This is why the Dub
eks regarded the events that took place in the Soviet Union uncritically. After the strange murder of Stalin's closest associate Kirov, the chairman of the Leiningrad Soviet on December 1, 1934, in the strictly guarded Smolny Palace, Stalin personally travelled to the city to investigate the murder. After arriving at the station, he smacked the head of the Leningrad police chief, Medved, and brought Nikolaev to the Smolny palace. After being questioned why Kirov was murdered, Nikolayev fell to his knees, pointing to the officers of the secret police and shouting, "They forced me to do it!" The secret police leaped on him, and before Stalin's eyes, pounded him with their pistols into unconsciousness. Stalin had Borisov, the head of Kirov's personal guard, smashed by iron sculptures. Just for having carried out his orders. Among the top-ranking Bolsheviks, it was whispered that Stalin was afraid of his popular, young rival. And then it started. 40,000 people from Leningrad, who allegedly were involved in Kirov's murder, went to concentration camps. Kirov's assassination gave Stalin the heads of Bukharin, Kamenev, Zinoviev and other leading Bolsheviks. Everyone was sentenced to death by shooting. A reign of horror began during which

from 1935 - 1939 nearly five million Soviet citizens were murdered or died of hunger and exhaustion in the camps.

In 1935, Soviet and German began secret talks, during which Stalin allegedly asked Hitler to produce evidence of contacts of Marshal Tukachevsky with Hitler's generals. Hitler's "evidence" was delivered and Tukachevsky was executed after a short time. This was followed by another seven generals and thirty thousand officers and noncommissioned officers of the Soviet Army. All those who had worked in the party and with leadership functions before the party was dominated by Stalin. Of the 150 delegates to the 17th Leningrad party convention, only two survived. The purges in Moscow and Ukraine were under the charge of Yezhov, whom Stalin later shot, and Nikita Khrushchev. One of the main organizers of the purge in Leningrad was a certain Alexei Kosygin and in his beastliness in Ukraine his accomplice was a certain Leonid Brezhnev. At that time, the ten-year old Gorky student, Alexander Dubček, didn't realize that he'd be dealing with these Stalinist thugs in person in thirty years time.

"Dad, do you know what my grandfather is called?" Sasha asked his father, who was reading Pravda in the kitchen, at the beginning of 1935. "This is unbelievable," Štefan said over the top of the newspaper. "Listen to this. According to the latest results of the investigation into the murder of Sergey Kirov, the murderers Zinoviev, Kamenev and others went so far as to say that Zinoviev, while urging the assassin to commit the crime, wrote a controversial obituary on the death of Kirov and asked that it be published ... What do you say to that?" He leant over to his wife who was sewing laundry at her table.

"Well, what do I know. You say they are still investigating and the newspapers say they are murderers?"

"The evidence is already clear now that there is no doubt. The main inspiration and organizer of this band is the Judas, Trotsky. "

"He's been living outside the Soviet Union for a long time."

"Please, do you think there's a problem in organizing a plot over the telephone?" Pavlína silently continued sewing.

"Dad, do you know what my grandfather is called?" Saša said.

"Your grandfather? What's on you mind?"

"Do you know what he's called?"

"I know that exactly. Andrej. He died of tuberculosis. "

"No. My grandfather lives and is called Ilyich," Saša laughed.

"What's this about Ilyich? Don't I know what my father was called or not? He was glassmaker in a glassworks!"

"At school, we're told that Ilyich Lenin is our Grandfather and Stalin our father ..." Štefan laughed and looked at the son who had taken on a serious expression. "Some of my classmates had their actual fathers taken out of their homes without a single word and they did not appear again. They didn't even ask where they had taken them, because ... um," the 14-year-old Šanko thought. Then he put on an optimistic expression. "Our teacher said that this month is very important in my life, because I'm going to lead the newspaper display of Ilyich's grandchildren in our class ... It's a great honour ... In December, the whole class will become komsomol members ..."

"You don't seem excited," his mother said. Saša was silent.

"All of us are called this," Julko broke in. "We are Lenin's grandchildren. All pioneers are his grandchildren. But chiefly us. His brother, Alexander Uljanov, was born in this city. I'm already a Komsomol and I'm not going to show off!"

"In your place, I would be utterly silentl!" Their father was angry with the older son. "I was summoned by the local Soviets about you. Because of your brawling."

"There was no brawl. Us lads from Ruttenberg ran into boys from the port. What happened?" said Julo.

" I'll tell you what happened. One said you have seriously injured Sergei Vasilievitch Kormanov. His father filed a criminal complaint against an unknown perpetrator. But if I know Russian investigators, they will in short time knock on our door ... "

"I didn't hurt anyone. When they ran off, he banged his head on a candelabra and hurt his forehead. It's a lie."

"Lad, it doesn't matter what you say. What matters is what the investigator will say. And believe me foreigners are usually not in the right. According to Soviet laws, they can send teenagers to gaol ... " his father said. Pavlína was thinking that her boy could end up in a Soviet prison.

"Even they can't punish anyone without proof," she tried to object.

"My dear ... what do you know ..." replied her husband. "The Soviets have asked me what the sentence means 'I'm old, I don't feel well, I won't be here a long time', which my father wrote to me."

"Surely they don't check our correspondence!" Pavlína said in horror.

"Lads, go out and play. Go on ... ... " The boys reluctantly got up up and went out of the kitchen. "Here they check everything. Especially foreigners. Julko's teacher, Satrov, an older man came to me warned me in a friendly way that they were after the boy."

"But he hasn't done anything," Pavlina scowled.

"They know very well that he hasn't done anything. However, they need to make an example from among the young. That's what the school leadership has decided. They're one of the last schools in this city where no children have been punished. You understand? They haven't complied with the quota of juvenile offenders determined by the city's party committee. The grammar school director has resisted for a long time, but no more can be done. This ordinary prank of our Julo is very convenient. It exactly corresponds to the famous paragraph 58 of the Criminal Code. It saves a home-grown boy and yet shows that he isn't afraid to propose the punishment of a foreigner. Don't forget that Julko has American citizenship. And fifteen-year-old spies have already been sent to the executioner. The director has filed a proposal for his punishment and the investigators can visit us every day. It doesn't look good."

"What do you want to do?" She put her head her palms

"You'll go home with Julko as soon as possible. Best right now. "

"How soon? When? "

"How long will it take you to pack?"

"You don't mean it."

"I'm deadly serious. They're coming after Julko. It'd be best to leave tomorrow. They can be here after tomorrow!"

"You've gone completely mad. And where do we live at home? "

"At my brother Michal's in Nové Mesto. And I've already picked up the train tickets."

"But it can't done ... Just pack and escape before."

"Pavlína, we're wasting time. Who whom. Here no-one can be sure of anything!"

Eventually she hastily packed the bare essentials and the next day she and Julko made their way quickly towards Moscow. Events moved so fast that the promising Komsomol recruit, Alexander, only realized that something had happened when the flat was deserted and he had to take over some of his mother's housework. He ironed. cleaned and helped his father as he could. After his mother's and brother's departure nothing was the same again. Saša seemed to have matured prematurely. The flat was empty and cold. Similarly, life in Gorky became sadder. The young Komsomol didn't understand why they had to cut out the photographs of Tuckačevsky, Bukharin, Zinoviev, Kamenev and other revolutionaries from their history textbooks who shortly had been cited as examples for them. The idea that the executions could be judicial murder was so outlandish that no-one entertained it. The defendants confessed after bestial torture so convincingly that even the well-known writer Leon Feuchtwanger, who was personally present at the Pjatakov trial in his book "Moscow 1937", wrote, "There is no reason to believe that the trial is something drummed up or artificial." The builders of socialism didn't know that about a thousand people a day were executed in the Soviet Union.

The new heroes were Stakhonovites, workers who had almost supernatural working abilities. A miner from the central mine in Donbass, Alexei Stakhanov produced 102 tons of coal in five hours and forty-five minutes in August 1935, thus surpassing the usual level of coal extraction by an individual by fourteen times and creating a world record. Miners from France came to see him. Lincoln University in the United States asked him for a signed photograph.. Šaňko, like other Soviet pioneers and comrades, dreamed of the heroic deeds he had performed. When he read that Alexei Stakhanov had got a new apartment and a three piece suite shortly after creating the record, he thought he would be a Stakhonovite. A vision of a couch for his mother motivated him to excellent study results. When he sometimes received a letter from Anička from Bishkek, his happiness was complete even though He missed his mother and brother very much. Letters from home came less and less often and he felt that his father and mother were estranged.

The chances of Štefan Dubček being dragged off to the gulag were all too real. All the more so if his previous work in America, the epicentre of imperialism, had been known. His American citizenship was also an unwritten secret. Vojto Palúch, who had remained in the joiner's workshop in Pišpek, wrote to him that several friends had been taken to the camps and others had been shot.

When the Supreme Soviet passed the decree according to which foreigners had to leave the country or accept the Soviet citizenship, Štefan made up his mind. In November 1938, he and Šanko took the train home. In Čop on the border, he ordered his son to throw all their remaining roubles into rubbish basket. He wouldn't risk a possible arrest as the export of money from the Soviet Union was banned.

The Dubček's train arrived at Trenčín station exactly on the day of Šaňko's seventeenth birthday. When he looked at his mother and brother on the platform, he burst into tears with joy. His father was grave and merely greeted his mother with reserve. They lived for a short time in Uhrovec in the house they had repaired, but later they moved to a flat that their uncle Michal lent them.

CHAPTER 9

TO THE HEALTH OF ADOLF HITLER

The times in which the Dubčeks returned were bad. Italy, France and the United Kingdom, despite the Czechoslovak Mutual Assistance Treaty, signed a shameful diktat in Munich on September 29, 1938, which ordered Czechoslovakia to surrender to Germany a fifth of its territory and a quarter of its population. 800,000 Czechs were in the German Reich and 250,000 Germans remained as a fifth column in Bohemia and Moravia. President Beneš was forced to accept the Munich agreement and after a week, resigned on October 5, 1938. By destroying the Czechoslovak armed forces, Hitler released thirty divisions for future deployment in other parts of Europe. Less than a year after British Prime Minister Chamberlain, when returning from Munich, declared that he had saved peace for the world, Hitler began a world war by invading Poland. A week earlier, on August 23, the foreign ministers of Germany and the USSR, Ribbentrop and Molotov, signed a non-aggression pact in Moscow. After the signing, the German Nazi delegation got drunk in the Kremlin with the Communist leader, Stalin. Josif Vissarionovich proposed the health of a great son of the German nation, Hitler, and congratulated the leader on how the German nation loved him. Minister Ribbentrop embraced the Soviet leader and claimed he felt as if he were among his "Parteikameraden" in the Kremlin. They made jokes in bad taste about the Comintern, which had instructed all Communist parties to stop regarding Germany as an enemy and to declare Wehrmacht soldiers as German proletarians in military uniforms. On the basis of this, during the Nazi invasion of France, Maurice Thorez, the President of the Communist Party of France, broadcast on Moscow Radio calling on French soldiers not to resist the Germans. Despite the difficult situation in his own country, Stalin gave Hitler a million tons of grain, 800,000 tons of oil, 100,000 tons of aviation gasoline, iron ore, manganese and other raw materials. In return, Hitler provided him with aviation engines, plans for shipbuilding, submarines, torpedoes and mines.

On 2nd November , representatives of Italy, Germany, Hungary and Czechoslovakia met in Vienna's Belvedere Palace to solve the borders of Czechoslovakia with Hungary. The foreign ministers argued over and over again until their pencils were worn down, as a result of which the boundary lines have become increasingly harsher on Slovakia. Some towns were located on the opposite side of the original bordersas had been previously. The head of the Slovak delegation in Vienna, Jozef Tiso, was so shocked by the results of the arbitration that at first he refused to sign the protocol.

On March 13, 1939, Jozef Tiso and Hitler negotiatedin Berlin. "If you don't want Slovakia to disappear from the map of Europe, I'll give you the time until 12:00 a.m. to agree," Hitler said categorically. On the second day at 10:45 a.m. at a secret sitting of the Assembly of the Slovak Lands, Tiso presented the matter to the deputies. The formation of a Slovak Republic was voted by acclamation, no one was against. On September 1, Tiso's government despite their refusal forced soldiers to join Germany in the Polish campaign. Slovakia became one of the two countries that started the Second World War.

CHAPTER 10

I ARREST YOU IN THE NAME OF THE REPUBLIC!

At the time of Dubček's return, the Communists were completing the construction of an illegal network, since the party had been banned from October 1938. Štefan was hardly at home and his wife didn't ask where he was going. The network usually met in a small house on Jančova cesta in Bratislava near Bôrik. Štefan Dubček liked going to the meetings. Not only because of the illegal work, but also because of a sweet, young widow, Spaniková, whose smile lured him more and more. And her daughter, Elena, gradually came to love Štefan.

Alexander joined the Communists in the summer of 1939 when almost eighteen years old. Two leading officials, Benada and Osoha, vouched for him. Entering the Communist Party in 1939 was a courageous decision based on profound inner conviction. Unlike those who entered the Communist Party after February 1948, when the Communists seized power, the young Alexander sincerely believed in a socially just society and at that time the Communists were the only political force to oppose the rising fascism openly.

The Dubček family was known for its anti-fascist and anti-Ludak (the popular term for the clerical-fascist Nationalist Party) opinions and was therefore under constant surveillance by the police. Štefan was a courier for the first illegal leadership of the Communist Party of Slovakia, later its chief technical officer. Pavlína handed out leaflets hidden in a shopping bag in Trenčín market and the boys brought banned printing materials from an illegal printer to their flat. Constantly they had to find newer and newer hiding places. It turned out that the most trustworthy dead letter box was the dog's kennel. The police searched the Dubčeks' Trenčín apartment many times, turned everything upside down, even tearing up the tiles around the stove, but none of them thought of the dog's kennel.

Alexander, following the example of the older Julius, began apprenticeship as a turner at the Škoda Plant in Dubnica. In the factories, armour production was, of course, controlled by the Nazis, as it produced almost exclusively for German military needs. This was quite risky for a young Communist. However, work was in short supply and, although Dubnica was fifteen kilometres away from Trenčín, both boys were happy to have a job.

While in the Soviet Union Štefan and Pavlína had divorced and Alexander's father didn't live with his family. However, he sought to maintain good relations with his former wife and sons. Occasionally he came home. In the backyard behind the house where Pavlína and her sons used to live, there was a small workshop where Štefan repaired wheels for his friends or made other wooden goods.

This time Pavlína had called him to the table a number times, Štefan and his brother did not respond.

"Do you have to whittle your shingles right now? I thought you'd come to celebrate Saša's eighteenth birthday ..." she was angry at Štefan, who'd littered the entire yard with piles of shavings, splinters, wood chips and sawdust fallen to the ground from the shingles.

"There is nothing else for it. I have to manage to make two thousand pieces by Sunday. Havran from Vyšehrady is coming for them to the market in Bánovce. And the workshop is full of boxes that I made for a tobacco warehouse."

"Let's hope they'll come collect them ..." sighed Pavlína.

"Let's hope," Štefan lit up his favorite Memphis. "If not, at least you'll have something to heat with in winter ..." he teased Pavlína. Štefan and his brother, Michal, whittled the shingle that he produced at times when there was no contract for a joiner or carpentry work. He didn't like working on the shingles, but crowns were needed and so he'd take any work. Saša, as they used to call Alexander from the time of his stay in the Soviet Union, and Julko helped their mother with the hot-water boiling for large scale laundry. The radio played a favourite song of František Krištof Veselý, who had recently returned triumphantly home from Prague.

"Oh Šaňko, you could have waited to enter the Communist party," said his Uncle Michal all of a sudden. Probably Šaňko's recent joining of the Communists was at the back of his mind."Julo is smart. He's learning to use a lathe so that he can take care of his family in a respectable way."

 "And when did I have to enter?" He looked as if he were reproaching his brother. "So then, after the victory of the Soviet Union, when everyone will be rushing into the Communists? Now it's necessary to show courage," said Alexander, who from time to time twisted the radio tuner. "Wait, psstt ..." The sound of BBC radio could be heard from the ether - the beginning of the Josef Suk's Olympic march. Then came the well-known voice of Ján Masaryk, whose broadcasts from London they listened to regularly.

"We swear to you, our beloved country that we will remain faithful and that we will bring you back to freedom. We, the Czechoslovaks in England, know of your heroic resistance. In France and Great Britain our boys have entered the army, determined to sanctify your struggle with their blood. It is clear to each and every one of us that we can win victory with our allies. No son of a Czech or Slovak mother can accept a promise or gift from Hitler's hands ... "

At that moment, noise penetrated the kitchen; the dog barked, there were voices, shouting, boots stamping. Štefan Dubček sprang to the window, returned to the radio, quickly turning it off as the police and several members of the Hlinka Guard burst into the kitchen. They held their weapons at the ready. The Dubčeks kept calm as, they were accustomed to unannounced raids on their home. Julius and Alexander Dubček, however, recognised with shock one of the secret agents of the State Security Centre, their former Piškek acquaintance, Kulifaj.

"Kulifaj? You?" The two lads cried almost together. Their former classmate, Kulifaj, was silent as his commander ordered.

"Don't move. To the wall, hands over your head!"

"Me, too?" their mother asked, her hands raised from which water dripped.

"You too!" The mother put her hands on the wall on which her fingerprints remained. The commander motioned two agents to watch them. He indicated two more to search their home. He went over to Štefan Dubček, patted him on his shoulders and said, "Dubček, Dubček ... You don't let up. Well, as you wish. Kulifaj, put him in handcuffs!" Kulifaj obediently approached Alexander's father and wanted to handcuff him. "In the name of the Republic I arrest you!" At that moment Alexander and Július jumped on Kulifaj.

"You won't put handcuffs on our father, you dirty bastard!" Two of the guards jumped on them and with all their strength pushed the boys to the carpet and hit them as hard as they could on their shoulders with their batons. Their faces spasmed in pain.

"You're the dirty bastards, all of you who stand against the Slovak Republic. We'll settle accounts with you!" Kulifaj shoved his face into those of his former schoolmates.

"What are you arresting me for?" Štefan Dubček asked with a deliberate voice.

"For listening to prohibited radio and storing prohibited printed materials."

"Is Slovak Radio forbidden?"

"You've been listening to London!"

"You've got no proof."

"But we have." The commander went to the radio and turned it on. It was still tuned to London. The Commander laughed and dropped the radio. "And what's this?" One of the agents pulled out from under the sideboard an unfamiliar box and handed it to the commander. "Well, well ..." the commander began to read with relish. "Slovaks, Slovakia do not be fooled by the beautiful speechs of Tiso, Tuk, Mach and other bigshots. They have broken the republic, they let Carpathian Ruthenia and almost a quarter of our territory be torn off by the Hungarians. Not the Slovak, but the German rules Slovakia today,... "

"That's not ours. You put it there now. You're lying!" Štefan protested.

"Mr. Dubček, we decide who's lying!" The commander crushed the poster together with the others and turned abruptly to Štefan Dubček. "Let's go!"

Štefan put on his coat and went out to the courtyard. Behind their curtains neighbors peeped out. It wasn't the first time Dubček had been arrested. He didn't stop organizing new cells for the Communist Party, reproducing and distributing leaflets. He often hid in Bánovce, Topoľčany or with the Ondris family in the village of Velčice, near Trenčín. The Dubčeks knew the Ondrisov family from Piškek, where they were together in the Interhelp cooperative. The brothers would meet their father in secret although it was almost open knowledge in the village that Štefan Dubček hid out with the Ondrisov family. No one gave him away him. In the summer of 1941, a judge from Trenčín, on the basis of the Act concerning Crimes against the Slovak State, which the Slovak Republic had taken in modified form from the Czechoslovak Republic and that from the Austro-Hungarian empire, decided to force the Dubček family out of Trenčín. The court's decision was they should move to a village with no more than two hundred inhabitants so as to be as isolated as possible from people. By chance, Velcice at Chocholna, on the right bank of the Váh met this requirement. The Ondris family took Pavlína, with the boys living with the Štefan Zemánka family. No one minded moving to Velčíce less than Alexander. Once more he could meet the blue-eyed Anička, whom he had already known in Pišpek. She was now twenty-five and had grown into a real female beauty. They were friends. She told him that her father had died in the First World War at Pijav and her mother later remarried a fine man, Štefan Ondris, who loved her as his own. Although he was six years younger than her, Anička also felt that this cheerful, eternally smiling young man awakened something in her she had never experienced before in any man.

Chapter 11

LENIN FOUNDED THE STATE, WE HAVE PISSED IT AWAY!

On June 22, 1941, at 3.40 am Central European Time, the Chief of Staff of the USSR, Georgiy Zhukov, telephoned Stalin at his villa in Kuncev near Moscow, where he lived and worked. He worked and slept in one room. "Stalin, Germany, has attacked us." Stalin was silent for a long time, breathing hard. He didn't have any reaction. He didn't understand. The Ribbentrop - Molotov agreement gave Hitler's guarantee that he wouldn't attack the USSR, but could concentrate on the Western Front. Of course, military intelligence had reported the concentration of German troops on their mutual borders, but Stalin regarded it as a diversionary manoeuvre before the German attack on Britain. He didn't believe that a man who'd returned most of the territory that Russia had lost from 1918 to 1919 would betray him. In the spring of 1940 he'd given an order on Hitler's request to assassinate 15,000 Polish officers in Katyn. The Soviet NKVD, which until June 22, 1941 worked closely with the Gestapo, handed over to the Germans several hundred German Communists and Jews.

Zhukov's hands were trembling. Waking up the great leader in the morning, at half past three after a night of drinking, could be life-threatening. "Stalin, the Germans are bombing Kiev and Sevastopol." Again silence. "Do you understand, Comrade Stalin?" Zhukov raised his voice. Finally, he heard, "Come with the People's Commissar to the Kremlin."

Stalin suppressed an outbreak of hysteria and forbade his army to shoot at the attacking enemy. 149 Soviet divisions on the western border were not put on combat alert. On Stalin's orders officers went on leave. Even those commanders who disobeyed Stalin's order and started to defend against the Germans attacking them were executed by police commandos. On the first day of the Barbarossa operation, Goering's Luftwaffe destroyed 1,200 Soviet aircraft that didn't even take off. The Germans seized hundreds of thousands of Soviet soldiers in their rail wagons as 77 divisions moved to the western border. During the first weeks of the attack, three million Soviet soldiers fell into German hands. The Germans marched through Ukraine, Belarus and Russia almost without resistance. On June 24, an air alert was issued in Moscow at three o'clock in the morning anti-aircraft artillery opened fire. Soon, however, it turned out that the Air Force Commander had botched it and let them shoot down their own bombers returning from operations. On June 27 the Germans conquered Minsk and a shocked Stalin rushed to the People's Commissariat of Defense. He fell out with Zhukov and with Beria and literally threw him out of the Commissariat. As he walked out of the building, he said angrily, "Lenin founded our state, and we have pissed it away. Yes, comrades, pissed it! away"

Only when the German troops closed in on Moscow did the Soviet army began a counter-offensive in November 1941. The Slovak Republic, as an ally of Nazi Germany, declared war on the Soviet Union.

CHAPTER 12

LOVE IN THE SHADOW OF THE GESTAPO

Anička Borseková worked in the ammunition workshop in the Dubnica Armoury, from where she was later transferred to a department for forwarding finished products for the army. All the personnel in this department had limited movement outside the works and had to wear a red sash with black letters "Heeresabnahmestelle." Július worked in the armoury workshop and Alexander in the tool shop. On July 2, 1941, officers from the State Security Institute - USB appeared in the tool shop, accompanied by two secret officials from the German Gestapo. In the entrance hall hung a page cut out from Slovenské vojsko magazine with an army order from the Minister of National Defense, General Čatloš. "Soldiers! In the East of Europe, the greatest war of history has begun. The victorious German army alongside the army of affiliated states, including our army, has built a steel wall against the mortal threat endangering Europe as a whole and its civilization. Red Bolshevism has enslaved the great Russian nation and under the banner of false catchphrases on the equality of blood, suppressing even the most primitive demands for personal and religious freedom, wanted to embark on the conquest of Europe to confirm the power of the Red Jewish Commissars.

The leader of the Great-German Reich, Adolf Hitler, saw this danger and ordered his army to overcome it and bring Europe and the unfortunate Russian nation to redemption. A few days ago allied troops crossing the Russian border have been in combat. Almost all the peoples of Europe have with relief accepted the historic deeds of Adolf Hitler and stand by his decision. Slovak troops have crossed the border to join our German friends in the battle. The meaning of this battle is that, we can freely profess the faith in securing a lasting peace for our nation, which will bring us and Europe the blessings of work, prosperity and happiness."

All over the big poster, someone had written with a red pen, "Bullshitters, Stalin is our liberator, the Russians are our brothers!" Secret agents gathered in the room of the German security adviser, Richter, about the suspects. Richter was furious having only two months before been personally dressed down by the ambassador, Hans Ludin, over the matter of the red flag somebody had raised on Ostrom vrch above Dubnica. Jano Balko, Ernest Stanovský, Ondrej Sulak, Alexander Dubček, Anton Pätoprstý and several others from the secret party cell. Special production was under the continuous supervisiopn of the UŠB and Gestapo. Sabotage had spread as more and more information was received from the front that the shells or grenades did not explode. Some workers had "forgotten" to mount detonators. Anti-state slogans had appeared in the town and in other works, but in the armoury, something like that had also happened for the first time. There was evidence that, despite a strict vetting of employees, anti-state elements were also employed there. Both Alexander and Július belonged among them, all the more remarkable as their father was hiding in an unknown place.

"Wer hat das geschrieben ?!" the German agent made no bones about this with the men gazing silently at the ground. "So not one of you wrote it?" bawled Kulifaj, one of two Slovak secret agents. "If no one confesses, all four will be posted to the front! Whoever admits it will only be dismissed

55

from work. Think it over!" Then he added, "Have you got brains? You are here in locked down, you've got a decent position and instead of thanks you provoke! So who was it?"

At that moment, as if instructed, they took four steps forward with the word, "Me."

"Well, what do you mean? Are you making fun of us again ... " Kulifaj grinned.

"Alle mitnehmen. Sofort!" shouted the German secret agent.

"Nein. Sie brauchen nicht alle. Ich habe es getan. I did it," said Stanovský quietly and walked forward to the secret police.

"That's not true, I wrote it!" Dubček approached him in turn.

"Sie sind Komunist?" The Gestapo agent said to Stanovský. He shook his head. "Jew?" He asked in Slovak. Stanovský was silent. "Dann haben sie es getan! Kommen sie mit!" they stepped out. The others went back to work.

That day was ruined for Alexander. For the first time he'd dared to express what the majority of employees thought at the high profile arms factory. They disagreed with the Slovak army's participation in the campaign against the Soviet Union, but they kept silent and kept their heads down. He'd taken a few minutes when the guards in the hall were changing and exchanging weapons in a back room. He'd written the slogans on General Čatloš's order and inconspicuously returned to his lathe from the toilet which was in the hall.

On the way home from work on the train he sat in the compartment with his brother and Anička. After work they always met and embarked on the trip to Velčíce together. There were no words from him that day. He wondered how he could make amends as his Jewish colleague, Ernest, had taken the blame for him. He was indeed surprised when Stanovský appeared the next day at work. "That Kulifaj convinced them that it wasn't me and that they needed me here because I'm a specialist in cutting fine threads for grenade valves. He claimed that our department produces statistically the least defective products. And he gave the Gestapo his word of honour that it wouldn't happen again. So I'm here." Alexander couldn't help but give Ernest a strong embrace. The anti-state inscription didn't appear again. Dubček got Kulifaj's warning that if somehow it happened again, he and his brother would be the first to go to the front. And they would be lucky if something worse didn't happen to them. The worst happened to Tono Pätoprstý, who, after the outbreak of the uprising, was shot in the courtyard on suspicion of helping the partisans.

On 9th September, 1941, the Slovak Government issued Regulation No.198 on the legal status of Jews, known as the Jewish Code. Ernest Stanovsk7 didn't have a great appetite. He sat down during the midmorning break on a bench in the corner of the room silently reading an article in Ľudové noviny, entitled, "The Jews have been sliced off. The most rigorous racial laws on the Jews are Slovak. In a sense stricter than the German," the newspaper claimed.

Dubček noticed Ernest's frowning face. Although everyone had returned to the machines after the break, they were late. Ernest gave him the newspaper without a word. "We have to wear a yellow star. like cattle," he was breathing hard.

"You don't have to, you're excepted, you're still in the service of the state in the public interest ..." Dubček objected.

"To hell with Tiso's exception. It's an unbearable feeling, as your parents, brothers, friends are taken away... "

"What do you want to do?"

"I think I'm going to Štiavnica. Some Exnár is organizing a guerrilla group in the old mining galleries. Why don't you come with me?" He looked at Dubček. He was silent for a long time.

"It's bad. The Germans have conquered half of Europe. My brother and I were also thinking of this, but ... you know, my father has left and our mother is alone ..."

"Yet sooner or later we'll go to the mountains," Ernest clapped Dubček's shoulder. It would have been foolish to tell a friend that the main reason he didn't want to leave Velčíce was his blue-eyed Anička.

The Slovak Republic introduced childcare allowances, increased wages, social benefits for the elderly and the poor, a bonus month of wages and the Hlinka Slovak People's Party held an annual collection of Winter Assistance. People in Slovakia lived almost well in comparison with the surrounding countries. The Communists discreetly withdrew their slogans for the struggle for a new, democratic Czechoslovakia. The vast majority of Slovaks were satisfied with their own Slovak Republic.

When the police in the fall of 1941 broke a second illegal leadership, Štefan Dubček became a member of the third leadership of the Slovak Communists, with Jan Osoh and Jozef Lietavský. In July 1942, he was invited to a secret meeting in Bratislava, where he was arrested in the city park. He never returned home. Alexander was the only one in the family who visited his father in a prison in Nitra. He said that he wanted to marry and needed to ask his father's consent for the engagement. They allowed him a short visit, where they sat with a grill between them. Two policemen listened to everything they said. During the conversation, Alexander saw the police pulling with them a prisoner with the red band on his hand worn by political prisoners. The man's clothes were spattered with blood. When he saw his face, he recognized Ludoviť Benada. On February 19, 1945, Stefan Dubček, together with a hundred fellow prisoners, was transferred from the prison in Nitra to the Austrian concentration camp, Mauthausen.

CHAPTER 13

PERHAPS I WON'T RETURN

What's so interesting in there?" Pavlína looked over Julko's shoulder, who was reading the latest edition of a Slovak daily. Alexander sat at a table over a large map of Europe, plotting shifts on individual fronts. He was a little lacking in his father's experience. Above the village the sound of aircraft engines spread across the sky. It was a hot August day in the summer of 1944. they got used to the flights of unknown aircraft. Their mother emerged from the porch and looked for a moment at the sky. "The English are flying east. They say that in eastern Slovakia they've been dropping Russian partisans ... They've already bombed Bratislava, too," Julko read.

"Hitler is now in a tight corner and so our general has already shifted. General Jurech failed to move an entire rapid division to the Russians and they accused him of sabotage. The "Slovak" talks about a German tactical retreat ... cha, cha," he laughed aloud.

"The Germans are in headlong retreat since Stalingrad. At Kursk the Soviets completely crushed them. Peter Hron reported from London that there are 100,000 partisans in Ukraine and two hundred and fifty thousand in Belarus. Both in Greece and Yugoslavia there are the uprisings and the Italians have capitulated. The Russians broke through the siege of Leningrad, and the Americans and the English have landed in Normandy. It's going to happen in our country, too," said Alexander contentedly.

The twenty-ninth of August 1944 was a Tuesday. The heat bored into the shade and the fish swam in warm water. The tool shop was almost impossible to bear. Alexander was filing a piece, which was fastened in a vice, and wiping sweat from his forehead. Because of the noise, he did not notice when Anička came up behind him. When she covered his eyes he knew who it was. He was astonished; workers were not allowed to go to other workplaces without their supervisor's permission. The ammunition workshop, where Anička worked, was far away from the tool shop.

"What are you doing here?"

"Ondrej sent me. There are guards in the munitions workshop. They're looking for Jews, and they're coming here ... well, I have to ... " She'd told him and ran back. Alexander at once went to Ernest, who was drilling dug holes at a nearby work bench.

"Go by the back to the warehouse to Jožko Gul. Give him this key. He already knows where to hide you! "

"But I ... what's going on?"

"It's a raid ... run!"

Stanovský took the key without a word and had hardly made it out of the workshop when armed guards with dogs entered. The captain came straight up to Alexander.

"Where's your work mate?"

"I don't know ... Perhaps he went to the toilet ..."

"Then we'll wait for that Jew!"

"Mr. Stanovský is a Jew?" said Alexander pretending incomprehension.

"A Jew as you are a Communist, Dubček!", the commander gritted his teeth

"I'm not a Communist."

"If you're not a Communist, I'm not in the Garde ... he, he, he ..." the commander sniggered. At that moment a visibly disturbed colleague came up to him.

"Commander, Commander, we've got to stop this immediately and everyone must report to HQ in Trenčin!"

"And what's happened that's so serious?"

"They announced an uprising in Bystrica!"

The commander went pale, nervously licked his lips and in a trembling voice yelled, "Get all the men instantly formed up in the yard!"

When they'd left Alexander ran back to the warehouse where they'd hidden a radio. Ernest and several others had already tuned into Banská Bystrica. Lieutenant Colonel Mirko Vesel read in a serious, dignified voice, "On behalf of the commander of the Slovak army, General Viesta, as part of the Czechoslovak Armed Forces, I invite you soldiers to stand against the German occupation forces, to fight hard and inexorably against the alien invaders ... We call on the whole nation to take up weapons and to fight against our age-old enemies and their local minions so that all Slovaks in a free Czechoslovak Republic can arrange a life according to their will ... "

The train journey from Dubnica to Trenčín lasted that day an interminable time. Only Alexander and Anička travelled. Julko hadn't show up at the station.

"Will you go with him?" Anička asked.

"Yes," he said after a long pause. Though she was reserved she couldn't hold back her tears. Alexander gazed at her and stroked her hair. People looked at them as if they knew what was happening between the two young people.

What if you don't come back? It's war ... "Alexander was silent.

"If the Lord wills, I'll come back. It won't be long. The Russians are already on our border. "

"When do you want to go?"

"Tomorrow."

"Julko's gone?"

"I don't know. Probably. He said nothing ... I'll stop tonight ... "

The kitchen in the Dubček house in Velčíce had the scent of fresh jam doughnuts. A Bible lay on the table. Alexandra was surprised as his mother only read the Bible when her spirits were low. He went over and kissed her. She was surprised, as he wasn't demonstrative. Since Štefan had left the boys had been kinder to her, but were shy of embraces. He couldn't explain why he kissed his mother. "Are you reading the Bible?" he asked to avoid further speech. And there was silence. His mother shrugged. "Did you make cakes?" He asked another pointless question.

"Where is Julko? ... I hope nothing has happened to him," she asked, worried.

"Nothing's happened to him."

"Was he at work?"

"I don't know."

"You don't know? Didn't he travel with you on the train ...?"

"Yes, he came with us. To work. But not from work."

"Why not?"

"So. He didn't come to the station. He didn't come to me at the workshop either. We had a raid at work he could have been scared and escaped. He'll definitely be on the night train ..."

"I guess so ... And why are you so early from work?"

This time Alexander couldn't keep it up. He knew that his mother already suspected what he wanted to say. "Mama, I wanted to tell you ... um ... that I'm going to the mountains."

"Do you have some sort of youth outing?"

"Mama ... you know very well what I saying ... Golian today ordered us to resist the Germans. The uprising has begun ..." The plate slipped out of her hand, fell on the floor and broke. She took a broom and wanted to sweep up the pieces, but her hands shook so much that she could not.

Šanko knelt down and slowly, with his eyes lowered, he cleared them up. When he looked at his mother, her eyes were full of tears.

"Golian gave orders only to soldiers. You aren't a soldier ..."

"I promised you and my father that I'd fight for freedom. I've received instructions from Bánovce that my party group should join them and go to the partisans in Upper Nitra." Then this voice unexpectedly muffled and choked. All at once he couldn't utter another word. He wanted very much to say something beautiful and soothing. "Mother, Mama, there's no other way ... you raised me like this ... you've always said, if you see injustice, you have to stand against it!"

"So indeed, my son, you have to go ..." she stroked her kneeling son's hair as she shed tears. "Yes, you have to go, yet ... your father is in jail ... the two of you in the mountains ... I'll be here all alone ... and who knows if at all you'll..." her voice failed.

"Mama, yes, maybe I won't come back ... I don't know, but ... I know what I'm doing is right. My father wouldn't forgive me if I just sat at home ..."

His mother stood up abruptly, drew tears and began to pack a packet of sandwiches for Šaňko as if he were simply going on a school outing. When she put in the cakes into his bag he said, "You knew I would go ..."

"Knew, I know my sons. If you meet Julko, give him some of those cakes, I know you like them ..."

Šaňko put his bag on to his back, turned as he left in the doorway, smiled at his mother and was gone.

Early in the evening someone knocked on the window. Frightened she drew down the curtains. She made out the silhouette of a figure she knew. She opened the door and Julko entered. She couldn't say a single word. She'd already bade farewell to both of her sons in her soul and now one of them was standing in front of her.

"I'm sorry, Mama, I've been ... I came on the second train ..." he looked around the house seeking a glimpse of his brother. "Šaňko has left?" His mother nodded in silence. "Well, so ... at least I don't have to explain everything again. We agreed with the boys that they would take us on the goods train from Chocholna before midnight. And Šaňko where did he go? "

"He said he'd be in Upper Nitra. Maybe home to Uhrovec ... " she tried to smile.

"I'll also be going in that direction." As he packed up his things, she didn't say a word. She knew it didn't make sense and she actually didn't want to. When it got dark, the older son hugged his mother. It seemed to her that he had a tear in the eye. Some sort of unfamiliar feeling told her she was seeing Julko for the last time. But she stifled this gloomy thought, made the sign of the cross on her boy's forehead and quickly ran inside as if to stop him seeing that she was sobbing as if her heart would break.

CHAPTER 14

"KULI, WO BIST DU?"

In those moments when Pavlína felt alone she'd open her Bible, which strengthened her in difficult times. From the departure of her sons to the uprising she prayed for them every day. Likewise she begged God to protect all the worthy Slovaks. On the seventh evening, President Jozef Tiso broadcast on Slovak Radio. After him General Malar spoke to the soldiers. "Stop! Go back! Everything is rash, ill-conceived and it can bring to our precious Slovakia, as yet little damaged by war, the war where we do not want it. Why revolution, young men? Who is doing what to us? Haven't you been masters of your own house so far, are we sure that this will be the case in the future?" When the next day they announced in banner headlines that irresponsible elements wanted to destroy the Slovak state and to return the Slovaks to Bolshevik Czechoslovakia, many insurgents, as their initial enthusiasm died away, began to change their minds. "Better under the Germans, than Bolshevik bandits," said the men returning home.

In Trenčín it was said that most of the local workforce remained faithful to the Slovak Republic. Many lads turned in their weapons at municipal offices, barracks or threw away them into a ditch and went home. Pavlína Dubček was in two minds, wishing for her boys to come back and begging God to give her strength if they were taken from her. If they returned, she would be happy, but she'd never forgive them. From the moment the boys left, she'd listen to the radio with anxiety. She stopped strangers passing through the village or more often she'd go to the market in Trenčín in hopes of getting news of the Uprising, especially from the area of Upper Nitra which her boys had gone. Alexander Dubček was assigned to the Suvorov artillery unit, which operated under the Second Partisan brigade of Jan Žižka in Upper Nitra. It had about one thousand, five hundred men commanded by Teodor Pola. Dubček's unit supported the infantry in checking the German advance. All the time, he stayed with his friend Ján Bulko and former tool shop colleague, Ernest Stanovský. Three days after leaving home, he suddenly met by chance his brother, Julko, in the Nitra valley somewhere between Nováky and Prievidza. They embraced each other and the older brother gave the younger one of two pistols tucked into his belt. "Maybe it'll come in useful." Then, with his unit, he headed for Prievidza.

Anička Ondrisová, who often visited her, told her that a woman from Oslany had said that German troops had defeated the partisans' defence in Malé Uherce, killing about three hundred partisans, capturing their commander, Kapitan Weinhold with one hundred and fifty men and then occupying Oslany straight ahead. She prayed that her boys weren't among those slaughtered.

From the men coming from Bánovce, she learned that on 2nd September the Commander of the National Defense, General Ferdinand Čatloš, arrived in Uhrovec with a guide and surrendered to local partisans without resistance on Ľudovít Štúr Square. From there he was escorted to Banská Bystrica and later to Kiev.

On September 14 the radio reported that German troops had broken through the line on the river Nitrica and occupied Prievidza. On 19th October, units from SS Division 18 launched an attack on the territory in revolt from Hungary towards Brezno, as well as units from the SS Wittenmeyer division, prison sections from the cutthroat Dierlewanger, the SS Tatra Division and almost fifty thousand further experienced German soldiers. Special SS units trained to fight partisans had moved to Trenčin. In the battles the largely untested Slovak army, amateur partisans, confusion in command, a lack of co-ordination between Communists and the military command, Moscow's hesitation in helping the uprising meant that the Germans conquered the heart of the uprising, Banská Bystrica, two months after its start. A retreat of about thirty thousand soldiers and partisans into the mountains began.

Dubček's company, in which he had been for almost two months, moved mostly overnight. The fall of Banská Bystrica caught them near Kremnica. When they retreated to Handľova, the German tanks cut them off on the Sebedražie road. With Ján Bulko and Ernest he slid into a ditch on the other side. The rest of the group followed them soon after. There was a row of berry bushes along the road, beyond which at least a five hundred metre wide open space sprawled and beyond that wooded hills began. On their left side, a German tank stood in the place where two roads ran close with its tower slowly turning. It was clear that they could only save themselves by risking the open space to the woods. They had to be there before the German infantry arrived. At the moment they took a breath and began running, the German machine –gun chattered. They saw how the shots ploughed into the ground around them. Alexander felt a slight prick in his back, but he didn't slow down. When they'd gained the safety of the edge of the forest, he found that the wet patch on his back wasn't sweat but blood. In the woods his friends detected a wound, from a bullet which had luckily passed through his belt slowing it down. The bullet had entered muscle and hadn't touched his spine. They patched him up as best they could and marched on.

At the beginning of December, Alexander's decimated group reached Strazovské vrchy. There were only ten of them left. They were hungry and tired. Venturing out in the frost was dangerous, but a lit fire, visible for miles, was even worse. They walked along the shallow stream of the Machnáč towards Mníchová Lehota, where Ján Bulko had a relative with an isolated cottage. They thought he could hide them there and they'd recuperate for a couple of nights. They walked silently, their machine guns cocked in their hands. Suddenly the first of them raised his hand and indicated that they should hide immediately in the woods by the stream.

With his binoculars he tracked the ridge to the intersection of the paths where a German machine-gun nest was sited. Fortunately, the Germans hadn't noticed them. The partisans debated how to proceed. They had to get to the other side of the valley to the woods beneath Ostrá hora, which was between three hundred and four hundred metres away. They moved to a place where the distance to the nearest forest was the shortest, and they managed to ford the stream without the Germans noticing. Between them and the road there was a field with deep furrows. They decided to crawl through the furrows as close as possible to the road and run the remaining distance to the forest. The first three successfully crawled into the opposite forest, with Dubček, Stanovský and Bulko following. Under stress Stanovský had forgotten to take off his backpack. The machine opened up. They stopped crawling and lay in the furrows. They were trapped. The Germans were sure where they were and waited for their first move. It was at least minus fifteen Celsius and to hang on until dark was out of the question. The safety of the forest was two hundred metres away. After they'd taken off their backpacks the firing stopped. The Germans had lost sight of them, but they continued to watch the place, knowing that they couldn't lie there indefinitely. They knew they didn't have much time. The Germans had signalled their command, which would send out the nearest patrol. They knew only fast legs would help them. They stood up and dashed full pelt toward the woods. The machine gun started firing again. First Bulko went, followed by Dubček with Stanovský third. A few metres in front of the woods, Dubček felt a burning blow under the knee of his right leg. His boot filled with blood in a moment. He fell, but his friends quickly got him on his feet and scrambled into the safety of the forest. Dubček sat on a stump and Stanovský tried to pull off his boot and treat the wound. Suddenly there was a barking of dogs. A German patrol was approaching. They jumped into a nearby crevice, where they pulled leaves over themselves and waited. Two lines of German soldiers with four dogs and a number of Slovak Garde combed the forest. They knew the partisans must be in these places. The squadron commander guided them precisely with his transmitter.

"Die sind diesen Weg gegangen!" The words of the German commander accompanied by the barking of the dogs could be heard in the crevice. The Germans and the Garde approached the hole in which the three were hidden. Unless the wind suddenly blew away from the dogs that were now barking furiously, the Germans would find them, even it seemed from the sound of their hearts that were beating so loud that they might give them away. The soldiers slowly passed the hole. The last of the Garde had a long stick in his hand, which helped him walk on the slippery, frozen terrain. Suddenly he noticed the pile of leaves. Something made him go over to the strange heap. He pushed his stick into the leaves and felt something soft under it. He was wary. He poked around and observed the leaves were moving. Perhaps it was a fox burrow, ran through the head of the Gardista. He pulled away the leaves until he'd made an opening from which a human face looked at him. The gardista stepped back out, quietly pulling out his pistol. The face seemed familiar to him just as Dubček recognized him. Kulifaj. Alexander thought it was all over.

"Na Kuli wo bist Du!" yelled the German commander, who had gone further ahead. Kulifaj looked at Dubček. They were the longest seconds of Alexander's life. Then Kulifaj did something incredible. With his fingers he shoved back the leaves over Dubček's face and continued after the Germans. "I'm coming!" he answered the commander, striding after them and continuing to look for partisans.

They waited an hour or so for darkness to fall. The leaves warmed them up a little. Jan's cousin's cottage was only a kilometre away. Ján went ahead and after a while he returned and beckoned Alexander and Ernest to follow him. Ján's cousin let them stay overnight, but he didn't allow them to spend more time. Everywhere there were Germans, combing through isolated huts and cottages. If they found a strange person, they mercilessly shot the whole family and fired the cottage. In this way they burned down Poruba and Kosárovce, later Ostrý Grúň and Kľak, murdering 149 citizens.

When, Ján's cousin came to the shed to wake them up the three friends, almost shot him. They continued another eight kilometres through the densely forested mountains under Javor, the Vojtkova valley, the valley of the Sedličiansky stream and Cierný vrch in Selec where Ján's family lived. Alexander's wound was inflamed, it hurt, and he leaned on a strong stick. They came across another open space with a metalled road that was patrolled by German motorcycles and trucks.

They dodged back and forth. They took advantage of an interval when they were hidden by a bend in the road and crossed the road and field beyond it. In the stress of the pursuit Alexander forgot about the pain. It was very evident when they reached Bulko's house where they cut off his boot and pulled out his swollen leg. They treated him with herbs. They were hidden by a family with children which worried the men. They agreed that everyone would continue on their own. Ernest chose to go home to Bánovce, Ján stayed in Selce and transport for Alexander to Trenčianske Stankovice and from there to Velčíce was arranged. They hid him in the side planks of a threshing machine pulled by the white horse. Fortunately, the farmer knew a married couple, Katarína and Michal Petrov, who hid him in a backyard barn. They didn't have children and that made him calm. As Alexander saw Velčíce from between the slits between the planks his heart thumped with excitement.

In the meantime, his mother had moved back to Trenčín. Alexander communicated with her through Ondris, whose house was in the neighborhood. Anička was in almost constant attendance and looked after him along with her aunt, Katarína Petrová. She was an enormous, imposing woman and even German soldiers who from time to time strayed into her courtyard respected her. But Alexander's leg was inflamed. It was blue and red, swollen and infected. He was in great pain and needed a doctor. His mother found one, but when they told him what had happened he wasn't willing to take the risk. It was fortunate that he didn't turn her in. A few days after New Year in 1945, finally a Dr. Bojko, who had the reputation as an excellent physician and man, came from nearby Melcice.

"It's funny, you're called Bojko, which means fearful, and you're the only physician who has the courage to treat me," Dubček smiled.

"I'm not brave, I'm just a doctor and my duty is to help those suffering whoever it is."

"Yet, there's a risk in treating a partisan. If the Germans caught you ... Moreover, you're Russian," Alexander nodded as he lay on the straw pallet.

"My parents emigrated here after the Bolshevik Revolution in Nineteen seventeen. I was born here ... As far as I know, your father went to help the Bolsheviks in Russia ..."

"Do I have to understand that ... as a reproach?"

"No, I was just wondering about your father ... Bolshevik violence has not given and won't give anything good to the world."

"Is the liberation of Europe and Slovakia from the fascists Bolshevik violence?"

"Europe and Slovakia weren't liberated by the Bolsheviks, but by ordinary people ... Do you think Stalin's soldiers fought for Slovaks to be free? I know those reds well. They belong to Stalin. Their front is already in Moravia, Hitler will soon be gone from Czechoslovakia and what do you think will replace him?"

"Thank God!"

"Mr. Dubček ... you were in the Soviet Union for enough time to understand that it's a criminal regime."

"Doctor, forgive my question, but if you hate the Russians, why didn't you join the Germans?"

"I love the Russians. It's a great and heroic nation. I'm a Russian. But I don't like Bolsheviks and ... I'm sorry, not even you ... Communists. My people are cowed much as Hitler wishes ... I'm sorry ..."

"Why are you treating me then?" Alexander asked after a moment of silence.

"Because you're a man. A decent man. I don't understand why you joined the Communists. "

"Because we want to build a decent society for decent people."

The doctor attended to his wound for a moment. He nodded his head. "I'll go. It has greatly improved. In a week I'll come and see you again." He gave Dubček a broad smile, shook his hand and then took Anička's and kissed it gallantly. "Goodbye, Miss Anna."

CHAPTER 15

THEY SHOT JULKO

Although Easter Monday, April 9, 1945 was beautiful in Velčíce, the Easter water rites didn't take place. Shortly before lunch there was a loud explosion. The Germans blew the bridge over an anti-tank ditch under Vysoký Breh into the air. The last remnants of the retreating Germans crossed the village on a horse and cart, which they took from a butcher from Kochanovce Resek and retreated to Drietoma. For about an hour there was silence in the village. Then the soldiers of the Red Army marched in.

Alexander had been hiding out alternately with two families so as to be as prominent as possible. He knew, as far as he could work out from the distant rumble, how the front was moving. He thought how cleverly he had hidden during his almost half-year secret stay in the village. Only after the war he learned that everyone in the village knew about him. In Velčíce there were no traitors.

"Šaňo, Šaňo, there are Russian soldiers in the village," the enthusiastic Anička came into the hum. "Auntie Petrová, the innkeeper is feeding them in front of the tavern with slices of bread with fat and milk."

"So we finally made it."

"I saw them go through Močidlá, the street by the bakery and the paths between the houses beyond the backyard to the fields. The Town Crier has announced an order from the Soviet commander for people to get the shovels and go to fill the anti-tank ditch."

"I have to go to greet them," he stood up vigorously, but the pain in his leg didn't allow him to walk. He hopped and limped, pulling on his shirt and trousers.

"Where are you going? It's better if I get their doctor."

"I don't need their doctor, Doctor Bojko will see me. Oh, it was not long ago. I hope the Germans didn't get him ..." Dubček was concerned. In that moment brisk artillery fire broke down in the village. During the night it was hell. People who'd herded their cattle into the barn "pod Hajom" in the Chocholanska valley were right in the middle of the front line. When it was light, Grandma Fogltonová walked from her house to get water from a nearby brook with a white cloth on a stick and cried out, "Don't shoot, don't shoot, I'm a civilian!" Soldiers on both sides actually stopped shooting while she filled her the bucket. During that time, one or the other knew her and as the frontline changed, they alternately went to her for a drink. On 28th April, the 40th Soviet and the 4th Romanian Army began attacking German positions. This ended on 29th April when the Germans retreated to Moravia.

Shortly after Velčíce was liberated, the door in the room to which Alexander had moved burst open and Anička's enthusiastic father ran in. He was a little embarrassed to interrupt the young couple, but laughed and cried, "Your father has returned ... Your father has returned from Mauthausen!" No sooner had he finished, than a tall man consisting of skin and bone came into the room. He could only have weighed a maximum of fifty kilograms. Dubček could barely recognize him. "My God, Father?" He walked slowly and fearfully to him. Anička and her father left the barn. Štefan and his son stood embracing for a long time, both weak and tired. Finally, they sat down behind the table. They didn't know where to begin. Although they had last seen each other three years ago in a prison in Nitra so much as from many lifetimes had happened.

"I know everything about you ... I met your friend, Ján Bulko, in Mauthausen."

"I haven't seen him since we went our separate ways in Motešice ... Jánko saved my life ... When the German shot me, Jánko dragged me fifteen kilometres to Selec. And then he hid me on a cart in the planks and brought me to Velčíce. "

"I know ... he told me everything."

"How is he?" Štefan Dubček was silent. Alexander raised his voice uneasily. "Father ... how is Jánko?"

"A few days after he brought you here from Selec, somebody gave him away. He was brought to Mauthausen shortly after the New Year ..."

"How is he?"

"He died."

"What do you mean died?"

"Murdered. There, most of them were murdered ... A few of us survived by a miracle ..." He looked at the ground then looked at Alexander. "If we hadn't listened to Široký at the time, the men could have survived," he nodded angrily and raised his voice which expressed a grief he could not alleviate. "After the outbreak of the uprising, the commander of the prison in Nitra made us an offer that we should bind him and the guards and we could go. The guards opened the gates and some of them even came with us to the uprising. However, then came an order from Široký that the uprising was premature and the party would have nothing to do with it. We were told to go back to our cells and wait for further instructions ... Next day the Gestapo came ... I hope he gets struck by lightning ... How many men could have been saved ... In February we were transported to Bratislava, where we were loaded with a cargo and transported to Mauthausen. At Melka American planes started bombing, the column did not stop and so they levelled us to the ground. How I saved myself I don't even know. For two weeks I walked to Bratislava with the Russians beside the Danube. They caught us in Petržalka and brought us to the concentration camp ... Jáno Osoha stayed there ..." His eyes glowed. Then he calmed down. "How is your mother?"

"She lives in Trenčín ... by herself."

At that moment Anička entered with the old Telefunken radio in her hands. "Churchill spoke, Roosevelt and now Stalin." She plugged in the cable and waited a moment for the radio to warm up. When its magical eye was fully lit, she adjusted it according to its greenish light and Stalin's voice spoke: "Comrades, yesterday Germany surrendered. The great day of victory has come ..."
Father and son were listening to Stalin's speech with one ear, but they wanted to know more what was going on at home in the prison in Nitra and then in Mauthausen.

"And ... Julko, where is he?"

"Didn't Jáno tell you?"

"What is? Did something happen to him?" His father asked uneasily. Anička turned down the radio and went out.

"We met by chance as soon as the uprising started, somewhere in the upper Nitra between Nováky and Prievidza. We left for the uprising on the first day ... "

"What's the matter with him ?"

"We said goodbye and I didn't know it would be our ultimate farewell ... He had two pistols and gave one of them to me ... I have it with me all the time ... just in case ... It was 21st January he went with some others to reconnoitre near Látkovce. He had previously stopped at Auntie Hudec's in Uhrovec for his favorite bean soup. He came in a white topcoat as it was beginning to snow. He said goodbye instead of his usual 'see you later'. It was as if he knew something might happen. In the evening they went to Dolné Vestenice where they wanted to relax. There they were captured by Slovaks from the Edelweiss group." He stammered. "They say they were tortured and shot the other day ... They buried him in Vestenice. Mama was there."

Štefan Dubček nodded his head in silence and rubbed his palms in a nervous reaction. "Exactly a month later, on 19th February, I and the others were loaded on to the train and taken to Mauthausen. During the journey, the Americans bombed and nearly all of us died. A friend asked me if he didn't come back to take care of his wife. He was killed during the raid. And I ... I stayed with his wife. In Topoľčany ... How is Mama?"

A man's tear ran down his face, a father's tear. Alexander came over to him and embraced gently. A man bereft with large, protruding ears let himself be hugged like a little boy. The final words of Stalin's speech emerged from the radio, then the "Sojuz nerušimyj", the new anthem of the Soviet Union. Ondris and other neighbors entered the room. They saw father and son embracing as though at the Soviet anthem. They assumed they were tears of joy and joined them with enthusiasm. Ondris had brought a bottle of plum brandy. He filled everyone's glass. They drank the health of Stalin and Benes, spontaneously celebrating the end of the war. "It's over!", "We've won!", "Long live Beneš!", "Long live Stalin!"

CHAPTER 16

A COMMUNIST IN CHURCH

On Saturday, September 15, 1945, it was lovely in Kochanovce. In a cloudless sky the sun coaxed smiles on to faces. Father Ivan Kolesár came to the sacristy in the morning. After a long time there was to be a marriage again in the village. And not just any marriage. The son of a well-known Communist functionary, Stefan Dubček, was taking the daughter of Jan Ondris, Anička, as his wife. For the priest the wedding was all the more interesting as he had met the bridegroom during the uprising. He himself had fought in the uprising and so the young couple were even more agreeable to him.

He felt significantly better than the day before when he again had had a temperature and was afraid he wouldn't be able to unite the newlyweds. He'd caught a cold during a violent downpour in Trenčianske Biskupice, where he was sanctifying the refurbished hall of the Factory of Vehicles, which had been severely damaged by the bombing. The groom's father, however, had got hold of the miracle drug penicillin. It had been sent to Czechoslovakia by the United States government along with food, medical supplies and other military surpluses under UNRRA assistance. The ten-year-old Paľko Kubinec, who was helping prepare the necessary props for the ceremony, had on his feet the new "crocodiles", also from American aid. In his pocket hidden beneath his cassock, he had carefully hidden the white stripes of American menthol chewing gum.

Shortly before three in the afternoon, a Škoda truck with the bridegroom, the bride and a wedding company arrived. The car was borrowed from the former Kvasnica factory, where Ján Ondris, whom Anicka fondly called "Tatinko – Daddy", worked. In the vehicles there were benches and youngsters in traditional Trenčin costume were already merry. In those days weddings were usually transported in feathered carriages decorated with plumes and coloured ribbons. The vehicle was a complete novelty and sparked surprise among the villagers. Alexander and his mother and father at first came to the Ondris family, where the bride and grooms were taken away from their parents. His godfather, Alexander Trančík, gave a formal speech to his parents. He was a witness from the groom's side, the shoemaker Ondrej Ondris was the witness for the bride. Pavlína had come from Trenčín, his father from Topoľčany, where he worked in the furniture company, Sitno. Although he had already had a period of convalescence in Piešťany, long-term imprisonment and the concentration camp in Mauthausen had left their mark on him. The priest welcomed the arrival of the coach from Velčíce in front of the church and invited them in. Alexander walked in front in a shirt of hemp cloth tied round his neck with four white ribbons, with a waistcoat of black cloth decorated with a rich, colourful woollen yarn, in narrow blue "giaca" leggings with a rich, ornamental pattern made of black lace tucked into black leather boots. His jacket was made from a blue woolen cloth with embroidery around the edges and a thick row of silver buttons. In his hand he held a dark, woven felt hat with a high tilted brim and his boots glittered so that girls could use it as a mirror. There was no custom of having a young couple dressed in costumes, but Anička and Alexander loved Trenčín costume and from the moment they started thinking about marriage, they decided to wed in costume. Beside Alexander was the first bridesmaid followed, followed by unwed young men and girls as attendants and then Anička. Her hair was combed into a braid, the scarf on her head was tied behind with a knot, and hemmed with wonderful lace. The scarf and hair were fastened with a wooden hairpin. A pleated frilly apron "fjertuška ", a plush "kacabaja" jacket fitted round her waist, beneath it a white, pleated skirt and on her legs, like the bridegroom's, she wore leather boots. Over her arms she had a white napkin. Beside the bride was the best man and behind them the elder members both families; Dubček's parents, uncle Michal, the Ondris family. Neighbors and curious villagers occupied the benches at the back. in a place of honour were two of the oldest inhabitants of the village - Ondrej Tehlár and Ondrej Kováčech - their long hair greased with pork fat.

"Alexander, do you take Anna for as your wife?"

"I do."

"Do you promise before Almighty God that you will be a faithful husband to her, that you will never leave her, neither in fortune, nor in misfortune, neither in health, nor in sickness and that you will love and honour her all the days of your life?"

"I do."

"Anna, do you marry Alexandra as your husband?"

"I do."

"Do you promise before the Almighty God that you will be a faithful wife to him and never leave him, neither in fortune, nor in misfortune, neither in health, nor in sickness and that you will love him and honour him all his days?"

"I do."

The priest passed his stole round the joined hands of the newly-weds. "Those whom God has brought together, man wall not put asunder." Then Alexander and Anička exchanged rings made by the goldsmiths Pechanec and Gáborík, (P§G), from the gold cufflinks that their Uncle Michal had given as a wedding gift to them.

In front of the church, the village gossips shook their heads that a twenty-three-year-old bachelor ha a married a girl six years older than him. They knew, however, that Anicka and Šanko had long known each other and they wished them from the depth of their hearts for their love to last a lifetime.

CHAPTER 17

DEATH DOESN'T PICK AND CHOOSE

After their marriage, Alexander stayed with his wife with the Ondris family, but in a month they had moved to Trenčín, where his mother lived. He began working in a yeast works as a maintenance worker and operator of the distillation system. On the facade of the factory, beside a hastily written name "Droždiarne národní podnik", (National Yeast Works Enterprise) the original name of the factory - "Kornhauser and Hertzka" could still be read clearly.

It was before Christmas in 1947. Alexander was stubbornly repairing an appliance behind the table in the kitchen. Uncle Michal was gloomily reading the weekly "Time in the Pictures". The difficult atmosphere had been created not only by the political situation, but especially through the serious illness of their firstborn son, Peter, who was lying with severe lung inflammation in the Trenčin hospital. He and his wife alternated in watching over their boy. At the moment it was Anička and her mother-in-law. His uncle tried to lighten the atmosphere. He placed in front of Alexander the headline about Rita Hayworth, an American film star.

"After the flood of German film stars from the Slovak state, it turns out that the Americans also have pretty women, have a look ..." Alexander didn't listen to him properly. "Don't worry, everything will be fine ..."

"Must. We only go to half power. The pressure in the cooling system is constantly falling ... in my opinion it's in the regulator ... no one can figure it out. I'm just a toolmaker, but I guess I could do it ..." he tried to shake a screw out of the component that had loosened and was rattling somewhere inside.

"I thought everything would be okay with the boy," Michal remarked sharply.

"Hey, sure ... but we have to meet the two-year plan and it'll hardly work with a malfunctioning cooling system."

"It is said that you have offered old Hertz a job in the factory."

"They made him an offer," Alexander corrected him.

"But you can also decide there!"

"Me? I am only a member of the organization of the Communist Party."

"It's just this, giving somebody a magnanimous opportunity to work in a factory they owned before," said his uncle. "It seems to me that you communists are becoming more and more presumptuous. I'm sorry, I do not mean you, but I can see what's going on. I don't like what is happening to the Democratic Party. All those accusations about anti-state conspiracies are thought up on the orders of Prague, which your Široky and Husák are doing in Slovakia. It's said that Husák and Gottwald and his wife were enjoying themselves in Mori's villa at Strbske Pleso with Gypsy music and they've decided on the resignation of the Communists from the Commission of Representatives. I don't like it. In our tailor cooperative, people are afraid of nationalization. But I can tell you that if they bring me a nationalization decree, I'll wipe my arse with it. I didn't put in all my savings into this cooperative so that somebody can now come and stole it from me. I'll throttle anyone with my own hands who lays a finger on my hard-won property!"

"Uncle, you aren't an exploiter. We all know that you've carved out that tailor's cooperative. It's not going to be nationalized. "

"I have to get hold of that penicillin," his uncle's hand touched him.

"Even if he had it, the doctor couldn't give it to him, he isn't even a month old."

"The boy will hang on. Well, keep your head up. You must have faith, "said Michal to his nephew. He swung up a wickerwork pram. "How do you like it? I got it from Gizka the neighbor. She gratefully exchanged it for the suit I made for her husband."

"Uncle, you've done so much for me ... You're like a father to me ... Even the wedding in Velčíce it was actually you ... even the wedding rings, thank you so much for your help ..."

A sombre Pavlína came into the kitchen, brushing off her soaking wet coat in silence. Outside, rain fell with snow. "So how is he?" Alexander stood up and looked at her. He and his uncle stood in tense expectation. She sat down, tears streaming down her face. She walked over to Alexander and hugged him tightly.

"Is he alive?"

"Death does not pick and choose ... Petko died ..."

CHAPTER 18

DEMOCRATS FALL OUT OF THE WINDOW

On February 25, 1948, at 4 pm Alexander Dubček sat with three other members of the "Action Committee for the Cleansing of Mass Organizations of Reaction", behind the chair in a room at the national enterprise Droždiarne – Kvasný priemysel. The portraits of Stalin and Beneš hung over them. Behind the table sat Ernest Stanovský, the new commander of the People's Militia. Alexander met his former counterpart in the uprising in the yeast production company as head of the material - technical supply. When looking for a suitable candidate in the party organization for the new people's reserve militia commander, they unanimously voted for Dubček's proposal for

Ernest. Although he didn't have great desire for the post, he accepted the suggestion at Dubček's insistence. An experienced rebel fighter was ideal for this function even though he was not a member of the Communist Party. His participation in the rebellion and Alexander's guarantee were sufficient.

The men were dressed in work overalls and work coats. The yeast works employees were on strike in support of Gottwald's government, which was negotiating with President Beneš at the time. The room was full of people, there were cigarette butts in the ashtrays and the atmosphere was tense, full of expectation. At five the radio commentator announced that they are switching to Václavské námestie (Wenceslas Square) in Prague, where Prime Minister Klement Gottwald had just arrived. "I've just returned from the castle from the President of the Republic. This morning, I presented the President of the Republic with a proposal to accept the resignation of the Ministers, who resigned on 20th February this year and at the same time I suggested to the President a list of persons to complete and reconstruct the government. I can tell you that the President has accepted all my proposals exactly as they were submitted to him."

Not only in Václavské námestie and in the meeting of in the Trenčín yeast works, but also in many other places around republic, at that moment jubilation broke out. It was welcomed especially by the poor who had nothing. Those who owned factories, farms or even just little shoemaking workshops watched with worry what was happening in the Republic. A few days later Jan Masaryk, the Minister for Foreign Affairs, allegedly committed suicide. Uncle Michal commented laconically about these last events, "Communists get in, the democrats are thrown out of the windows. Lord knows if someone helped him." He didn't know how close he was to the truth. Only after the opening of the archives after the collapse of the Communist regime it turned out that a German citizen, Schramm, an alleged agent of the Soviet secret service NKVD, instructed by Gottwald and the Soviet ambassador, Valerian Zorin, in cooperation with a castle guard, Sedma, had thrown Ján Masaryk from the window of his apartment in Černínský palác when Gottwald learned that Masaryk was about to fly to England. Sedma and his wife later reportedly committed suicide. The government at Masaryk place was appointed by the then State Secretary of the Communist Party, Vladimír Clementis.

In Bratislava two months after the Communist Party took power, the first political trial ended. Sixteen leaders of the Democratic Party were altogether sentenced to 99 years of imprisonment. President Beneš, who refused to sign the new Constitution and disagreed with the undemocratic elections, resigned on 2nd June. He died in three months at the age of 64. After him, the National Assembly elected Klement Gottwald as the Chairman of the KSČ (The Communist Part of the Czech Republic). At his own request, the first Communist President of Czechoslovakia was taken right after his election to St. Vitus Cathedral, where the Prague primate, Beran, celebrated a solemn "Te Deum." All parishes were ordered to ring bells.

CHAPTER 19

MOLODCI – A GOOD GUY

In mid-September 1948, Stalin invited the new Czechoslovak president and his new wife, Marta, for a holiday in the Crimea. This visit was considered to be a sign for the transition of "the victorious protagonists in February" to the tough course of "building socialism." Gottwald was in a panic of fear over Stalin as all the other Communist leaders were with the exception of the Yugoslav President, Josip Broz Tito.

Stalin, this time received the Czech president with little emphasis on "reaction." However, for his successful handling of his Prague subordinates in February Stalin praised him with the impressive Russian epithet "Molodci (Good guy.)"

Stalin could never stop himself getting all those with whom he had lunch drunk. Of course, on Georgian cognac. Gottwald could not tolerate alcohol, so he drank wine. Stalin constantly poured vodka and Marta would take the glass with the words: "Allow me, Comrade Stalin, to drink for myself and for him!" Stalin was very put out by having to clink glasses with "a woman", while the Czechoslovak president drank "only" wine. Nikita Khrushchev was present during one lunch. Stalin suddenly asked Gottwald, "How does the cleansing look to you? Your Čekists are probably working badly if you don't have enemies in your own ranks!" Gottwald gulped and blushed for a moment. He was afraid of the question, but he couldn't evade it. Khrushchev lowered his eyes. Gottwald breathed. "Comrade Stalin we have no enemies in the party and I will explain why. Our party was strong before the war. It was a legal party and therefore our enemies didn't need to establish their own agents as they knew about everything." Stalin was terribly angry with him. When he and Marta had left, Stalin said to Khrushchev, "What a blind little pussy is that Gottwald. He doesn't understand that inside the party there can never not be enemies."

Stalin, on the basis of the experience of the Soviet Union of the thirties and forties, knew that the best way to ensure the potentially "disobedient" respected his will was through fear. All the leaders of the emerging communist satellites in Czechoslovakia, Poland, Bulgaria, Albania, Hungary and the eastern zone of Germany were potentially disobedient. When Gottwald departed from the Crimea, he had no suspicions that he would soon become the executor of Stalin's will. The most terrible period of his life, as well as that of the country of which he was president, was approaching.

CHAPTER 20

HE THREW HIMSELF UNDER A TRAIN

The early years of the Dubček marriage were happy years. On July 7, 1948, his son, Pavol, was born and Alexander was a hot candidate for the post of deputy director. He worked as one of the best technology experts and, despite being less than thirty, he had gained authority through workmanship, sacrifice and a sensitive accessibility to people. Since the director was due to retire in two years, it was very likely that the young deputy would take over the post of director. The deputy's salary was more than double that of an operator's salary. Anicka had already been to the furniture store to look for a new sitting room set when Dubček was summoned to the District Committee of the Communist Party in Trenčin in June. Whereas in 1938 the Communist Party had 80,000 members, in 1949 there were 1,788,000 organized Communists. Moreover, in Trenčín, the number of Communists had increased significantly and the organization had to instill order and system. Alexander had all the prerequisites to successfully run the organizational section of the KSS District Committee that they offered him. His professional work in the party attracted him, but his salary would be half what he was earning. However, Alexander didn't see the party as employment, but as a mission.

He accepted their offer.

His job was to take care of the administrative site of the district organization, to schedule membership sessions, to be in charge of registering members in local and factory groups, gaining new members and collecting membership contributions. Three months later, when his organizational talent was fully deployed, they sent the young secretary on a six-month political course of the Central Committee of the Communist Party (UV KSS) in Harmonia near Bratislava. On 18 February 1950, when the course ended, a second son, Peter, was born to the Dubčeks in Trenč9n. Alexander couldn't enjoy his boy as he'd been called for a military exercise in western Bohemia. Although he was only twenty-nine years old, after returning from the exercise, he was appointed the head of the district office of the Communist Party in Trenčín. A second report, which was been waiting for Alexander on his return from the military exercise, was bad. Very bad. When he learned it, he couldn't control his tears.

He sat down behind the kitchen table and for maybe the hundredth time he read an announcement of death dominated in big black letters by the name of Michal Dubček.

"You haven't eaten for three days," said his wife sternly whose eyes, too, were red from crying.

"I can't understand. Uncle was the best person in the world. Pride and honour. How did he die? "

"He threw himself under the train. He couldn't bear the false allegations. "

"He would never have committed any accounting fraud!"

"As chairman he was against the nationalization of the tailor's cooperative. In order to nationalize it, they needed to remove him. That's why they made this up about him ..." Anna whimpered.

"And he threw himself out of despair under the train ... terrible ... Even the former director, Kornhauser, hanged himself ..." It came to him that they had arrested the former Commander of the Upper Nitra partisan brigade, Jozef Trojan, before Christmas, a man of whose integrity he was absolutely convinced.

"I don't know, I don't know ... if what you do is good," his wife said aloud.

"It is good! Otherwise, it's won't happen. It's just ... we're doing it badly, "Alexander tried to persuade himself. It had got into his mind that maybe he'd had a part in the suicide of his beloved uncle. He convinced himself, that he didn´t know about it, that his uncle had acted rashly, that everything would have become clear. Try as he might, somewhere in his deepest interior a weak, hitherto unknown sense of personal responsibility or rather a remorse for his uncle's death settled. He was not only a member but also a functionary of a party under whose direction his beloved uncle had taken his own life. For a moment, he had the desire to turn his back on it all, but there was also the feeling that he had to do everything in order to prevent distortions. And this was only possible by staying in the party that made the decisions in society. Belief in the ideals of a just society had for a while exaggerated his doubts about the way his party wanted to achieve justice.

CHAPTER 21

THEY WILL KEEP IN LINE AND THEIR TRAPS SHUT

A new directive with changes to the priorities of the five-year plan came again from Bratislava. The Cold War had broken out in the world and fears of a military conflict between East and West grew. Two years before NATO had been founded and the countries building socialism were unable to fall behind in the arms race. It was therefore necessary to accelerate the construction of heavy industry, metalworking and armament industries. The manufacture of heavy industry had to jump four times! Expenditure on the military increased as the economy had militarized and resources were insufficient. The standard of living fell with rationing for bread, flour and potatoes reintroduced Coal as a part of wage in kind to miners and rail workers was stopped. The Trenčin district was one of the most industrialized districts of Slovakia and it had a key role in Czechoslovakia. The youthful Dubček was a key person in this district.

"And God help you if I get to Trenčín and the car is dirty!", the pudgy twenty-year old with a hard Western Slovak accent warned the tall, young man from Trenčín, in the courtyard of the Communist party's regional committee.

"Do not worry, you can come anytime," replied the young man, and calmly looked over the polished vehicle. He'd come to Bratislava in the spring of 1950 to take over a new service car. The black used Tudor, with blue fenders, had been removed from the fleet of the party's regional committee. The Regional Committee had received a decommissioned vehicle in place of the Tudor from the Central Committee of the Slovak Communists, who in turn had received a decommissioned vehicle from the Central Committee of Czechoslovak Communists in Prague. They themselves had received some new Tatra 600s, popularly known as Tatraplanes. The pudgy car mechanic didn't know that the smiling man from Trenčín was Alexander Dubček and Dubček did not know that the podgy car mechanic was Jozef Brinzík. In some years' time the fate of these two men would be joined.

Dubček tried not to burden the family with work problems, but his wife, knew from his almost perpetually furrowed brow that his head was spinning with problems. Housekeeping was becoming more and more her own and only responsibility. During his rare walks with his children he tried to get rid of the daily avalanche of tasks he had to deal with.

The last April Sunday afternoon of 1950 was surprisingly warm. So that Anna could make Sunday lunch in peace she sent her husband for a walk with the boys. His mother was supposed to come and Anna wanted to have space for preparation. It was one of the few Sundays when Alexander was home. Petko was lying in the pram his uncle had given the family and Palko was sitting on the side. Although Petko was only two and a half months old, his happy father was talking to him as if he understood. He remembered the words of his mother to talk to children from a very early age in order to avoid the use of baby talk which deformed a mother's language. The proud father cordially greeted passers-by, many of whom knew him. With some, he felt as though their salutations emerged from fear and others would have rather avoided the encounter. In the Brezina woods he sat down with pleasure on a bench after Petko fell asleep. Palko sat a bit on the warm, springy grass and played with some pebbles. Dubček was watching him contentedly when he noticed a man walking up to him.

"Hello Šaňo." Ernest Stanovský stood above him. "I hope you don't mind, I've been waiting for you here. They didn't want to let me into your office ..."

"Ernest," said Dubček taking his hand warmly. "Who didn't let you in?"

"No one else can help me only you," he said. Dubček watched Petko with one eye at the same time observing the diffident Stanovský.

"Why are you so formal? We're friends, aren't we? What's going on?"

"Well, then ... you are the first District Secretary ... A great man ..."

"Take your great man somewhere else. I'm the same Šaňo as I was in the yeast works."

"You're not the same Šaňo anymore. You can look as you always have done, but people take you for a great man. And ... some are even afraid of you ..."

"These are absurdities. There's no need to be afraid of Dubček,. I feel ... what's wrong with you? You're nervous ..."

"You know well that I fought on our side in the uprising. It's the unforgiveable accusation that I was with the Germans!" Ernest burst out. "I never had anything to do with them ... On the contrary! ... And to believe I was treating the Garde during the Slovak state. I wasn't allowed to practise and if good people hadn't hidden me, the Garde would have sent me to Auschwitz."

"You weren't exempted by the Slovak state?"

"And why do you think I was hiding with you in the works? Of course not. I still have Ďurčanský's certificate. Here he is," he furiously handed Dubček the paper who half-heartedly read it. 'Subject - Prohibition of the practice of medicine under Government Decree No 184/1939. The Ministry of the Interior, after hearing the Medical Chamber in Bratislava, shall notify you that you have not been included in the percentage specified in § 1, paragraph 1, nor the numbers above this percentage pursuant to § 1, paragraph 3 of the Government Ordinance no. 184/1939 and thereby lose the authorization to practice medicine ... There are no appeals against this decision. Minister Ferdinand Ďurčanský. "

"That's why you hid yourself. But it was quite risky. The works was controlled by the Nazis," Dubček responded.

"The darkest place is under the lamp," Ernest smiled bitterly.

"What does your chief say? There's is no problem proving you were on our side. "

"Trojan? ... He's been arrested ..."

"Oh yes ... sorry. There are no doubts about demonstrating his innocence ..." Dubček glanced at his boy who was sampling the yellow petals of a dandelion.

"Do you know who investigated me at the StB, State Security? ... Wait for it ... Kulifaj ..."

"What? Kulifaj? But he was in the secret service of the Slovak State," he almost jumped back from Dubček's anger.

"They are the most suitable ... They are trained and grateful. They will keep in line and their traps shut. The most suitable people in such services are those who can be blackmailed."

"Is Kulifaj in the State Security Branch in Trenčín?!"

"And from where are the new secret services going to find ready personnel? Why not from the old guard?"

"Then I'll have to get on to his chief ... captain ... what's his name ..."

"Kardoš ..."

"Kardoš, and call and ask him if he knows who he's got there!" his anger exploded. "Damn!"

"I'm afraid you can't call him. State security isn't accessible to you... But as a Communist Secretary you can summon Kulifaj directly. He's a member of the party, but in Bánovce ... I guess the local chairman could do you a favour...."

"So Kulifaj is now one of us ... I would have thought that the former People's Party were only entering the Democrat Party ... But they don't seem to be disdained by the Communists either."

"And there will be more and more of them ... As you have more power, they'll be crawling all over you to you."

"Why don't you join us? You're an honourable man, you were in the uprising. I can testify that you were. "

"I just came to ask you ... I've already written it here ..."

"If confirmed by the District Secretary of the Communist Party, they have to admit it!"

"Yet Trojan was a Communist," Ernest said bitterly.

"Trojan was not caught because he was a Communist and a partisan, but because he had been engaged in sabotage of the two year and five year plan after being liberated in Baťovany and there is serious suspicion of murder. Don't be afraid, the courts are fair. If his innocence is proved, they'll release him!"

"Do you believe that?" Dubček was silent. "And your Uncle Michal? The most honourable person I ever met ... It's an unforgiveable nasty thing!" Dubček helped Paľko collect the spring flowers for the Sunday vase. "Do you believe that Clementis is an imperialist spy?"

"I believe ... um ... I believe the party is just and the truth will out. I have no doubt that they will throw out the charges ... And the others. They must," the young district secretary shook his head, as if he wanted to convince himself.

"It's said that people are fleeing to Austria ... They have banned bathing in the Danube and in Moravia, pulling barbed wire along the border ..."

"The truth will out." Dubček repeated himself as though only to himself.

"It also came out in your uncle´s case. But it was for nothing then."

"It turned out that the accusation was wrong ... He reacted in a panic ... his suicide was futile ... Show me your paper."

"Alexander Dubček, the first secretary of the District Committee of the Communist Party in Trenčín, confirms that Doctor Ernest Stanovský was an active participant in the Upper Nitra Resistance."

"Put Comrade in. Why don't you write there that you were in Pavel unit, which was integrated as part of the second Czechoslovak parachute brigade? It would be more convincing! "

"Well ... because Trojan was a commander there..."

Dubček breathed, then nodded, took the pen and signed. "After the 1st May celebrations come and see me. I'll talk to Kardoš in the meantime. Don't worry, everything will be fine. I'm sorry, I have to go, my wife is waiting with the Sunday dinner ..."

CHAPTER 22

I HAVE COMMITTED SERIOUS CRIMES

The Yugoslav leader, Jozef Broz Tito, refused to submit to Stalin, and so Informburo, the Moscow headquarters of the Communist parties, excommunicated the Yugoslav communists. A letter in which Stalin criticized Tito was given to Gottwald on a day he was visited by Gustáv Husák and Ladislav Novomeský. He told them to read it. These high-ranking Slovak officials read the letter as though it were Alice in Wonderland. They ate the frankfurter sausages that Gottwald's wife had prepared for them and couldn't believe their eyes. After the Soviet Union Yugoslavia was a model for Czechoslovak Communists.

"Tito a spy of imperialism? What is this nonsense?" Husák asked.

"Sign it so that you've taken note of it ..." Gottwald said laconically. Then, without hesitation, he drew a bottle of Mikulovsky Frankovka from a compartment in his desk eager to pour for all three of them. "Klement, you shouldn't drink so much!" His wife warned. Klement was drinking more and more. He drank especially when a new report came from Moscow. Even when he heard the name of Stalin, the hands of the most powerful man in Czechoslovakia began to tremble from fear.

Doubts gradually and inconspicuously penetrated Dubček's interior. When the District Chief of Staff, Kardoš, told him that if he wanted something, he should come to him, he understood that, as the highest representative of the party in the district, he'd become a secondary cog in the wheels of power. For the sake of Ernest he went. Kardoš's sentence: "Let me tell you, Comrade Chairman, that we are not here for you but you for us," remained in his ears from that time. State security had become a state within the state. Husák and Novomeský also began to understand this when they were arrested on 6th February, 1951. Bishops Gojdič, Buzalka, Vojtaššák realized that when they were sentenced to long years in prison. And thousands more.

Dubček was relieved that, as district secretary, he had no authority to decide on Public or State Security, which was governed by other elements in the state apparatus. They knew of them in the district and everyone tried to get along with them. Therefore at the first opportunity he attempted to correct his tactical error when he'd almost quarreled with the District Commander StB Kardoš over Stanovský. Kardoš had acted coldly and gave the District Secretary an ostentatious demonstration of his power. Consequently Dubček was pleased with a request to move to the UV KSS in Bratislava. Anna was less excited. She lived in Trenčín and had her family in nearby Velčíce. In October 1951 the Dubčeks moved to Bratislava. They lived for a while at Alexander's father, who worked as head of the personnel department on the Board of Trustees. Later they moved to Sokolska Street nearby. Alexander joined the organizational section. In addition to his own work, he was deputed at the beginning of 1952 to represent the sick chairman of the National Committee of the National Front, František Kubač. Dubček was selected for this position because he had been a deputy for three months for Trenčín to the National Assembly. During the 1948 elections, he came second on the candidate list for the yeast works. The deputy who was elected died and Dubček took his place. Before František Kubač, the former head of the Slovak partisans, Karol Šmidke was the head of the National Front.

At the UV KSS he was responsible for party-related organizational work as well as non-party activities. As part of the political processes in the early 1950s, campaigns were also organized to express the "anger" of the working people. Workers in the assemblies approved judgments and expressed support to the party and the government. The headquarters of the KSS were flooded with hundreds of consensual telegrams and resolutions that condemned the crimes committed by bishops, traitors and minions of American imperialism. Shortly after Dubček's arrival, the most intense phase of what was called Relocation Action B was begun. "Politically unreliable people" were forcibly removed with their families from their homes and flats. The young official monotonously folded letters, papers and decisions prepared for approval by the Central Committee Secretariat. Sometimes he admitted that he had hardly started working in Bratislava and he was already tired of the work. But it wasn't due to the quantity of work. He was accustomed to work, but not to work where he wasn't always sure of its point.

In the office he listened to the radio from morning to evening. Always the same. Optimistic songs alternated with information on successes and those who prevented them from achieving even greater successes. As for those their conviction was demanded by millions of workers in 10,500 resolutions.

"I have committed the most grievous crimes that anyone can commit ... I know there are no mitigating circumstances, no excuses, no forgiveness for me. I deserve a just contempt. I do not merit any end to my criminal life other than the end that the prosecutor proposes ..." in a penitent voice the former general secretary of the Communist Party, Rudolf Slanský recited the confession extracted from him by brutal torture. A broken Vladimír Clementis added more through the same process: "As I said in my confession, I committed serious crimes against the interests of the Czechoslovak people and thus against all progressive humanity. I betrayed the people, the Communist Party and the Soviet Union ..."

On 27th November, 1952, Dubček celebrated his birthday. It was after work and so with his colleagues, they symbolically drank a little wine. Today, judgments were to be given on the conspiracy centred on the leadership of Rudolf Slansk7. Nobody was in the mood to speak and so everyone was pleased when some of them eagerly began to debate the new football championship and newcomers, the Red Star team in Bratislava. The fans of Slovan club opposed them because they feared the departure of their best players to this club. The company was a little drunk began to argue if Slovan stars such as Pažický, Vičan or Reimann would leave or stay. The debate gained a political tinge as the new Red Star club in Bratislava had been created on the orders of the Minister of Interior as a club, bringing together mainly sportsmen from the ranks of public security. Debating on a political subject in the Central Committee building of the Communist Party was risky and so Dubček's colleagues gradually excused themselves to him. He knew, however, that this wasn't the reason why everyone returned to their office. He remained alone. The old Titan radio was on the cupboard. In a moment it would be six p.m. and the evening news would begin. When he switched it on, his hands were shaking a little. The news began. "Today, at 9.30 am, the President of the Court issued its judgment against the members of the anti-state conspiracy headed by the former General Secretary of the Communist Party, Rudolf Slanský. Under Section 78 3 of the Criminal Code, the defendants Rudolf Slanský, Bedrich Geminder, Ludvík Frejka, Vladimír Clementis, Bedrich Reicin, Karel Swab, Rudolf Margolius, Otto Sling, Otto Fischl and André Simone are charged with treason, sabotage, espionage and military betrayal and are sentenced to death . Under Section 78 3 of the Criminal Code. Having regard to the provisions of Article 22 1 of the Criminal Code the defendants Artur London, Vavro Hajdu and Eugen Löbl are accused of treason, sabotage and espionage and are condemned to life imprisonment. All the accused are declared to have lost their citizenship."

Dubček sat down and didn't even realize when he drank up one of the leftover glasses of borovicka. He called his father to see if he could spare time for him. But he was busy, so Dubček left the building and chose Hlboka Road to Horsky Park. He walked through the narrow walkways of the forested park that reminded him of the woods round Uhrovec. His head was whirling as the thoughts, the testimonies of the defendants, their confessions the names of the convicts began to merge together in him. He walked as if he had no soul. There was a heavy bell in his head, which once rang enthusiasm for the achieved successes, a second time for the price paid to attain them. Somewhere meanwhile doubts began to form. He had no reason not to believe the party, hundreds of thousands of workers, poets, scientists, writers, teachers, students who condemned the destroyers and demanded that they be punished with severe punishment. The newspapers and the radio daily broadcast convincing evidence of their guilt. "We are still threatened, because we have not yet learned irreconcilably, to hate immeasurably these evil-doers for their ravages. That's because we have not learned to hate irreconcilably in ourselves, in our thoughts and actions, what this gang has sown. But we will learn it!" the poet, Dominik, had written. Before his eyes Dubček had the portraits of Tukachevský, Bukharin and Rykov, which, after their executions, were cut out from the textbooks in Gorky. He had strange feelings in his soul. When he came home, his wife saw him for the first time in his life under the influence of alcohol "So they must have celebrated with you properly ..."

CHAPTER 23

FOR CHRISSAKE WHEN WILL IT STOP!

"No appetite?" Anna asked cautiously. She knew that when Šaňo had made two wrinkles over his nose he didn't want to be disturbed in his thoughts. It was less than ten days before Christmas in 1952. As long as Alexander was not on a work trip, Anna tried to have a proper Sunday lunch. Behind the clean, modest table chair sat Alexander, four-year-old Palko and on a raised chair two-year-old Peter. The radio was broadcasting cheerful, optimistic songs. The commentator described the achievements of workers and the peasants in the construction of a socialist society in superlatives. "We have broken the through limits ... peasants in the whole of Slovakia with joy and enthusiasm have entered united peasant cooperatives ... an increase in yields per hectare ... milk yields has grown ... We have achieved a record production of eggs ..." Then they put on a moment of Sunday poetry:

Our native party is pure

Like a blue and cloudless sky.

In the light of Stalin's morn

Under the earth a shadow lies.

Comrades, trust only in the Party's dawn

Whose fist slays every snake for sure.

And tomorrow Gottwald's Party

Will be stronger a thousandfold or more.

"I don't want porridge ..." Paĺko grizzled from his chair.

"Eat and don't answer back!" Anna came over to him and began to feed him vigorously.

"Don't force it on him! You could at least put an egg in it for him."

"We don't have one."

"You should buy one."

"There aren't any."

"How is it there aren't any?"

"There aren't any."

"No eggs?"

"There are ... but only on the radio and in your reports ..." she smiled bitterly.

"The purchase system still isn't working ..." Alexander explained.

"Your smallholder cooperatives aren't working! The newspapers are full of odes on the cooperative farmers, you demonstrate tremendous successes. They are all working splendidly. There's just one tiny little flaw. There is no butter, milk or eggs. And bread is only early in the morning!

"It may happen that some suppliers don't deliver, but on the whole the situation is improving."

"You talk like a newspaper. Co-operative workers make better use of new, modern technologies, precisely ... there's precisely no butter, no milk, no meat! You've introduced coupons again!"

"We have many enemies. outside and especially at home. Many of our efforts are sabotaged!"

"Doesn't there seem to be an excess of saboteurs, enemies, traitors and who knows what? This thing with Šmidke doesn't appeal to me ... You know him. He's a worker, not a stuck-up intellectual ... I don't believe he's a bourgeois nationalist. Do you know why they called them all that? Because

Široký, Bacílek and those like them are jealous. Bacílek began to quarrel with Husák to get him recalled so he could take his place." Dubček listened in silence. "And he succeeded. He was the Chair of the Board of Trustees and is now in place in Prague! "

"The party cannot be mistaken. At least not in so many cases. Certainly they'll be released ..." Alexander tried to convince himself.

"You also said that about Clementis ... A few days ago he was executed. Nice of them not to hang him on Christmas Eve!"

Dubček, with his head down, was silent. "I never knew a more honest man. The same goes for Šmidke ..."

"You see, they've accused them of bourgeois nationalism. Every one of you has gone insane from this bourgeois nationalism. Here it's enough to say you're Slovak and immediately you're a bourgeois nationalist!"

"I also think that Široký and Bacílek bow under pressure from Prague. And they recalled Šmidke, But it he didn´t come out of it badly.. He is, however, the director of Tesla and it's a major enterprise ..."

"Please they're hounding him like wild animals!" Anna sat down and impulsively tenderly took her husband's hand. "I'm scared. I'm scared we've got into a spinning wheel that we can hardly jump out of ... I'm afraid for you Alex ... I'm afraid for our boys, I'm afraid ... They're already suspicious about this Bojko. You run from pillar to post just to find out something about a Russian emigrant, who has been dragged away by SMERSH."

"I'm immeasurably committed to Doctor Bojko and his wife and I will do everything to help them!"

"For sure, just as long as we don't suffer ..." Anna was worried.

"We're building a new society. Don't you see the tremendous successes that we've achieved since the inauguration of Gottwald as president? Slovakia is more industrious than ever, we are building HUKO in Košice, an aluminum factory in Žiar, engineering in Martin, Chemko in Strazsky, Slovnaft in Bratislava, Plastics in Púchov, and a hundred and fifty new plants. New colleges, theatres, a railway is being built by young people. Thousands of new flats are being built, the young are dancing in the ensembles, Sluk and Lúčnica. Occasionally, there are no eggs ..." he raised his hand and tried to smile. "They make mistakes, but nobody makes them deliberately."

"Except for saboteurs, enemies and traitors. Please, you're starting to talk to me as if you were at a promotional meeting."

"Is that onion burning there?" Alexander closed the conversation tartly.

"I have to economize on fat. That's why our family in Velčíce occasionally sends us a pot of fat."

The news began on the radio. "... Today in the early hours aged fifty-five after a long, incurable illness the former Chairman of the Slovak National Council and the Chief Commander of the Partisan Movement at the time of the Slovak National Uprising, Comrade Karol Šmidke, died."

Dubček and his wife looked at each other for a long time, unable to speak. Little Petko put his spoon in his eye and started crying. His mother hushed them, but the boy didn't stop crying. Alexander's face was twisted with pain. "No, no ... no, it's too much ... That man didn't do anything. I don't believe it! He was my father's best friend. I don't believe it! For Chrissake, when will it stop?"

Dubček stood up and walked out silently. At first he wanted to go to his father, who lived in the Mudroňova Street nearby with his second wife and stepdaughter. Eventually, he decided to breathe in the fresh air of Horsky Park. He felt that he and his father were moving apart in their opinions. He was a sharp, uncompromising man and things were usually resolved by commands. He didn't discuss much. Alexander, on the other hand, was calm, patient, persuading people and winning them over. It seemed to him that his father had become embittered because Široký and Bacílek didn't let him back into active politics.

He came to the well on the Hlboka Road. It wasn't frozen so he drank, splashed his face and wondered if anyone by chance had seen him. The road was deserted and he took a few energetic steps up the stairs to the nearby grotto of the Virgin Mary. A few old women were praying silently. He sat on a bench, closed his eyes and breathed in deeply the soothing atmosphere of the place. It was quite dark and he was confident that no one knew him.

CHAPTER 24

CLEMENTIS 'S BED LINEN

Two days after Šmidke's death, Dubček sat in his office at the Secretariat of the UV KSS and read a draft resolution by UV KSS approving a new Soviet-style planning system that was to be valid from the New Year.

"Comrade Dubček, you have to go to Comrade Secretary Benada," his secretary interrupted him.

"To Benada? When?"

"Immediately."

Dubček shook his head in surprise. A strange intuition, however, told him that this was not a coincidence.

"Welcome Šaňo, we haven't seen each other for a long time. Sit down," the old party member warmly welcomed him. Dubček would never forget the image when in 1943 he was visiting his father in prison in Nitra and he saw guards dragging the body of an unconscious, bloody battered Benada along the ground. "How are you? What do you say to that?" he pointed at the wonderful gleaming set of antlers. "I shot him at Muráň last year. Now they have sent me the antlers."

"Well ... it's fine."

"You don't sound very enthusiastic."

"So ... the work here is interesting, but ..." he reflected.

"But what?"

"I'm sorry comrade secretary, but I'm still under the influence of recent events ..."

"Do you mean the trials with Slanský, Clementis and others?" Dubček nodded.

"The party has decided and the party is always right!" Then he added unexpectedly. "Well ... I think Clementis certainly wasn't responsible for what he was convicted of. Those Prague Jews Slanský, Frejka, Geminder and the others ..." He hadn't renounced his Moravian origins and his aversion to Prazaks (people from Prague) and Jews. Most Slovaks had an attitude to the trials like

Benada's. The executions didn´t bother them too much. "Let the Communists and the Jews kill each other," was whispered in the taverns.

"The Prague Presidium has agreed to Gottwald's proposal for all eleven capital punishments ... Hm, we live in complicated times ..." Then he changed the subject. "I have a request for you. Karol Šmidke, although he was no longer in any party or state position as a one-time President of the National Council, will have a state funeral. I've heard that there won't be many going for various reasons. They also tried to talk me into it. I can't not go there. He was my good friend. Our families were and are very close. We're even godfathers. You know my boy and his daughter are friends... So we were ... I've been talking to some older comrades to speak at Karol's funeral ... None of them wants to ..."

"They're scared?"

"I guess so... I wanted to ask if you might speak ..."

"Me?" Dubček looked at him in surprise.

"You. If your father was in some position, I'd ask him, so I'm asking his son in his place. You're young, no black marks against you ... and a Dubček. Everyone knows that your father had a very close relationship with Karol. Unfortunately, I can't ask Husák or Novomeský ..."

"Can't they do something to release them?"

"We are trying something, but ... you know, the Communists don't rule here ... nor State Security, as many think. There's someone else in the world ... Perhaps if I called Stalin ... he, he ... and so I don't give it much chance ..."

"Tell me, Comrade Secretary, is it true that the wife of the President, Comrade Gottwaldová, auctioned Vlado Clementis's bed linen and dining set at an internal party auction?"

"I heard something ... Some say it was Novotná ..."

"If it's true, it's horrible ..."

At that moment, there was a knock on the door. "Come in!" His secretary came in. "Comrade Secretary has a call from Comrade Bacílek."

"I don't have time."

"But it is Comrade Bacílek ... from Prague ... the Minister of State Control ..." The uncomprehending his secretary tried to persuade Benada.

"I have an important visitor. Tell him that when I'm done, I'll call him! "The Secretary chuckled and nodded. "I'm not going to be bothered with some nobody from Smichov when I have the son of Štefan Dubček with me..." Benada laughed. "So what do you say to this?"

"I don't know if I'm worthy. At the funeral of such an important person ..."

"Write your speech and give it to Gosiorovský."

"Why Gosiorovský?"

"To make sure. He is an ideological secretary. So you're covered if someone doesn't like it ..."

Gosiorovský not only looked at Dubček's speech, but also adjusted it. He didn't actually edit it. His cuts were so drastic that he practically wrote a new funeral speech. Dubček found himself in a stupid situation. He did not want to go to the funeral of an important party and state official with the phrases and neutral banalities written by Gosiorovský. Finally he solved the dilemma. He decided to read his original speech.

A nervous official requested Comrade Dubček to present a funeral address on behalf of the Communist Party's Central Committee staff. Dubček began quietly, but with a strong wind as if he had entered into an unfamiliar resistance. An icy wind blew and Alexander was almost shouting. To many it seemed he shouted much more strongly than would have been required to shout down the wind.

"... today we bid farewell to a man who has left an indelible mark in our country's history. Despite the fact that not all of his life and his work have been fully understood in recent times, Comrade Karol Šmidke deserves respect from all of us ..." Grimaces of surprise appeared on the faces of some officials. "In all his functions he consistently promoted the interests of the people and the unity of the brother peoples of Czech and Slovak origin ... The role of the fifth illegal leadership of the Communist Party led by Comrade Šmidke, should also be appreciated whose members include Comrade Husak and Comrade Novomeský." At that moment, the funeral congregation murmured. Dubček noticed it, and continued with an even stronger voice than before. "History undoubtedly proves that Comrade Karol Šmidke was one of the most important agents of the Slovak National Uprising and that the accusations against were unjust. Let us be proud of people like Karol Šmidke. We promise, Comrade Šmidke, that we will complete the historical work of building the socialist society that you began."

Dubček bowed and returned to his original place. He felt surprised eyes on his back. An unknown person standing beside him cautiously tapped his hand and nodded his head. But he quickly withdrew it. No one else came after him, no one else squeezed his hand in agreement. Not that day, nor the next.

CHAPTER 25

DEATH OF A PROLETARIAN GOD

Even though the secretary headed enough young people without a family he, the father of two small children, had viciously been put on duty at Christmas Eve. He sat in his office and felt somewhat lonely. From Smidke's funeral, it seemed as though Dubček had begun to be under a cloud. He decided to go to his "party" father, Ľudovít Benada and pour out his heart to him. Benada listened to him smiling mysteriously all the time.

"You don't feel good here ... I can see it. Well, Bratislava is somewhat different from Trenčín. But you won't be going back. I've got a proposal for you. We're moving Miša Bakula to Nitra and we need ae head of the party secretariat in Banská Bystrica. What do you think about it?"

"Regional secretary? I'm only just over thirty-one. "

"You'll be thirty-two in the autumn. So what? Collectivization there is fraying us at the edges. In Trenčín you had excellent results. People liked you and we also need people like you in the Central regions. It's more complicated there; conditions and, traditions are tougher, but you can do it ... The Comrades and I have talked about you. In mid-February in Prague, there will be a national congress of combined smallholder cooperatives. New directives and model statutes of the JRD

(Combined Smallholder Cooperatives) will be adopted there. Those directives will make it easier for us to work. So how about it?"

"Well, I won't think too hard about Bystrica. I don't know what Anička will think, but she certainly won't object."

"What are you talking about? If the party sends you there, Anička will go ..." Benada smiled. "You like her, though?"

"I'd give my life for her and my boys. And now we are waiting for a third ..."

"Now you see. You'll have a Bystričan! You'll also have a Central Slovak in your planned football team. "

"You know it?"

"Everyone knows you want a lot of kids."

They left for Banská Bystrica in mid-February. Alexander Dubček joined the regional secretariat of the party on 1st March, 1953. They moved to an older, two-storey villa near Hron pod Urpínom with a garden from which Dubček gained the greatest pleasure. He was friendly with the caretaker who bred chickens at the end of the garden. One day Dubček was given two rams, so he started to breed them in the garden, to the great joy of Palko and Petko.

At midday 1st March, the staff of the government villa in Kuntsevo near Moscow began to worry. Stalin had not come out in the morning or called anyone. Going in to his room without calling was forbidden. Whoever dared to do so risked their life. It was eight, nine, ten o'clock in the evening and there was the silence of the grave in Stalin's room. An hour before midnight Starostin, who was on duty, with the words .... - "friends, if anything happens, remember the good in me," decided to enter. When he switched on the light in the small dining room, he saw Stalin in a pool of his own urine, in his pajamas and an undershirt. He lifted his hand with a great effort as if he was calling Starostin, but could not say nothing. Starostin´s hands and knees were trembling. He called servants in order to place Stalin on the sofa. Calling the doctor for the god of the proletarians was only allowed with the approval of Lavrentij Beria, a feared executioner, head of the secret service, the NKVD. Beria, however, was carousing with one of his many mistresses and it took five hours to find him. At three o'clock in the morning Beria arrived with Stalin's personal secretary Malenkov. He entered the room in his socks holding his boots with his thumbs so as to not creak the floorboards. The drunken Beria scolded the servants that they were panicking for the God of the proletariat had no pre-death rattle, but was only asleep and snoring. Three hours later, the whole politburo arrived with Khrushchev. Beria, who was already planning to seize the God's power, was kneeling at his bed and kissing the hand of the unconscious dictator. After a four-day struggle, in one of his last moments he suddenly opened his eyes and gazed with his wicked eyes at all who were standing near him. Then he suddenly lifted his left hand, which he could move, and pointed upwards. Or he was threatening all of them. Then his tyrannical soul departed from him. The god of the proletariat died on 5th March, 1953, at 9:50 in the morning. In another nine days, one of his proletarian angels had died, Czechoslovak president Klement Gottwald.

On 1st June, currency reform took place in Czechoslovakia, although the new president, Antonin Zápotocký, had said the day before that no reform was being prepared. Any citizen who didn't have an employed labour force could exchange three hundred crowns at a rate of one for five. Whoever possessed more money could get new crowns at a ratio of one for fifty. The government thus gained enormous resources.

The fourth year in a five-year period went by, the main focus of which was the industrialization of Slovakia. Though predominantly heavy industry plants without environmental protection were built, people were happy because they had a job. Kysuce, Orava, Zemplín, the area below the Dukla and others, which before the war had escape en masse, became regions where work arrived. Thousands of new homes, roads, hospitals, cultural buildings were constructed. Health care was free and educational and cultural levels were raised. State propaganda uncritically exaggerated the achievements of building socialism. Officially there were no weaknesses and if there were, they were caused by saboteurs, wreckers or bourgeois nationalists.

CHAPTER 26

I'LL GIVE THE COOPERATIVE A TRY

There was a good mood at Jednota Krásno football club. The stadium was packed. Everyone wanted to see the new, perpetually smiling secretary who'd come from Bratislava. Jednota men played against the young officials of the Banská Bystrica district. The match ended in a draw and the players and officials in the dressing room derisively remarked that the home team wasn't allowed to win because the team of youngsters had the chief regional secretary in attack. Dubček had the reputation of being an athlete, he skated superbly, played volleyball and hockey and hiking along with football was a great passion.

"Your goal was straight out of the first division," laughed Selecký.

"I told you not to be formal ... I'm Šaňo," said Dubček shaking his surprised colleague's hand.

"But you're up there ... a great man."

"What kind of great man? You're a greater man! You have a farm," Dubček laughed

"Whatever, there are two horses ... I heard that as a regional secretary, you're breeding rams," Selecký muttered. Dubček started to laugh. "So I breed them. Isn't that allowed?"

"Right, it's just strange that the top man in the region breeds rams."

"If you come into the cooperative, I'll give you my rams ..." The other players were laughing heartily. "But seriously, Jožko, you could be a big man ... You are a well-known farmer. But you toil like a goddamn ox! In the cooperatives there are tractors, harvesters and threshers. Everything is done for the people. We just have to get them in there."

"Secretary, you don't give this a rest even for football," Dubček was reproached by his chauffeur, Jáno, who was playing as one of the team.

"When I'm surprised I have to talk about it. The cooperatives are like American farms! Jožko, if you come in, the others will, too. And I'll tell you this that I'll see you as a chairman!"

April 29, 1953 was a beautiful spring day. Dubček, together with the Chairman of the Local National Committee, Regional and District Secretary for Agriculture, several other officials and co-operatives stood beside a wide, endless field, over which the innovative tractor Škoda Zetor 25 had been tried out with a plough. As the tractor approached the debating group, the chauffeur turned off the engine and smiled broadly at them.

"How was it?" Dubček gave him his hand.

"It's different from walking behind a cow," Jožko Selecký nodded his head appreciatively.

"You see men, it ploughs like this in modern agriculture. Six furrows at once," Dubček nodded eagerly.

"And the tractor goes even faster," the MNV chairman said.

"It doesn't even eat," came another joke.

"Yet a Selecký has worked in these fields from time immemorial ... Great grandfather Selecký, grandfather Selecký, my father, now me and my boy has already started ..."

"Jožko, you don't work in these fields ... you break your back in them. All you want is for the boy to go and study and not live out his life just like you in drudgery ... How many hectares are there?"

"Which of his fields?" Fero Kuhl added an envious note to the debate.

"Don't pull faces, titch. And what if I have five fields? They've been in my family forever ... It's not my fault you haven't got any."

"How many hectares have you got?"

"Seven"

"How long does it take you to plough them?"

"So ... I guess if I don't use up a horse in a week, ten days ..."

"Do you know how many horses this has?" The engineer Kubovčiak placed proudly on the hood of the tractor. "Twenty-five! That will plough a field in a day! When I start in the light, when you go to church in the morning, I will be ready! "

"The church doesn't have anything to do with this, that's my business!" Selecký protested.

"Unless your Lord God has helped you in with the ploughing," Kubovštiak put in. The others laughed.

"Well, let's leave out things that don't belong here," Dubček said with in some irritation with Kubovštiak.

"I'd like to come in ... It doesn't appeal to my better half. Could you give us a guarantee that if it doesn't work you'll return the fields?" asked Kuhl.

"What fields? You've only got a cottage and a piece of ground!"

"That's not relevant! The main thing is that together we'll use technology; tractors, ploughs, seed drills, harvesters. And we'd need a suitable chairman. What do you say?" Kubovštiak urged Selecký and he winked at Dubček.

"Where are we going to take the machines?"

"The National Committee will assign them to you. The chairman has already received funds for machinery. Look, men, if you're afraid of this, you don't have to mark your boundaries as a preliminary. Everyone will have their fields, only they will work together. With machines in common and livestock in common," Dubček said persuasively.

"So it means that I'll plough Bucko's field with my horses?"

"Exactly. And he'll help you with sowing, mowing or other work. "

"Secretary, and what I mow, you say will be with the harvesters," Bucko caught Dubček.

"The harvester can't work under Holý vrch It'll have to be mown by hand there. And while there Jozo will be mowing with some people, others will take care of the livestock. As on an American farm. All of you look at America, but don't you see how they get their yields, because they do things on an enormous scale?" Dubček argued.

"OK, Secretary, don't compare the American farm with our cooperatives. There those who work on them own them. Here do we hand over everything and then work on the land of strangers?" one curious observer asked.

"What about these agitators in Lehota? They were driven out with pitchforks. Blood even flowed there. If your cooperatives are so amazing, you wouldn't have to force us, that's clear! In Eastern Slovakia, people from the cooperatives are leaving in droves because they aren't working. A person can make something of what he has, his own, but it's his. This way it will not belong to anyone," Hurtaj was upset. "And in Hačava, they condemned Pekárik, Šumný and Belica to move to the Czech border. Because they didn't meet their quota. They set it so high it couldn't be met.

"As far as I know, Pekárik and Belica had full lofts of the grain they'd hidden ... And workers in the towns also need bread as you need their machines?" Dubček turned to Selecký. "You will continue to own everything but you will be able to use machines."

"And how will the crop be divided?"

"Everybody gets out of their fields."

"We can do that on our own as we've always done."

"Of course, I won't come with the tractor to plough or sow for you and when you're sorting out your homestead at Tomala I'll go to Balaton for three days, you twit. What don't you understand?" Kubaštiak's nerves were getting the better of him.

"The work you do for the benefit of others is credited to you. And when you make the quotas, you can sell everything else and you'll be able to dispose of the funds as you like."

"That sounds interesting," agreed Selecký.

"And if it doesn't work, you'll return to your homes and you'll do business just as before. You aren't risking anything ... Jožko, you'd be a good chairman. You're an experienced farmer, you have authority." Selecký smiled uneasily.

At that moment, Miško, the driver for the Regional called out to the whole village from a distance: "Comrade Secretary ... Šaňo ... You have a son ... Milan ... they called from Bratislava ..." He switched off the engine and warmly congratulated Dubček, whose face had lit up with his characteristic smile. Those standing round congratulated him. Perhaps it was Dubček's disarming smile that convinced Selecký.

"Congratulations. Well, I'll give the cooperative a try," he looked directly into Dubček's eyes.

"This is the most beautiful gift I could get on my son's birth." He turned to the others. "Men, we're going to the village. I invite you all for a glass. Today is a great day. I have a third son and Jožko finally decided to join us. It's worth a celebration. "

"The tavern is still closed."

"So get the landlord," commanded the chairman of the National Committee. That evening, Alexander came home in his best mood for some time. The business apartment was prepared for the family who moved from Bratislava on the following week.

CHAPTER 27

YOU'RE THE CRIMINALS!

The United Smallholders' Cooperative in Krásno was among the larger agricultural enterprises owning twenty-one hectares. When it became known in the village that its chairman, was the renowned smallholder, the daring Selecký, many also joined. But there were many who weren't willing to share their inherited land with others. Those who didn't want to enter found that their children couldn't study and were prescribed quotas that were disproportionately high. Failure to deliver was punished by confiscation of part of their harvest or even by prison. Or they were forgiven, provided that the smallholder joined the cooperative. The promise of forgiveness was an effective tool to force the farmers to join.

"Comrade Chairman, this is the draft of the poster," the secretary of the Selecký's office said. The Chairman took the poster and read: "Smallholders! Don't plough with your cows. You reduce their milk yield by a third. Do not order from the village rich man, his work is twice as expensive! We charge you per hectare, medium ploughing 450 Czech crowns, deep ploughing 603 Crowns! As a member of a JRD of the higher type, we carry out a medium plough for 315 crowns, a deep plough for 422!" He sighed, signed and returned the draft to the secretary.

"Put it in front of the church. So as many people as possible see it."

The secretary nodded. "And don't forget that you have a meeting of the Communist party at four. The first one. The first." she looked significantly at Selecký.

"Well, I joined as Dubček was so insistent on me ..."

The Krásno cooperative initially worked, personally assisted by the regional secretary. After a while things on the cooperative didn't develop as promised. All machines had to be handed over to the Strojnotraktorova stanica (The Machine Tractor Depots) under the 1950 Uniform Mining Cooperatives Act. Whatever Selecký and his people tried to do, the new purchase system approved by the National Assembly meant, in fact, a further increase in quotas, reinforcement of direction, centralization and administrative paperwork. The work of Co-operative was less and less managed by Selecký and his men and the officials from the District National Committee and the District Committee of the Communist Slovak Party meddled more and more. Instead of the promised contracts, mandatory state quotas were introduced on the basis of fixed standards per hectare. Although the Krásno co-operatives farmed on difficult stony ground, they were ranked in the top type of cooperatives, requiring the highest quotas. Standards were so high that they simply couldn't be met and there was nothing left for free sales. There was no money to buy new machines, which again led to low returns. Added to this was a growing theft of crops. Keeping watch didn't help as the guards stole the most. It happened that when the harvester came to harvest maize there was nothing to harvest. All the ears of corn were broken off because at night villagers had taken them home in their carts. Everybody stole and everyone pretended they hadn't stolen. They hadn't a pang of conscience about it. Uncle Klčo took his scythe on during daylight, went into a co-operative field and mowed undisturbed. When they caught him, he uncomprehendingly explaining that he wasn't stealing and mowing his own property because from the pear to the other one that stood in the wide field, it had always belonged to the Klčos.

If that wasn't enough, the supplies of spare parts didn't work. The socialist planned economy produced something different each quarter. If the engine of the tractor was accidentally damaged and the spare engines had not been produced at the Brno production plant, the tractor could be laid up. Not even the new STS (Machine Tractor Depots) helped, because the spare parts weren't there. In order to save the situation, there was nothing left for Selecký except to cheat. They filled in endless forms and tables with quantities that did not exist. It stuck in Selecký's craw, but since it was done by all the cooperatives, if they were honest, they'd be the worst. So he found himself in a vicious circle. The cooperatives ceased to function, gradually collapsed and party and state authorities, instead of seeking solutions, sought out the culprits.

The district court in Banská Bystrica, where Selecký's trial was underway, was painted in two colors. The lower half was painted with a green oil paint, separated from the upper dirty white by a brown strip. The portrait of President Zápotocký hung on the front wall. Beside him was a large banner, "There are no places for the village rich man in the JRD!" There was a judge in the middle of the presiding table, on either side of him peoples' judges. Opposite them, standing behind a lectern for the indicted, was a grim-faced Selecký. The room was full of people. Seated one bench from the back was Dubček. The judge announced the judgment. Selecký listened as if he weren't present. Occasionally, he looked among those present at those he'd expected to defend him. His head was crowded with images from his debates with Dubček where the young party secretary had convinced him to join the cooperative.

"The defendant, Jozef Selecký, abused the trust of the co-operatives and immediately after the founding of the co-operative he began to speculate how to break it," the words sounded as if from far away in the chamber. "He himself was elected chairman and from that time he began his destructive sabotage activity. He even entered the ranks of the Communist Party. He conspired with two rich villagers, Guzik and Hlucháň, and established a common goal to break the Untied Smallholders Cooperative in Krásno. The membership was wrongly informed on the possibilities of development, with statements of false data and other results, so that they constructed a fait accompli for the membership that the JRD was not and would not be viable. The co-operative members did not have time to consider and therefore approved written decision for the dissolution of the JRD ..."

"That's not true at all!" Selecký abruptly interrupted the judge.

"Be silent! The trial is over! Through your subversive activity you have caused incalculable damage to our socialist agriculture." Then the judge lectured on his moral discipline to pronounce sentence." So the defendant can to correct his mistakes, he is sentenced in the name of the republic to five years' removal of his freedom!"

The chamber murmured. Selecký's legs gave way and he had to hold the rails in front of the lectern. There was a desperate cry from his wife in the chamber, "It's a crime! He did nothing wrong! It's unjust..." The woman was crying and desperately looking at the man to whom she could turn to for help. Gradually, everyone looked at him. The confused Dubček didn't understand what had happened. The Chairman of the Regional Court, however, had clearly promised to release Selecký. "You are the criminals, you are the criminals!" Elena cried out desperately. Her words were mixed with weeping and sobs. Dubček stood up and briskly stepped out of the room. He sat down in his service Tatraplan.

"To the regional court. To the Chairman!" he said sharply to the driver. From Krásno to Bystrica was only thirty kilometers, but it lasted for eternity. The Chairman of the Regional Court, Doctor Peter Ivanko was in session. As the head of the regional committee of the party had come in person, the hearing was adjourned. He invited Dubček to his office. He offered him coffee, but Dubček refused. He neither took off his coat nor did he sit down.

"I'm sorry, but I don't understand this. It is clear, however, that this person is innocent. I've come from the hearing he's got five years. Five years! Do you understand?" he was almost shouting.

"Šaňo ... Comrade Secretary, I'm sorry, we know Selecký is innocent, but ... but ... I can't rule. Goddamnit I wash my hands of this justice. I've got no balls, no heart or guts ..." Ivanko sat down at the table and put his head in his hands. "I can't rule on this ..."

"What happened?" Dubček's voice quietened.

"I was called by Bakoš ... the head of Bacílek's Secretariat. That Comrade First Secretary of the Secretariat insists on the exemplary punishment of Selecký ..." Dubček sat down and stared at him for a long time.

"What can Bacílek care about some obscure person from Krásno?"

"That's what I asked Bakoš. He was in rebellion along with Selecký's father when a reportedly drunk Bacílek had appropriated some insurgent money that Mayor Šmidke had given him. Selecký's father was the only witness. That's why Bacílek demoted Šmidke. Selecký's father died two years ago. Maybe Bacílek was afraid that his son might know the devil knows what ..."

"But the man is totally innocent. And I got him into the cooperative. You know! I am actually responsible for what happened. He has a wife and two little children. Goddamnit!" Dubček was beside himself.

"Well, have one and calm down," Ivanko poured himself one and gave one to Dubček. He didn't even know how he got it into himself. "If you dare you can go to war with the comrades in the party, you can start fighting Comrade First Secretary ..." The two men fell silent. It was clear that the fight against such power didn't stand a chance. Behind Bacílek were both Široký and Novotný.

"I'm going through Benada. Yes, through him. There's no other chance," Dubček thought to himself. "Please could you ask your secretary to call the Central Committee, Secretary Benada of the Secretariat!" Ivanko opened the door and rang the phone for a minute. "You have the secretariat here," and handed Dubček the phone.

"Honour to Our Work, Dubček from the Central region. Will you please connect me with Comrade Secretary Benada?" Dubček was listening and held the receiver unsteadily. "Well, then ... thank you." He put it down, sat down, breathing deeply. He felt he had begun to lose this battle. Ivanko stared at him silently. "Benada doesn't have time ..."

"Doesn't he have time for you?" Ivanko looked surprised. "'has something happened between you?"

"There was nothing between me and him ... But my father mentioned that he told him and Bacílek has something of his soul ..." Dubček shook his head.

"Will you have one more?" Ivanko offered.

"No Thank you." He stood up and went out. He got into the car. The chauffeur knew that something serious had happened from the way his jaw was set.

CHAPTER 28

ASSASSINATION OF DEAD LENIN

"Take me to Moštenica." Jáno the chauffeur already knew where to go. Before Lučatín they turned off the main road, they went high up into the Starohorské hills, to the point where the road was leading. "Come and get me before lunch ... And call the woman that I had to talk to ... I don't not know what they have made up ..." Jáno nodded, he was used to it. Behind the car there was dust in the bend. It was beginning of September when the mountains are the most beautiful. Dubček went to a large clearing at the end of which stood an old hunting lodge. It was his favourite place to come with his friends and family. He went in. He glanced at the wooden beams, then went out again and sat on a massive stump. He came there when he needed to be alone, when his head was filled with ballast which needed to be cleaned out. Again he began to mull over the question more intensely about why he had come to this. Perhaps he could have a sacred room and live a peaceful life of a tool-maker, go for walks with his boys and his wife, take care of the garden and play football with his friends. He was thirty-four. Others were chasing girls and he solved housing construction, reconstruction of a factory or trade union. And there was Selecký whom he had unwittingly got into gaol.

He crossed mountain paths which were covered by moss and fallen pine needles. The sun rays warmed his face. He felt that the splendour around him was giving him new powers. Nature directed by pure and divine laws gave him energy and his head was cleared. No, he wouldn't abandon Selecky. He wouldn't give up even if Bacílek had to send him to gaol alone. He would fight not only for Selecký, but would try to overcome his own fear and battle with himself. If he succeeded in freeing Selecký, it would be the first victory over his own cowardice.

When the chauffeur returned, he ordered him to go straight to his office. His secretary was used to being at work until he personally sent her home. When it was less busy, he'd let her go before midday and so she would work in the evenings. He went into his office, folded his coat and asked her to put paper into her typewriter. He started to dictate.

"Dear Comrade Antonín Zápotocký, President of the Czechoslovak Republic. I turn to you in the matter of exercising the mercy for the Chairman of JRD Krásno, Comrade Jozef Selecký...

The end of August 1955 was unusually warm, so the Dubčeks used the beautiful weather for excursions to the surrounding countryside. Anička had moved with her sons to Alexander in Bystrica. They had just returned from a family trip to Šachtičky. That evening Anička helped to remove dusty tracksuits from their boys, in which they walked around Banská Bystrica for a number of kilometres. Seven-year-old Palko, five-year-old Petko and two-year-old Milanko, looked as if they had just returned from the cinder playground where they sometimes went. They were dusty and dirty, but happy they with what they had achieved. Alexander looked at his sons and tried to be cheerful. The boys shouted and capped each other with bragging about who did the most walking and who carried the longest on his father's back. Heating under the boiler in the bathroom was already on and so hot water poured into the bath. Anička prepared the bath and the first one in was the oldest, Palko. He washed and then Milan and Petko went in... As the boys in the bathroom splashed and yelled, Alexander slowly took his father's old suitcase out of the cupboard and began to pack. Anička brought his shirt, underwear and socks. They both kept silent. Just a year ago they had moved to Banská Bystrica. Now they were returning to Trenčín. But only Anička and the boys. In two weeks Alexander was leaving for three years in Moscow University to study at the political centre of the Committee of the Communist Party of the Soviet Union.

Dubček wandered through Arbat and the old quarters of the capital. Although he'd spent thirteen years in the Soviet Union, he was in Moscow for the first time. At the hostel in Miušsko Square for the college of the political centre of the Committee of the Communist Party of the Soviet Union he and Miloš Jakeš were welcomed by a third year student, Jozef Lenárt. They had a double room on the third floor. There were two wardrobes in the room, a large oak table and two bookshelves. Immediately after their arrival, they were given two hundred rubles, which they couldn't wait to use seeing the city. The Metro, the Kremlin, Red Square were places that the young students of the party school wanted to see in Moscow as soon as possible. On the way to the Metro station, they passed a drunken man who had thrashed a woman with a stick from a fence. She was also drunk. Onlookers watched with a smile. It was obvious that such scenes were not unusual.

No matter how hard they tried, they could not hide their disappointment. Besides a few high-rise buildings on Arbat and Gorky Prospekt, the new complex of Lomonosov University in the Vorobyovy Gory, the Ministry of Foreign Affairs and the Koteľnitsky waterfront, most of the houses were wooden. Even the shops were made of wood. The streets were dirty, there were drunks every step of the way, the shops were empty and the faces of people were gloomy and silent. Street gang fights were nothing unusual. Most of the young Communists from Czechoslovakia, who at that time studied at Soviet universities, experienced an agonizing period of schizophrenia. They came to Moscow in the hope that they would find the future, but what they found was dismaying. Scruffy buildings, a lack of goods, corruption, fear, constant control, hypocritical, ill-bred and arrogant people. Soviet reality differed diametrically from their idealized ideas of the Soviet Union, which they knew only from newspapers and film magazines. Gradually they have lost faith, that the Soviet Union would be the country to accomplish their ideals. It turned out that those who claimed that if you wanted someone to lose faith in Communism you should send them to the Soviet Union were right. And these students lived in Moscow, which was the dream of every Soviet citizen.

The winter semester 1955/1956 had an unusual conclusion. Examinations were held at a time when the Twentieth Congress of the Communist Party of the Soviet Union was held in the Kremlin palace.

The hostel of the Political School had unusually modest furnishings on the third floor. Above the window was a portrait of the party leader, Nikita Sergejevich Khrushchev, whose secret speech at the Twentieth Congress of the Communist Party of the Soviet Union caused an earthquake. The portrait was much smaller than Stalin's, the contours of whose portrait frame remained on the wall. There was a table with fifteen chairs along the wall, two antique cabinets by the wall, brought there from an abandoned noble residence by God knows who.

In the study room, there were about twenty students aged mostly from twenty to twenty-five. They were mostly Russian or Ukrainian, but there were also Kazakh or Kirgiz. The four oldest were from Czechoslovakia. They were around thirty-five years old. Alexander Dubček, Milos Jakeš, Jozef Lenárt and Ladislav Abrahám. The young students debated vigorously. On the tables were bottles of Stolichnaya and Moskovskaya. The room was full of smoke with crumpled packs of the popular Belomorkanal. Some were drinking Zhiguli and Riga beers. With more and more alcohol their souls opened and revealed hidden corners which in a sober state would remain strictly hidden. Of the Czechoslovak students only Alexander was involved in the stormy debate. The smoky air bothered him and from time to time he opened the window to let the air in. In front him there was a bottle of the Georgian mineral water, Borzomi. Jozko Lenárt and Miloš Jakeš didn't speak Russian well enough to keep up with the impassioned future cadre leaders of the Communist Party of the Soviet Union. Predominant among them were simple rural boys who had survived the war in the kolkhoz or in an armament production factory. There were, however, among them a number of front-line soldiers who belonged to the elite. These Frontoviki were shown a natural respect by the youngsters from the countryside.

"I'm a swine, I'm a real swine ..." the drunken Aljosa shouted, with his head lying on his desk.

" It is impossible that Czechoslovak houses in the villages are made of stone and brick...." Ivan was almost shouting at Alexei. "You mean that they've got normal tiled roofs? You mean like ones on Kremlin?" and spat into the ground. A handkerchief was at that time in the Soviet Union a bourgeois luxury for some. "You should be ashamed of lying to your comrades!"

"So you don't believe a front-line soldier? I crossed Czechoslovakia from the Dukla to Prague, and there were brick-built houses in every village. There were wooden ones, but more were brick built! "You're a liar. I believe in the comrades in the Central Committee and they issued a directive according to which our citizens live in the best accommodation. And if our best-housed citizens have wooden houses, it's impossible that Hungarians and Czechs can have houses that are brick-built! " Ivan scowled and drank from a glass the kvass, which he'd bought from a tank in front of the hostel.

"Who are you to call front-line soldier a liar? Half of my mates fell, while you were banging your balls empty on your kolkhoz! ", Alexei grabbed the befuddled Ivan by his throat and shook him. "Was I at the front or you? You can't tell me what it looks like in Prague or Berlin. I fought there. Do you understand, you peasant cockroach!" If the strong Sergei hadn't jumped between them and pulled them apart, Alexei would have injured Ivan.

"Friends, well, well ... let's not quarrel. However, we've got our comrades from Czechoslovakia," Sergei turned to Lenárt, Dubček and Jakeš, who were sitting together on one bed and following the dispute without a word. "Osja, Sasha, tell me how it is!" Dubček, seeing that Lenárt and Jakeš did not understand what the boys were saying, quietly explained the nature of the dispute. Lenárt screamed with laughter. "Of course, people have brick houses!"

"And do you have flushing toilets?" Ivan asked.

"We do in the towns and there are also already some in villages."

"And you have asphalt roads?" teased an astonished Míša. Lenárt turned to Dubček, who again translated Míša's question.

"Well, we mostly have," Jakeš contributed to the debate.

"In Slovakia, there are still many which are ordinary, but it is gradually improving," said Lenárt, trying to calm the astonished Soviet students.

"Is there radio reception in the villages too?" Sergei asked cautiously.

"Where electricity has been introduced. And that's almost everywhere," Dubček said, smiling.

"Pavol Pavlovich, tell me that I am ... God, I'm such a swine ..." Aljos moaned ever louder and every desperate self-accusation call was flushed down with a glass of vodka.

" What is it you´re upset about?" Pavol placed a hand on the boy's shoulder caringly..

"I betrayed my friend ... I'm a swine ..." The students turned their attention from the dispute about asphalt roads and the brick houses which was stifled by a topic that had begun to be closely discussed in the USSR at that time. The myth of a pre-war thirteen-year-old hero from the small Russian village of Gerasimovka, Pavlik Morozov, who betrayed his father, grandfather, uncle and his neighbour had begun to be called in doubt. Moreover, somewhere, an article appeared that Pavlik didn't betray his father, the kulak, because he hid undeclared grain supplies, but because he'd left Pavlik's mother for another woman.

"And why?" Pavka asked the question on behalf of the others.

"Haven't you heard? Voloďa said he runs through the corridor in the hostel only in his underpants."

"Did he do that?"

"Clearly ... They all saw it ... They threw him out of his studies!"

"Don't mumble, everyone saw it, you didn't betray him!" Pavka comforted him.

"But betrayed, god help me, betrayed ... hall porter asked me if I saw it ... Do you understand? Me! They all saw it, but they asked me! ... If I said he hadn't done it, they'd've thrown me out of school ... So I said that well ..." Aljos muttered. "Tell me I'm a swine! Say it!" he demanded directly from Pavlik or anyone in the room to call him a swine.

"You're not a swine. No-one among us is a swine ... They are elsewhere!" Boris said quietly. It seemed as if Aljos had calmed down and his sobs were quieter.

"Even so I am ..." he added and finished his purgation. There was silence in the room, which was disturbed by a careful knocking at the door. The boys chuckled. It couldn't be that someone was hearing them, for God´s sake no one managed to report Boris's words, that swines are elsewhere. But the knocking was becoming more and more persistent. Ivan, standing closest to the door, opened it slowly. Something appeared in it that resembled like a man. An old, toothless, gaunt man guy with his eyes sunken in, strong eyeglasses in a bone frame, with white thinning hair, a face raddled with scabs, a nose red from brandy, a deep scar across the whole right half of his face a deep ugly scar. In his hands he had a military haversack, he was dressed in an old tattered military uniform. He stood there somehow unnaturally, in humility and fear, waiting for permission to enter. He was in such a sorry state that the lads fell silent and looked at him wordlessly.

"Hello ... I have not been reported, but please humiliate for sorrow. Excuse me, I'm called Stepan Ivanovich Bogatyrov. Colonel Bogatyrov. I think my son should be here ... Piotr Stepanovich Bogatyrov ..."

"Come in, don't stand in the door," said Misha, staring blankly at Piotr.

"I'm Piotr Stepanovich Bogatyrov ... Excuse me, aren't you making a mistake? My father, Colonel Bogatyrov, is a man like a mountain ... and he has black curly hair ..." Piotr slowly began speaking. He pulled the father's photograph out of his breast pocket, kissed it and showed it to the stranger. "This is my father..."

"I'm sorry ... my son I'm sorry. I can't believe it. I went home to our village, to Kumerovka, but no-one is there anymore. Neither your mother nor your brother, no one. I don't know where they are, what has happened to them ..." the man said slowly in whom Piotr began to recognize his father. "I even wanted to smarten up a little to meet you more appropriately, so I bought a new hair gel on the market at the Belarusian station, which cost almost all my rubles. I tried ... I know I don't look my best ..." the stranger apologized. "This was your father twelve years ago, before they put him in a camp," he took his picture from his son's hands and looked at it for a long time. There was a frozen silence in the room.

"My God, Father ... Is you it?" They fell into each other's arms and could not break away. Some of the boys gently handed the Colonel a chair, another an empty cup and poured. "Father, my father, papa, my papa ... is it you? My God, you understand, he came back, he survived ... he lives, he's alive here and ..." He wanted to say healthy, but he realized that these words did not suit the decrepit old man. The Colonel pulled out the crumpled pack from his breast pocket, lit one, and inhaled the smoke. He smoked silently, as did almost everyone in the room. The smoke replaced words. They would have to have been invented at that moment although the most angelic wouldn't have been more appropriate and symbolic than the smoke that got lost on its way to heaven. His hands trembled so much that he could barely stub his cigarette into the bottle top from a jar of pickled cucumbers that served as an ashtray. Dubček watched the stranger and before his eyes he had the image of his father, who had returned from Mauthausen in May 1945. An almost hundred kilo man returned weighing just 45. He looked at Colonel Bogatyrov and couldn't understand.

"My apologies, my father was also in a concentration camp," he said without knowing how he said it.

"And where? In the north, in Vorkuta? Beyond the Urals or in the Far East? "

"He ... he .. was in a German concentration. In Mauthausen ... "

"In a German concentration camp ... I was also in a German camp. In Dachau ..." Colonel Stepan Ivanovich Bogatyrov began to speak. He was interrupted only by the occasional trickle of vodka, which was poured into the empty cups as quietly as possible. Piotr sat next to his father, holding his hands all the time, occasionally kissing him, sometimes caressing his father like a small child and his father lovingly returned them. The loving and tender behaviour of two tough men hardly suited them and seemed out of character. Stepan pulled away from time to time, where - he wiped his head, sometimes he bent to the right and they watched it as he was tried to return to his original position. Sometimes he thought and fell silent looking for the words to go on.

"Yes, I was once a man like a mountain ... In forty-three I was captured by the Germans near Makayevka, north of Kharkov. They caught all of us ... except those they shot ... We didn't have a chance, they were a huge force. They transported me to the Dachau concentration camp. After the liberation, I only replaced a German camp for a Russian one. I'll never forget when we returned to Soyuz at the beginning of winter and entered our native land. We wept out of emotion, we embraced each other. I figured the men would leave the train at the places they came from. But the train was guarded by the NKVD and they didn't let anyone out. We didn't understand at first, but then we did. We were prisoners of our own. When the train approached Vspolie station in Yaroslavl, I thought I would go mad. There we lived, you were there, I knew nothing about you. There were crowds at the station and I looked for you, but the train just accelerated ..."

"Yes, father, I remember. We were standing with my mother on the platform. It had been rumoured that there would be a train coming with our soldiers and officers returning from the German prison camps. We'd been staying there for weeks as no-one knew when the train would come. And then it came. Railroad carriages, small windows with iron grilles, windows with wretched, pale, confused faces ... On the platforms there were wailing women and children. Our mother called your name, maybe you were there somewhere but the train didn't stop ... Yes, it was as you say ..." Piotr broken into his father's narrative in a low voice.

"I was looking for you, too, but the train was going to the east. At first I was hoped it would end somewhere in the Urals. But when we passed Omsk, Krasnoyarsk, Bratsk, I knew we were going to the edge of the world until we arrived in Vladivostok. Then those who had survived, arrived. They left us in the bitter winter for three days in the wagons and then moved us to Nakhodka. They took us on a ship and sailed alongside Sakhalin to Magadan. But even that was not enough suffering. From there they drove us on a frozen road to Orokutan. Ten thousand kilometers from Moscow ..."

"Why did they send you there? Didn't you fight Hitler?" Boris asked naively.

The colonel smiled bitterly. "Supposedly we had betrayed ... I don't even know how many camps in Siberia ... I was in. I learned about Khrushchev's condemnation of Stalin only half a year ago... In Orokutan, Kolyma, five hundred and six kilometres from Magadan..."

"Are you scarred from fighting?" asked Aljos

"I have the scar from a whip ..." he lowered his eyes in shame. "Overseer Prokhorov like to flick us with a whip. We used to live there in wooden barracks, with one bucket of coal dust for heating every twenty-four hours. In the winter it was minus forty. We didn't have beds, we slept on the ground. To get warm, we lay on each. Those who were in the middle lived. The ones on top froze, the lowest ones suffocated ... People died like flies ... It was in Dachau that everybody got their cause ... We, front line soldiers guarded by murderers and the other vermin ... We once tried to revolt, but those scum murdered everyone..." tears trickled from Colonel's eyes. No one wanted to interrupt him. Dubček had occasionally exchanged uncomprehending glances with Lenárt and Jakeš. For the first time in their lives, they saw a real prisoner of the infamous shameful Gulag camps - Glavnoje upravlenie ispraviteľno - trudovych lagerej.

"One by one they brought us to house number three, they pounced on us, and each of us stuffed rags in everyone's mouth, tied their hands behind their backs, and then, after five, six, they threw us in a truck and took us to the camp cemetery." He'd smoked all his cigarettes and the lads offered him their own. "I was glad they were going to kill us as it would be the end of our misery. They didn't shoot us, but they threw the living into a hole that had been dug out. It wasn't cruelty, but they found that handling the living - carrying them, lifting them ... was easier than the dead. So they threw us in and buried us there. The night when they threw me in they got their vodka ration, all of them were drunk on the moon, and they had buried us carelessly. They'd my hands badly and I managed to get out of there ... I came across a frozen guard in an old Chekist uniform. He had died only recently and was still warm. So I put on his garments and one of the drivers took me back to the camp. The next day the Commissioner from Magadan came with a list of those to be released. Out of the entire list I was the only one alive ..." He thought for a moment, then laughed, unnaturally. "Imagine it, they also buried Oleg from the village of Ugolsk in the Yakut region ... The village had three hundred souls. He'd been in a camp since thirty-seven ... Do you know why they locked this little rascal up? Someone accused him of being the head of a terrorist group in the village preparing the assassination of Lenin ..."

"Of Lenin? For he couldn't even suspect that Ugolsk exists ..." he asked one of the students with surprise.

"That's right. They accused him of preparing the assassination of Lenin if Lenin came to Ugolsk. He got twelve years. Best of all, he was accused of this at a time when Lenin had been dead for fifteen years ... he, he, he ..." Colonel Bogatyrov roared with laughter. And he laughed and laughed until the students noticed that this wreck of the old front-line soldier was shaking from crying. "Sorry ..." he pulled himself together and wiped off his tears.

"Father ... let's go to the park ..." The colonel stood up and walked to the door. "Excuse me, please ..." There was a grave silence in the room, which was interrupted by Miša. It was the howl of a wounded animal rather than sobbing. "I don't believe it! Why would they sentence anyone in thirty-seven for preparing the assassination of Lenin, who hadn't been alive for so long! It's nonsense! I don't believe what they say now about Stalin. Without him the world would never have freed from Hitler's yoke! What would be the world without Stalin?! I don't believe it, I don't believe ..." He sat down and stared at the wooden floor. Several times he repeated, as if he were persuading himself. "I don't believe, I don't believe ..."

"I'm a little older than you," Dubcek said in a low voice. "In thirty-seven I was living in Gorky and I remember how we had to tear the photographs of Tukachevsky, Kaganovič, Radek and others from our textbooks, accused of things they never did. Even then, no-one believed it." Then he turned to Jakeš and Lenárt, who nodded silently. "Even with us, the General Secretary of the Party, Slanský, and Minister Clementis thought to their last minute that their allegations against them were a bad mistake. They only believed when they a noose round their neck ..."

"I don't believe what's written here. It can't be true," Miša slapped the paper he'd pulled out of his pocket with all his strength. "I've been carrying excerpts from Khrushchev's speech for months, reading them from the front and back to front and I don't understand. Josif Vissarionovich Stalin – the instigator of the massive persecution of millions of innocent victims. The founder of the gulag system which totally destroyed human lives. He was the executor of a criminal project to exterminate all smallholders, intelligentsia, clergy and all other foreign class elements. Because of him famine occurred in Ukraine between 1932 and 1933, which it is estimated killed three to six million people. A five-member smallholder family had eighty kilograms of grain a year. From hunger human beings ate mice, rats, tree bark, their own waste and in some areas there was cannibalism. Stalin is the inventor of the category of "enemies of the people" who were identified with their families for extermination. He is directly responsible for the lack of preparation for war and the resulting death of thirty million Soviet citizens. He is responsible for splitting the Russian people into hostile camps, resulting in a state of permanent civil war. He is the founder of the genocide of nations of the Soviet Union. He is responsible for the martyring of two million Soviet soldiers and officers who returned after the German captivity. Under all the principles of international law he is posthumously guilty of crimes against humanity ... Terrible ... Unbelievable ... This can't be true!" Miša sat down and took another shot of vodka. He shook his head uncomprehendingly.

"I also think we can't just condemn him out of hand. Certainly there were mistakes, but we can't suspect Comrade Stalin of doing things against the interests of the workers and the smallholders," Jakeš objected in broken Russian.

"Bandits. They're all bandits. All these old Bolshevik scum must be shot! Destroying six million hungry smallholders was in their interests? In my opinion, Stalin was sick and Khrushchev's speech should be considered heroic, because only through his personal courage did the innocent prisoners of the gulag began to be liberated, newspapers began to write more freely and the people roused from lethargy. Who can't be believed here!" Boris said, his voice booming. He was not among the youngest and he'd to fight for the admission to the Party college. It was known that he'd finally got to the college only on the basis of a letter he'd written to Khrushchev, who'd ordered the school to accept him. He was clearly following Khrushchev's line." The colonel has told you so clearly. How do you want not to believe him? Is there anyone who says he was lying?" He looked at his fellow students. They all looked away. "Because our farmers were actually slaves," he almost shouted, poking Ivan's shoulders. "Ivan, tell us how your parents lived?"

"Well ... they didn't have any personal papers, they weren't allowed to travel. The reward for their work was poor food ... I, I don't know ... I don't know ... I grew up with my aunt. She said our family had died of hunger ..." He burst into tears. He poured a glass of vodka into himself and ran out of the room.

"I was on the front and I won't tolerate anyone who slanders a Soviet soldier!" Alexei called out. "And Stalin was our first soldier."

"How was he a soldier? He didn't stick a toe out of the cosy Kremlin for the whole war. Nobody here is slandering the Soviet soldier, we just want to know the truth. If we don't know the whole truth about our past, however bitter, we'll never have any future. I don't want to be a Communist in the party that the Colonel was talking about!" Boris was irritated and somehow his gaze met Dubček's. The young Slovak student nodded.

"Even so, there won't be a storm from Khrushchev's revelation... The higher comrades will make a few changes, Khrushchev's people will take over the Stalinist posts and everything will be as before. Not the way our minds work," Alexey said skeptically.

"A new war can only be avoided if socialism is as strong as possible," Ivan calmed the atmosphere in a statesman-like manner.

"What you say is true! And we'll build it whether we like it or not. And we are ready to make any kind of sacrifice to reach this noble goal. The Soviet Union is the leading country building socialism, and it will be forever!" spluttered Stepan, whose tongue was increasingly affected by the amount of vodka he'd drunk.

"Comrade Lenin in The State and the Revolution says that if the socialist revolution wins in a developed country wins, this advanced country would take the lead in the international socialist movement ...", Dubček cautiously remarked.

"You want to say that the Czech Shweikists could lead an international labour movement? Ha, ha, ha ..." Miša laughed heartily.

"And why not?" said Dubček with a red face.

"Because you don't have the guts for it. Communism must be imposed with force. Understand! How are you going convince American workers? You have to ram it into their exploited heads!" a completely pissed Miša argued.

"People need to be convinced. Otherwise they won't trust what we do," said Dubček.

"Well, go ahead and convince them, but I'm curious how long it'll take you ... ha, ha, ha ... And don't think you're the leading force in the labour movement, because you have toilets that flush and ... hic... asphalt roads ... well, that's not ...", Miša said and fell dead drunk on the bed.

The lads slowly started to leave the room. Jakeš and Lenárt went out. Dubček opened the window and let fresh air into the room. Someone began to sing in a subdued voice, a heartfelt "The Song of the Criminal". "Beyond Baikal I hurry to meet you, mother. Is my father in good health? And my brother? Your father's been in the grave long since, covered with cold earth and your brother rattles round Siberia in irons ..."

"Alexander Stepanovich, I almost forgot. I've got something for you ..., Boris beckoned to Dubček. They left the room together. "I got some information from my friends in the Central Committee ... They found Dr. Bojko ..." Dubček stared at Boris. "Your doctor from the uprising!" He pulled a piece of paper from his pocket and handed it to Dubček. "Here it is. He was in the Vorkuta camp ... Ten years. He's seriously ill, but he's alive."

"That's wonderful. Boris, you have no idea how grateful I am. This man saved my leg in the uprising. When everyone was afraid, he cared for me. After the war, I wanted to find him, but I knew your special section had removed him..." he added sadly.

"Smersh?" Dubček nodded.

"Why?"

"His parents emigrated after the revolution to Czechoslovakia in 1917. He took our nationality, but he was still considered to be a Russian emigrant. So they packed him off..."

"I hope his suffering will end. The main gulag administration has decided to release him these days. He can return to Czechoslovakia. Don't be afraid Saša, it'll be fine." Then he thought and as if he had convinced himself. "Everything!"

"Sometimes I doubt if what we are building is right ... So much suffering and pain ..." thought the young Slovak.

PART II

CHAPTER 1

WE'LL BURY YOU!

In Moscow, Dubček felt increasingly abandoned. His spirits were troubled with sadness for his home and family. He went to Slovakia twice a year and his wife was allowed to come to him twice a year as well. He missed his boys, Anička and his friends. The family had moved from Bystrica back to Trenčín on Vajanský Street in the middle of the town. Anička and the boys were helped very much by his mother, Pavlína. Fortunately Anička had a sister, Pavla, in Trenčín, who also often helped them.

Spring in 1956 was the busiest so far in Alexander's life. After the devastating revelations of the cult of Stalin's personality, he bitterly recalled his student days in Gorky, where a large banner hung in the hall: "Stalin is the best that mankind has. Because Stalin is the hope, he is the expectation, he is the beacon that shows the way to all progressive humanity." N.S. Khrushchev. Moscow and the entire Soviet Union seemed as if they'd been taken over. There was a wave of prisoners being released from the camps. The ten to twenty-year-long or even longer isolation of these people from the world, their incredibly cruel conditions of everyday struggle for survival, had made many of them barbarians. Moreover, they were released en masse from the camps and prisons, but no-one cared what would become of these people. So they mostly gathered in Moscow, Leningrad, Kiev and other large cities where they were more likely to survive. Incidents of robbery and murders occurred almost daily. In a carriage of the Moscow Electric Railroad Dubček saw a dead man lying on the ground and the passengers indifferently stepping over him. He tried to persuade himself that he was drunk, though it was obvious that he wasn't breathing. They roused themselves a little when the person lying down was blood-stained as it was a sign of life. When he went swimming in Lake Kuskov at the end of the year with some classmates, they swam to an island in the middle of the lake, but on their return they found only their underwear on the shore.

Foreign students didn't live badly, their scholarship was at the level of the monthly salary of a Soviet worker. With Hungarian, Polish or Bulgarian classmates, they often went to the renowned café at the Metropole Hotel or the Prague restaurant in Arbat. Dubček often went to the theatre, Moscow ballet and opera. Foreign students got preference for tickets. He didn't ingratiate himself with his Soviet classmates. An unforgettable experience was the performance of the world's prima ballerina, Maja Plisecka in Tchaikovsky's Swan Lake. But whenever he was in the theatre, the stadium or fishing, he kept coming back to the stinging revelations about Stalin. The enumeration of his sins was so compelling that it could not be disbelieved. Colonel Bogatyrov and other Soviet citizens, whom his friends had introduced to him, confirmed that the facts were much worse. Dubček felt that the Communist movement was coming to an historical crossroads. It could continue on its dictatorial path or embark on a new path of decency, debate, tolerance and openness. Khrushchev gave him a new hope and new thinking. He refused to go the old way and decided to do all he could to promote Khrushchev's course. It was the only way to stand before history before his conscience, to admit the guilt that, although indirectly, still weighed on his spirits. He would try in his branch, as his capacity allowed, to reform the party so that it could strive for the fundamental values of its communist beliefs.

The thaw in Moscow after Khrushchev's speech was reacted to most stormily in Hungary. The recall of the reformist communist leader, Imre Nagy, prompted an anti-Soviet uprising. The immediate cause of the uprising was the brutal shooting by the Hungarian secret service against a student demonstration on 23rd October, 1956. The revolt forced Imre Nagy's return. On 25th October, the Hungarian insurgents took down Stalin's statue, invaded the Central Committee of the Hungarian Workers' Party and lynched several dozen Communists. On 1st November 1956, Imre Nagy announced the resumption of a pluralistic system of several political parties, the termination of Hungarian membership in the Warsaw Pact and declared neutrality. On 4th November 1956, the Soviet Command issued the order for a large-scale military operation involving hundreds of thousands of men and a thousand tanks. The young Soviet tank soldiers in Budapest wondered where they would come to the ocean. When the Hungarians explained to them that they had no ocean, they didn't want to believe them. Their commanders had told them they were going to fight English imperialists in Suez...

The Voice of America and Free Europe radio stations maintained the Hungarian rebels in the hope, intensified by the hopeless resistance of Hungarian patriots, that NATO troops would come to their aid,. However, neither the US government nor any other NATO member ever had any such an intention.

Khrushchev at a reception in the Kremlin mocked the ambassadors of the capitalist countries. "History is on our side. We will bury you!" Out of nearly 15,000 people actively involved in the uprising, 229 were sentenced to death. More than 200,000 people fled to the West from Hungary. The ambassador of the Soviet Union at the time of the Hungarian uprising was Yuri Andropov, later head of the KGB and the secretary general of the Central Committee of the KSSZ.

On 17th June 1958, the former Prime Minister, Imre Nagy, was executed. The establishment of a new Hungarian government was entrusted to János Kádár.

Dubček had mixed feelings about the Soviet intervention in Hungary, despite the Soviet media's unilaterally reporting of Western attempts to exploit some shortcomings in the People's Democratic Hungary to provoke the anti-Soviet uprising. According to Soviet newspapers, tanks had to intervene, otherwise world imperialism threatened to dominate the situation in Hungary and the country could be thrown out of the socialist camp. In the Soviet newspapers, he read with horror articles about Hungarian counter-revolutionaries and his brow furrowed when he saw photographs of communists hanging from candelabra in the Hungarian capital. The official Moscow explanation of Soviet intervention interpreted the Hungarian Revolution as an attempt to re-establish a fascist regime. In Moscow, there was no access to any information other than Soviet. From many debates with Soviet friends Dubček understood that they had the same ideas as him. Removing the iniquities of the past, yes, but not at the cost of throwing the baby out with the bath water. It was necessary to remove errors, not the system.

Looking at the Hungarian communists lynched by the mob, even the most fervent reformers tucked in their tails and waited for the situation to develop. Fear was once again an important factor in helping Novotný pacify the critical wave triggered by Khrushchev's criticism in the Czechoslovak Communist Party.

CHAPTER 2

RETURN HER EGGS

In Moscow, Dubček learned that Dr. Ivan Bojko and his wife returned to Czechoslovakia in 1956. Again he became a doctor in Melčice, where he worked until 1962. President Antonín Novotný granted amnesty to several former officials of the United Smallholder Cooperatives on the occasion of his appointment at the end of November 1957. Among the amnesty was the former chairman of JRD Krásno, Jozef Selecký.

Alexander completed a three-year study with a red diploma for the best study results amongst foreign students, but a damaged belief in Soviet-style Communism. In September 1958 he returned to Slovakia and was immediately appointed to the post of regional secretary of the Communist Party in Bratislava. On the second day after being appointed, he introduced himself to a new fellow worker. He walked from office to office, went to the kitchen and beyond the drivers and the mechanics into the garage. Jozef Brinzík became his personal chauffeur, protector and gradually a friend for life.

His family bade a final farewell to Trenčín and the Dubčeks moved to a five-room apartment under Slavín at the beginning of Donovalova Street, over the residence of the Soviet consul. From the first moment they felt at home in the four flat house. The house had been built in 1944 by the Nobel Dynamite works for its top management and the apartments had a room for servants. In every room, including the kitchen and the bathroom, there was a bell to call the maid. Maids in a classless society had already been liquidated, but the bells remained. Until Dubček cut off the cables, his boys would ring down to their grandmother who, during her frequent visits, lived in the former maid's room. Beneath them was the family of the Secretary of the Central Committee of the KSS for Agriculture, František Dvorský, whose son Fero quickly became a friend of the Dubček boys. Dvorský and the Director of State Forests, Miro Hanák, were Dubček's most frequent companions on his favourite hunting trails in the Tatras, Topoľčany or Pusté Úľany. Although there was a fruit garden around the house, Paľko, Peťko, Ferko Dvorský, Oleg Tatarka and other boys, with whom they played, especially loved the strawberries from neighbouring gardens better than their own. In every fence in the neighborhood the boys had secret holes to escape an angry farmer if they were caught. The only nearby little street on the slope below Slavín, on which there was a short straight stretch, was the nearby Mišíkova. The boys would make nets for football or hockey and as cars came in those times hardly once an hour, they could play their games undisturbed. In the abandoned concrete pillboxes over the nursery they found war cartridges from time to time. When they started to explode in the evening fire, they ran away as fast as they could. The racket of the exploding cartridges couldn't be hidden from the district superintendent.

The best were the late mornings when their fathers were at work and the boys had afternoon classes. The primary school in Čapková, to which they went, was nearby, so they could romp about in the playground opposite to their heart's content. It was terraced, the boys playing football and soritas (a blend of football and handball) at the top. In the middle there were sandboxes and booths for supervising aunts and at the bottom there were climbing frames and swings for the smallest children. Occasionally, the Dubček's came to the playground to bring her boys prune cakes and gossip with her neighbours.

Although Bratislava was an exciting city compared with Trenčín, they never felt at home. Yet, however, they discovered a lot of secluded and magic places that grew into their hearts. In addition to the football and hockey stadium, where Dubček used to be a regular visitor to the VIP sector, he liked the narrow streets of the old town. He also liked to walk to the castle hill where the ruined castle looked over the city. Though from 1953 measurement works from Prague on the castle had been under way, following the condemnation of the Husák group of bourgeois nationalists and the party congress in 1954 a strong anti-Slovak wind had rumbled. The Council of Trustees had managed approve the reconstruction of the almost total ruin, but in 1957 the chief architect of the castle reconstruction, the Czech professor Alfréd Piffl, was arrested for alleged defamation of a friendly country. However that tireless engine of reconstruction, the national artist Janko Alexy, did not give up. By letter he also turned to the new secretary of the Communist Party of West Slovakia, Alexander Dubček, who was in fact the senior chief for investment in reconstruction - the West

Slovak National Regional Committee. Dubček, despite Prague's negative opinion, gave instructions for the creation of resources for the reconstruction. In 1961, the Bratislava Castle was declared a national cultural monument and in 1968, after signing the law on the Czechoslovak Federation, it became a symbol of fundamental significance for Slovakia.

After the feast of the Three Kings in 1959, Grandmother Pavlína needed to repair torn trousers or shirts for the boys, but found that there was no thread. After the long holiday Alexander needed to get out and so happily took his wife to Halmoš's haberdashery. They walked down Kuzmániho and from Tolstého to Obrancov mieru where Anička bought yarn at Suche Mýto and they continued to their favourite inn, Fajka, on the corner of Veterná, where they drank two glasses of Račianska Frankovka. They hadn't been in the old town for a while, so they headed for Michalská Veža, when suddenly Dubček' heard raised voices. In the narrow passage beneath the gate, a grandma in a headscarf had placed a small basket with a few eggs on the ground. The public district guard sternly rebuked her, took her eggs and expelled the woman in a brutal manner, threatening that if he caught her again, she would be fined.

"Why are you screaming at that citizen?" Dubček said calmly.

"She's engaged in illegal activity!"

"What?" There was a group of people who terrified at seeing a man who had let himself to stand up to an all-powerful public security officer.

"And who are you sticking your nose in this? Your ID card!" Dubček handed him his service card. The embarrassed "Esenbák," apologized in a servile manner to the regional secretary of the party.

"But I'm just doing my duty. The selling of goods in the street is forbidden. I don't care personally one way or the other, but a byelaw is a byelaw."

"All right. Give the woman her eggs back."

The flustered policeman returned the eggs. The woman looked at Dubček with gratitude and cleared off.

"Now you know at least why there are no eggs," observed Anička angrily.

"Yet there is a new poultry farm in Cífer," he said nodding his head.

"They don't manage. And the grandmas from Záhorie have enough eggs, they just don't have anywhere to sell them."

At the next meeting of the regional committee, Dubček proposed to re-authorize the market in Bratislava. It wasn't unusual that even a few years before markets had operated in all the cities of Czechoslovakia. But according to the Soviet model they were cancelled on the grounds that it was a return to capitalism. The First Secretary of the Slovak Communists, the all-powerful Bacílek, was furious, but citizens welcomed the recovery of the central market so spontaneously that he didn't dare ban them again.

CHAPTER 3

YOU'RE BUILDING SOCIALISM AND THE TELEVISIONS AREN'T WORKING

"The soup was excellent," Dubček praised his wife.

"We got a new spice from the diplomatic store. It's called Vegeta. It adds taste." She noticed that her husband's thoughts were elsewhere. "What are you still thinking about?"

"Well, I don't want to talk about it very much, but the draft of the new constitution ..." he sighed deeply. "Imagine, they've suggest that the Slovak Double Cross be removed from the state emblem. It's supposed to be replaced by the triple fire of the Uprising. I don't know if it will be good. The Double Cross is the ancient traditional Slovak symbol. Of course, I revere the fire of the Uprising, I warmed myself there, but this doesn't seem to be good," he sighed. "And they propose to cancel the Council of Guarantors, so everything will be done in Prague. The Slovaks will become subordinate in this constitution."

"What do you want to do about it?" asked Anička.

"Me? I'm just a regional secretary ..."

"You're also a member of the Central Committee of the Czechoslovak Communist Party (UV KSČ), so you can take them to task in Prague!"

Dubček blinked and without looking at his wife added as if to himself, "It's almost too early for us to oppose Novotný's centralizing efforts openly. He's convinced that when we build the foundations of Socialism, the Czechs and Slovaks will naturally merge into one nation. But there are already enough people in Prague who are aware of the risk of centralization."

"Will it really be said that we have built socialism?" Anna asked.

"Even that. It's stupidity when we're still building socialism ..."

"And I've already got socialism!" laughed grandmother Pavlína, who had come to visit after a while. "Yesterday, I bought the soap powder for three crowns twenty and before that it was a crown more. They say in the advertisement that "Pěnik" is the best powder to get. Not to get another, so it will probably be true. And I bought the boys blue, green and gray galoshes and until recently they were only black." Dubček looked at his mother. He knew the ironic undertones she had often been using for some time. "Novotný announced on May 22nd that 'meat will be there in no time at all and since then all the Czechs have been asking where's No-time-at-all?" she added.

"Dad, are we going to the football this afternoon?" Paľko asked.

"I don't know yet," he said surprisingly. If he had time, he didn't miss a Slovan game and sometimes went to see Red Star. "Hradec?" Paľko nodded.

"It's on TV."

"You know that the image flickers on this old box?"

"And you deserve a new TV? People complain that with the bearings on your carts carriages you make a racket all the way down to Šuleková" he reproached his boys.

"Actually we're cycling. The carts are for little kids to ride in," said Peťko.

"And who goes walking under Slavín by the old pillboxes? Didn't I tell you not to play there?" The boys were silent. But they saw that their father was grinning. "I hope you win at least ..."

"Clearly. We are the Julo Dubček partisan section. We always win! ... Only ... hardly ... anyone wants to play the Germans ... What's in the box?" Paľko insisted, looking at the big box by the front door that Dubček's driver had bought. Both Milan and Peťko joined their brother's pleading.

"Only after lunch!" Their father decided. The fried chicken disappeared from their plates like lightning.

"Did you like it?" asked their grandmother who'd prepared the crunchy delicacy. The boys enthusiastically nodded.

"They're from the new poultry farm at Cífer," their father said happily.

"Dad, we've eaten now ..."

"Don't keep them in suspense," Anička smiled. It was obvious that Alexander couldn't wait to pull the treasure out of the box in which he'd hidden it. When he got up from the table, the boys held on to the box and their father pulled out a new Mánes television before their delighted eyes.

"A new TV!" grandmother clapped her hands enthusiastically. "Will you have two?" she asked, pointing to the old TV with a screen little larger than a postcard.

"That one's had it." The boys were eager to install the TV set. "And do you know what we're going to watch?" Alexander sat calmly in his armchair as the black-and-white test card appeared on the screen. "Football. Red Star and Hradec Králové. The Reds have a chance to be a champion. "

"Agh! the Reds, the police squad," Peťko, who supported Slovan, looked derisively at his father. "Slovan has no chance. The Reds have a strong team. Nothing but internationals. Matlák, Buberník, Cimra, Dolinský, Kačáni and especially Dolfi Scherer. You'll see that it's going to be the best squad in the league," said Paľko.

"I thought we would be watching only football and hockey," she contentedly brought in a tray with cakes to the table for her husband and boys. She sat down, too. Grandmother took the smallest, Milan, on to her knees. In a few minutes the test card disappeared and the reporter announced a live broadcast from the match of the sixth week of the football league. When the words were spoken by Rado Siváček, the faces of the Dubčeks were a sight to behold. They felt as if the commentator had spoken only to them. They watched the big screen, which they could not compare with the little "portholes" they'd had so far.

"Our Slovak manufacture," Alexander nodded proudly. "Made in Nižná na Orave. Boys remember it. Nižná was until recently a tiny village where only linen carpets were produced. And now there are TVs!"

"This Scherer is great," asserted Dubček, when the football star from Petržalka fired the first goal past the Hradec goalkeeper. The boys and their father were excited. At that point, however, the picture started rolling and ran unstoppably upward. Dubček picked up the instructions for use and nervously worked out which button would stop the image rolling. Finally, he managed to get the game back. At the moment Kačáni headed dangerously below the crossbar, the image resumed moving. It changed direction and rolled downwards.

"Paľko, turn the knob on the side," his father directed the oldest son to the TV. He turned the knob a bit and the image went in the opposite direction. "Not so fast. Try it more gently!" Paľko tried more gently and the picture paused. But only for a moment. Then it set off again on the road that the designers had directed it in the Tesla works at Nižná.

"Will I always be running to the TV" Paľko asked in irritation.

"You can alternate," grandmother suggested.

"Go there!" Dubček almost shouted when Scherer found himself with a huge chance at goal. The closest was the smallest Miško, but he wasn't fast enough, so the Dubčeks lost Scherer's second goal to. "To hell with that television!" Dubček muttered. At that moment a message, "The error is not on your set" appeared on the screen.

"You see, I told you it isn't the TV's fault. They know how to do it in Orava. They produce only good things there." After a while, the notice disappeared. Football continued. The rolling image, too.

"Oh, an Orava TV shouldn't be like an Orava cheese whip," grandmother threw in.

"It's said you can get good ones in Vienna," said Paľko annoyed by the constant jumping of the TV image.

"No Austrian TVs. Our technicians are just as good. Tomorrow we'll take it for repair! Turn it off and turn on the old one! "

"That's jumping, too."

"Then ... we'll listen to the radio!" Dubček decided. Paľko anxiously switched on a tiny transistor radio, a T 58, a Tesla Nižná product from Orava. Fortunately, it worked.

Frustrated the boys shoved the TV back into its box.

"You're building socialism and the TVs aren't working," said Grandmother Pavlína.

CHAPTER 4

FIVE YEAR PLANS UP SHIT CREEK

After almost two years in Bratislava, the Dubčeks had got used to it. Although every morning the service Tatra 603 waited in front of the house, Dubček liked to walk to work on foot. The Regional Committee of the party at Žabotova was a hop, skip and a jump from their home in Donovalova Street. If he could, he used the service car as little as possible. There were very few private vehicles at this time and he sometimes lent the very attractive Tatra with Jožko Brinzík to one of his subordinates for a wedding. He earned the criticism of the county committee's bookkeeper, who was irritated that his chief boss lent the car without first signing a travel order.

The boys most enjoyed the rare Sundays when their father had time and took them to the Central Committee's Recreation Centre at Železná studnička near the final bus stop. The facility was in an enclosed area of the State Sanitarium, where only staff and officials of the party and state institutions had access. The lawn was kept in exemplary condition as were the bowling alley, the football pitch and a volleyball court. As the boys romped in the pool, the men played football. Šlapka, Janík and Colotka excelled among others at football. Dubček was better at volleyball. Sometimes Karol Bacílek stood under the net, but because of his figure he would quickly stop and go bowling or play cards. When the abrasive, this eternally smoking bearded character played 'Mariáš, children circumvented him. Bacílek didn't like children larking about nearby when he played cards. Dubček liked best to dive from the five-meter-high board. He'd acquired an almost professional style from his time as a student in Moscow, where he was a member of a diving team. He noticed that women sunbathing at the pool occasionally cast a glance at his sportsman's figure.

Dubček would take his boys fishing in Parina or to a pond by Biela skala near Papiernička in the Little Carpathians. This place was a particular favourite of Dubček's. The trout, which had the honour to be caught by party officials, were grilled by their wives. The successful fishermen drank drams of vodka or good Orešanské wine. After a successful fish the Mariáš cards would be pulled out. Dubček didn't play preferring to carry on catching fish or playing with the boys in the stream. Paľko, Peťko and the youngest, Milan had found friends and were content with their life in Bratislava. When they'd begun to feel the same certainty in their new environment, there was bad news. They would be moving to Prague. After two years, their father, in his capacity as the West Slovak Regional Secretary, had, on the recommendation of Comrade Novotný, been elected as the Secretary of the Communist Party Central Committee for Industry. For the boys it was another loss of friends and a move to a new, Prague environment in which the unknown 'uncle' Novotný lived, about whom their parents had no high opinion. In Prague in the Bubeneč district they were given an apartment in a state villa.

Dubček's activities included the metallurgy, engineering, chemical and construction industries. Despite the restructuring of these sectors problems had accumulated. Dubček understood that the problem was not in bad management, but in the system itself. The lack of independence of individual plants, their lack of interest in economic results, their blind fulfillment of the tasks planned by the centre were a sure way to inefficiency. Centralization had hampered people's initiative. Pilfering, fraud and false accounting of economic results proliferated. The system had reached its limits. Everyone knew the country was affected by the crisis, but no-one said so. In April 1962, the third five-year plan was abolished. "The five-year-old plan is up shit creek, and all the upcoming ones will be up shit creek as long as competition is not allowed!" said their neighbour, Valášek, when he was with Mrs Dubček queuing at the Dělnická Street butcher's.

As an industry official, Dubček sought solutions within the possibilities that the then-centrally planned economy allowed. He began to meet experts such as Ota Šik or Karel Kouba. He criticized unrealistic plans, had different opinions from Novotný and his people on the investment priorities in Slovakia. Moreover, he was surprised to find that the first man in the country knew nothing about Slovakia and, even worse, he didn't want to know.

In Moscow they removed Stalin from the mausoleum, Stalingrad was renamed Volgograd and changes began in Czechoslovakia. Unfortunately, they were only symbolic. Stalin's peak was given back its old name of Gerlachovský, the embalmed Gottwald was removed from the mausoleum in Prague's Vítkov and from Letná during the month of Soviet-Czechoslovakian friendship in November 1962 the statue of Stalin disappeared. It took eight hundred kilos of explosives to blow it into the air. Stalin's head broke off and plunged into the Vltava River. The largest statue of Stalin in the world had been removed, but the year before, on the night of 12-13 August 1961, another Stalin mega-memorial, the grimmest building that Stalin's godchildren could think of - the Berlin Wall, began to be built. The chief constructor was the East German Communist leader, later the initiator of Dubček's fall, Walter Ulbricht.

CHAPTER 5

THE STRUGGLE BEGINS

Dubček repeatedly and stubbornly urged Novotný to rehabilitate Vladimír Clementis. He laid siege regularly to the presidential offices at Prague Castle. The President sent word to him that he had no time for him. Yet Novotný gave in and accepted the stubborn Slovak secretary unwillingly. Dubček told the most influential man in the country that rehabilitation was a question of human dignity and it was a moral obligation for the Communists to correct the mistakes they had made. Novotný was afraid that an avalanche would start, which would eventually end by finishing him. Since the time the interior minister, Barák, had tried to remove him he feared this even more. Eventually, Barák was falsely convicted and sentenced with Khrushchev's blessing to twelve years in jail. Dubček added to his demand for rehabilitation criticism of insufficient financial resources for some Slovak regions. For the first time he deplored Novotný's degradation of Slovak national authorities in the new constitution, upon which Dubček had been silent up to this point.

"We must stop this Dubček," Novotný said to the circle of his intimates. He started gradually. First he transferred Dubček back to Slovakia, where he was elected by the Slovak Communists on November 25, 1962, as a member of the presidium and Secretary of the UV KSS. At first glance it looked like a promotion. In fact the Secretary at the central level became Secretary at the regional level. In Bratislava he was surrounded by Novotný's creatures and supporters, Bacílek, David, Chudík and Sabolčík. He couldn't count on his fluctuating classmate from Moscow, Lenárt. So he began to renew contacts with old friends and search for new allies. In spite of Novotný's disapproval, he was elected a member of the commission, chaired by Drahomír Kolder, a member of the Central Committee of the Czech Communist Party (UV KSČ). The commission's task was to investigate the repression and political crimes of the 1950s. Dubček directed the group that revised the case of Mária Svermova, former Deputy to Secretary General Slánsky. For more than half a year, the Kolder Commission investigated top secret archives on the political trials in which thousands of people were unlawfully convicted. Dubček was shaken by documents and evidence of inhuman treatment of the accused. He was horrified to realize that when on the occasion of the 19th anniversary of the Slovak National Uprising he received a group of twenty partisan commanders, all except two had been persecuted. Page after page, as they passed through his hands caused shocks and new questions. Although the trials were controlled by the Soviet secret service in cooperation with the ŠtB (State security), and only the narrowest circle of the highest party leadership knew about their real background, Dubček felt a share of complicity. In those times, he was the district and regional secretary of the party that had perpetrated them. The Kolder commission only investigated the repression of the Communist Party functionaries. The rehabilitation of thousands of innocent convicted priests, partisans, scientists, teachers, peasants and others who were convicted only so that someone could be brought to the altar of victims for the paranoid proletarian god in Moscow had yet to be dealt with. The results were published at the Communist Party of Czechoslovakia Central Committee in April 1963. They set off a breeze that gradually turned to a wind in 1968. Novotný prevented Dubček from speaking at this meeting.

What he wanted to say he said four days later, on 8th April at the meeting of the UV KSS in Bratislava.

At the words of guilt of his closest allies, Bacílek, Kopřiva a Široký, Novotný narrowed his eyes slightly. Only those closest to him noticed this. Dubček thundered from the podium, "It emerged that the so-called anti-state conspiracy centre, headed by Rudolf Slánsky, did not exist. It was artificially constructed by the security authorities whose conclusions were fully adopted by the court and the prosecutor's office. The sentences of Slánsky, Geminder, Freik, Frank, Clementis, Reicin, Švab, Margolius, Fischla, Šling and Simone to the death penalty and Löbla, London and Hajdu to the punishment of a long-term prison were illegal! It is not true that the convicted ganged together against the party and the state. The anti-legal trials of Mária Švermova, Gustáv Husák, Ladislav Novomeský and others were the same. They were artificially constructed. Klement Gottwald, First Secretary of the CPC, was personally informed of the criminal punishments and court decisions and even proposed sentences himself. After the departure of Ladislav Kopřiva, who was replaced by Comrade Karol Bacílek as Minister of National Security, the arrest of party workers continued."

The chamber boiled and Novotný's eyes narrowed more and more. Bacílek glared icily at the hall. He felt the chair beneath him start to shake. Dubček seemed to have run amok and those who knew him knew this was the right, fighting Šaňo who, when he saw injustice, ceased to control himself. He raised his voice and spread his arms wide. "The individuals who were involved themselves directly and brutally have to take responsibility for their actions. The then party leadership in Slovakia bears full responsibility for the violation of socialist law in the years when the Chairman of the Communist Party of Slovakia was Comrade Široký. Under the leadership of the Secretary of the Central Committee of the KSS, Bacílek, chairman of the KSS, discussed the preparation of the trial of Husák, Novomeský and others."

Novotný anxiously watched the gestures of agreement from the listeners. He realized that to save himself Široký and Bacílek would have to be sacrificed. In his speech he cordially thanked Dubček for his open words and suggested that it might be him who could replace Bacílek. Behind the scene he campaigned for his stooge, Chudík. It turned out, however, that Dubček's position was so strong that at that meeting he was, at the suggestion of Novotný, who in the meantime was travelling back to Prague, elected as the First Secretary of the Slovak Communists. It was Dubček's first victory over Novotný. As a result of his new function he automatically became a member of the Prague Presidium of the UV KSČ. Novotný could not prevent his return to Prague. The struggle of these two men had begun.

CHAPTER 6

IT'LL TAKE A LONG TIME TO CLEAR THE AIR

The office of the First Secretary of the Communist Party of Slovakia was in a white, five-storey building at the beginning of Hlboká Road on the first floor directly above the main entrance. It wasn't very large, about six by seven metres long. On the front wall, there was a large image of Lenin, attached to a working table was another table with four chairs on both sides, covered with glass. There were four ashtrays full of cigarette ends. A portrait of President Novotný and the first secretary of the Communist Party of Slovakia, Bacílek, hung over the wall with a bookcase behind the work table. Beneath his portraits Karol Bacílek sat at the conference table and lit one Bystrica after another. He picked them out of a soft pack of a hundred. The second hundred pack of Bystrica was on his work desk and a third on a second table in the corner of the room. A kilim carpet of indeterminate colour was burned in many places by the ash that had spilled to the ground from the trailing hands of the sixty-seven-years old Communist pasha. The room literally smelt of smoke, which was permanently in the curtains, the walls, the carpets and the furniture. Everything, especially Karol Bacílek, was constantly dusty from fine cigarette ash. He was a former auxiliary worker from the village of Choťánky near Prague, who had risen to be the strongest man in Slovakia, a fanatic, for whom the most sacred church was communist.

Twenty-five years younger, a non-smoker and sportsman Dubček looked irritably at the heaps of papers that were stacked on all the tables. A secretary followed him and carefully wrote the handover protocol. Tomorrow Dubček would officially take over from Bacílek.

"You're young and I see for you that you've also succumbed to what Khrushchev started. But it'll pass and the party will walk its proven way. I don't say that we did everything well and we made mistakes, but we did learn. But the main thing is not to deviate from the way. They tried it on me from all sides. Even with this movie ... but what you call, you know ... They wrote about it the paper ... "

"The Sun in the Net," said Dubček reading his papers.

"That's right. I banned it. They do not love me. There, such a young man tells his mother that the Danube is a great and powerful river and yet in the scene the Danube was dry. They were shooting on purpose when it was dry. I know they meant the party ... That's right, but what do you call it ... amphora? "

"Metaphor," Dubček corrected him.

"Metaphor. But I know they thought the party was drying up ... Even the song," he stood in the last minutes of his position in his office job and tugging at his braces he began to sing. "That life is a worn-out vest for me ... how can life be a worn out vest ... So they're young, they have something to look forward to. I'm not saying, so and we were young, we ran after girls, we got up to mischief, but we were more modest. We did what we could ... they want jazz, well, but why not our beautiful folk songs? I know those musicians and writers. It isn't that that they're against the party, they just don't understand the theme ... Sometimes Mňačko and other writers came here. But Mňačko was the best player at Mariáš. Discussing things with artists is difficult ... But I like them basically. If they don't write against the party, let them write," he said to Dubček, who was looking at a hard-to-read text with many grammatical errors written in green ink.

"Good, eh?" Bacílek winked. "The green ink. You can do as I did. I was the only one using in the UV. Immediately they saw that it was in green ink they knew it was from me." Dubček was silent. "Take care, Sasha! From the twentieth congress, reaction has begun to stick out its horns." Dubček laughed. "Why are you laughing?"

"I'm introducing myself as a reaction to sticking out its horns ..."

"I mean like a horn, don't you understand? I also had to ban this Dr. Zhivago. Don't allow it! It's clear provocation by the Paštrnák." Dubček laughed, Bacílek looked at him blankly.

"Pasternak," he corrected him.

"But you're a smartypants like Husák. And he's starting to jump. While I was doing black work in the party, organizing strikes and organizing the workers, Clementis, Husák and the like, were writing articles and talking to the intellectuals. After the uprising and liberation, they sat down in an office and wanted to discard us, the old Bolsheviks. "

Dubček had thought for a long time how to ask him. Then it came out of him. "Comrade Bacílek, can I ask you ... Does the name of Selecký mean anything?"

"Seleck, Seleck ... it was," he began to remember. Then he frowned. "No, he doesn't. Why?"

"He was the best guy I ever met. They closed him for five years. It's said his father was with you in rebellion ..."

"I don't remember, I don't remember ... It was years ago ... Look, there's a fine looking fellow, yeah?" Bacílek tried to change the topic and proudly showed him a photo where he was in the dress uniform of a general of the National Security Corps adorned with medals. Gottwald had had to bestow this rank due to the Moscow pressure at the time when he was the dreaded Minister of national security who, along with the NKVD, had prepared and directed the trials of Slánsky and others. It was notorious that he had a large mirror in his office where he'd admire himself in this general's uniform.

"At that time, the sections kissed my ass and now they chase me over Slánsky. You could have stood up for me."

"I don't have the slightest reason to stand up for you." Dubček's gaze fell on a pale-green envelope with the inscription "Information on the trial of members of the Slovak side of the anti-Partisan terrorist unit Edelweiss. Banská Bystrica November 12, 1962" For a moment he weighed the envelope in his hand.

"That Nižňanský was a pretty dirty bastard," Dubček put the file in front of the secretary who added it to her list of selected materials.

"You know ... you yourself were in the uprising ... He was a Slovak soldier, he was in the uprising, but the Germans captured him, so he made them a promise and took over command of the Slovak part ..."

"You met him?"

"Why do you ask?"

"Just asking."

"After the suppression of the uprising, we and Čulen went with him to the mountains. We broke up there, somehow the Germans captured him near Čierny Balog. Why are you so interested? "

"And how about Šmidke and Clementis?"

"Why are you asking?" Bacílek burst out. "I didn't create the bourgeois nationalists here! The party uncovered them revealed them and sent them behind bars! But so what? Now they're being rehabilitated. Clementis's widow will get a thousand and sixty crowns widow's pension. I've seen the materials."

At that moment, Dubček couldn't hold back. "I don't think, Comrade Bacílek, that the party uncovered them. You and Široký sent them behind bars! Don't hide behind the party! And I assure you that while I am head of the Slovak party, the people will learn everything the Kolder commission has revealed. Husák, Novomeský and more! Also about you! "

"So we see how official you've become. But you liked to bowl with me at Železná studnička!"

Dubček thoughtfully pulled aside the smelly curtain, opened the window and breathed deeply. "It'll take a long time to clear the air ..."

CHAPTER 7

IF WE DON'T STOP HIM WE'RE IN DEEP SHIT

Although the leadership of the Communist Party tried to conceal the results of the Kolder Commission from the public, many of them made their way to the public. Rehabilitation has become a public matter. A wave of complaints and dissatisfaction began. Society shook off its lethargy and the breeze changed into a wind. At the beginning it was stronger in Slovakia. Artists, scientists, writers and journalists, in particular, dared to publish unprecedented materials. Immediately after the turn of the year in 1963 the weekly, Život, brought out in its New Year's issue the first part of Solzhenitsyn's One Day in the Life of Ivan Denisovich. The tale of the convict Shukhov in the Stalin Workers' Brigade 104 became a sensation. In the Soviet Union, Solzhenitsyn, forbidden until recently became a favourite author during Khrushchev's rule.

Less than three weeks after the election of Dubček as the First Secretary of the Central Committee of the Communist Party, the Third Congress of the Slovak Writers' Union was held in Bratislava. The congress became a forerunner of the political movements that Czechoslovakia experienced in subsequent years. The surface was broken by Ladislav Novomeský, who engaged in a passionate defense of Vladimír Clementis. Novomeský renewed his membership in the union. Kultúrny život began to publish unprecedented articles and became a forum for critical attitudes, efforts to correct injustices both in Slovakia and in Bohemia. Mňačko's Delayed reports, which were published in a series, literally roused its readers. Kultúrny život was the most read weekly of these times. Its issues were regularly sold out and requested under the counter. The editorial office provided space for the rehabilitated Husák, Novomeský, Löbl, as well as the Czech writers, because the atmosphere in Prague was substantially more stifling than in Bratislava.

On 28 May 1963, a Slovak journalist congress was held in Bratislava, which became a key event for the prospective settling of accounts with conservative forces. Slovak journalists pointed out the necessity for freedom of information and the democratization of political and public life. The speech of Mieroslav Hysko, Editor-in-Chief of the rebellious Pravda exploded like a bomb. In his hour long performance he criticized the political practices of the cult of personality and accused Viliam Široký as the instigator of the campaigner against so-called Slovak bourgeois nationalism. Široký was still the powerful Chairman of the Czechoslovak government. The publication of Hysko's performance in Pravda was a public sensation and terrified conservatives. The Editor-in-Chief of Pravda was Ondrej Klokoč, one of Dubček's close friends whom he had known from work together in Banská Bystrica. The article was published prompted by criticism that Pravda, in terms of publishing courage as the central authority of the KSS in terms of journalistic courage, lagged far behind newspapers and magazines such as Kultúrny život, Smena, Práca, Roháč and others. It was clear to Novotný that without Dubček's consent it wouldn't have been possible to publish this article.

The recreation complex on the Vltava River near Orlík Castle was built by Novotný for himself and his henchmen in the early sixties. In this fenced, police-guarded area, there was a large main building, modern villas equipped according to the Western European standard, allocated for recreation to individual members of the Bureau of the Central Committee. Separated from the other buildings, alone in a high place was a house called "the Eagle's Nest." It belonged to Antonín Novotný, proud to be first man in the country. He was so self-absorbed that he sometimes hit his head in the glass door to the main building. The Eagle's Nest was not an imitation of a Western capitalist villa, but a Czech village cottage. There was a huge brewing barrel and inside it a large table with chairs. The fundamental issues of the Communist Party of Czechoslovakia in Novotný's times were addressed in this barrel. He and his cronies solved them playing Mariáš. Those who belonged to the "barrel" party were the key people of the country. Miroslav Mamula - head of the feared Security and Defence department of the Central Committee, Pavel Auersperg - head of Novotný's secretariat, Jiří Hendrych - ideological secretary, Drahomír Kolder, Vladimír Koucký - secretaries of the Communist Party of the Czechoslovak Communist Party. Dubček, although he was entitled to recreation, ostentatiously did not go to Orlík.

"What mess is Dubček making in Slovakia?" Novotný cried out furiously after Mamula had placed a paper in front of him.

"I think Toník our Sasha knows very well what he's doing. He's going to attack you through Široký! said Auersperg.

"Slovakia is going wrong! It's a bad thing ... The weekly, Život, is continuing with the Solzhenitsyn, Kultúrny život is doing its best to get banned.To top it all is the performance of Hysko at the journalist's congress. Did you read it?" Novotný hit Pravda on the table so violently that a number of playing cards fell to the floor. "Allegedly we don't have freedom of information. He's calling for the democratization of public and political life and actually refers to Marx! Can you understand that? Who is this Hysko?"

"Such a wretch ... He was the editor-in-chief of Pravda in the Slovak uprising ..." Mamula said coldly.

"The resolution called for the congress of Slovak journalists 'to make the most of the effort to make the press a permanent parliament of the masses!'" Novotný read from Pravda in parodic Slovak. "What is the press?"

"Print," said Mamula.

"And the editor-in-chief Klokoč is who?"

"Dubček's pal," said Hendrych.

"Damn ... I myself suggested Dubček as the first secretary of the Slovak party. I told him that I trusted him that I knew his father from the concentration camp and that I believed he was a brave comrade like him. And you see what this person does...! What have our comrades done with press supervision? What do our comrades do in Bratislava? David, Chudík, Sabolčík, Lenárt? He wants Husák and Novomeský to return to leading positions in the party!"

"I told you that replacing Bacílek with Dubček would not be good," Mamula sighed.

"I know that too, but neither Chudík nor Lenárt could get the support in instead of him. Almost absolute support! This indictment of Comrade Kohler is an inconvenience! "

"This is a dangerous route! We can't allow this! It'll lead to Hungary in fifty-six!" Mamula was scared.

"I know that the arrests and repressions in the 1950s contradicted the law, but then that wasn't taken into account. I personally initiated the directive that the laws must be observed!" Novotný nodded. "Now that we have come to real socialism, I won't allow our efforts to be challenged! Dubček directly attacked the new Institute. They don't like that I've cancelled some Slovak authorities! They were not only useless, but they were centres of separatism and Slovak nationalism! Yes, the attack on Široký is an attack on me! That's clear! This is the beginning of the campaign against all the pre-war comrades. It's the start! So, as Khrushchev began in Moscow, Dubček is beginning with us!"

"But he's supported by many party organizations. Especially in Slovakia," Mamula said.

"We won't keep Široký, Lenárt instead of him will become Prime Minister and Chudík will be the chairman of the Slovak National Council. What do you say?" He turned to Auersperg. Novotný lost a hand Mariaš and sighed sadly. "Recently I've been losing somehow ... But that'll work. I won't an opposition from the left. The right doesn't matter, but the left shouldn't be allowed to form a group! Not even on the pretext of correcting mistakes, as Dubček claims," Novotný ruminated.

"We've got to stop this man! At any cost! If we don't succeed, we are all in deep shit!" Mamula said dryly.

CHAPTER 8

DANGEROUS JOURNEY

During the next meeting of the UV KSČ secretariat, Novotný didn't initially raise the matter of the situation in Slovakia. But all of them there felt a tension hanging in the air. Finally, Novotný couldn't contain himself and during the break came up to Dubček.

"What's going on over there?"

"What do you mean?"

"A congress of writers, journalists, those articles in the press. Why don't you have it under control?" He said cautiously, but felt like he was seething inside.

"Could you be more specific?" Dubček asked. Novotný thought for a moment, then started out. "Hysko's Critique of Široký."

"That's not an easy thing," Dubček said calmly. "We both know that in the 1950s he dipped his fingers in the worst sort of pie. It is clear from the Kolder Commission's report. Hysko can't know what we know, but obviously he and others know enough and his criticism has its merit. In such a situation, I don't think I should do anything about it. "

"It's too risky at this tense time to let such things out of the party. Isn't the Široký case a party internal affair? "

"I think that's just the problem. The public isn't informed of the party's efforts to rectify illegality. People see developments in the Soviet Union and think rehabilitation in Czechoslovakia is going too slowly."

"Comrade Dubček, Sasha, I strongly urge you to make Hysko and Klokoč aware of the implications to the party!"

"I don't know exactly what they have done wrong..."

"If you would oblige me!"

Novotný decided to clean out the stomachs of Slovak party officials personally. At a meeting on 12th June in Košice, he wagged his fingers and shouted at frightened officials. "The problem that has been recently discussed is the problem of bourgeois nationalism in Slovakia ... I read the article from Comrade Hysko in Pravda, I read a number of articles in Kultúrny život and I say it is a dangerous journey taken by the writers of these articles, as well as the editors. I also openly say that we will not allow the organ of the Central Committee of the Communist Party of Slovakia Pravda to become a platform for reporting false opinions and hysterical assaults on the party! "Dubček sat a metre away from the shouting Novotný. The silent hall followed the first man of the Slovak Communists. He stared coldly in front of him.

The pressure of Novotný to recall Klokoč was resisted by Dubček. He punished him at a party meeting with a warning. Likewise, Miroslav Hysko wasn't punished. In his criticism of Hysko's article, Dubček laconically stated that "He could not agree with everything that Comrade Hysko had written and besides he could no longer agree that Pravda had brought about a rise through his contribution in such a form at this time."

20th September, 1963 Novotný dismissed Široký as Prime Minister of the Czechoslovak Socialist Republic. Half a year after his appeal his wife, Margita, shot herself. He was totally alone, gradually losing the ability to walk and was about to be confined to a wheelchair. It was as if nature wished to avenge this once powerful man. His friends and enemies abandoned him. The only one who sometimes came to see him was Alexander Dubček.

Gustáv Husák and Ladislav Novomeský were acquitted of bourgeois nationalism. The Kolder Commission held that the judicial trial of the "bourgeois nationalists" was irrelevant, rehabilitated them as citizens and restored their membership of the Communist Party. However, it did not examine the legitimacy of the Party's allegation of nationalist deviation based on the principle that the conclusions of IX. The KSS offensive in 1950, when they were officially criticized, was correct. This judgment caused such outrage in Slovakia that in June 1963 a new, the Barnabitská Commission (named after the former Barnabitská monastery in Prague, where it presided), which in December concluded that the allegations about Husák, Novomeský and others of bourgeois nationalism were unjustified and fabricated. The highest party bodies subsequently fully rehabilitated Clementis, Husák, Novomeský and Šmidke. Clementis and Šmidke were dead. Novomeský had no political ambitions.

The educated, imprisoned and weather beaten lawyer, Husák, with the hallmark of a victim of injustice, however saw his chance. He was increasingly using his skills and, in particular, furthering his ambition. He raised fears not only with Novotný, but also Dubček could see a certain danger in this well-known and respected person with a significant intellectual potential. In July 1963, he invited him to discuss Husák's position and complete rehabilitation. He also tried to establish human contact with him, unfortunately he didn't succeed. Their first encounter ended in awkwardness.

A number of Communist functionaries opposed Husák's new acceptance by the party. They argued that he had remained a man who was calculating and ambitious for power. This was confirmed, in particular, by those who knew Husák at the time of the war and the beginning of the 1950s when his political star rose. Dubček took no notice of these opinions, nor the opinion of his father, who knew Husák well. Above all he wanted truth and justice to triumph. Finally on 5th February, 1964, he handed the renewed identity card of a member of the Communist Party in person to Husák. He was offered the position of Deputy Minister of Justice, but Husák refused and continued to work in the Slovak Academy of Sciences.

On 15th March, 1964, Gustáv Husák gave an unusually courageous speech at the Bratislava Communist Party Conference in Bratislava. Alexander Dubček sharply criticized him. As a result of this criticism, a proposal was withdrawn that Husák should stand as a candidate for the National Assembly. The tension between Dubček and Husák didn't ease up. Rather on the contrary...

CHAPTER 9

MAKE SOMETHING UP

"Comrade First Secretary, Comrade Minister of the Interior," his secretary told Novotný.

"Let them come in," Novotný laconically called, smiling nervously. Lubomír Štrougal entered his office in the building of the Communist Party of the Czechoslovak Communist Party on the Vltava River with a man

"Honourable Comrade President," said the minister "Let me introduce to you Comrade Lieutenant Colonel Kulifaj."

"Good day Comrade President," Kulifaj greeted Novotný.

"Sit down comrades ... Excuse me, we don't have much time, there are comrades waiting for me ... so I'll be brief," he turned after a moment's thought to Kulifaj. "Comrade Lieutenant Colonel ... You know Comrade Dubček well."

"Yes, Comrade First Secretary."

"I think the Comrade Minister explained the sensitivity of the matter."

"Yes, Comrade President."

"Call me Comrade Novotný," he said, putting Kulifaj, who did not know how to address him, in his place. "How do you know Dubček?"

"Um ... We were children together in the Soviet Union within the Interhelp teams with our parents. Comrade Dubček was from Trenčín like us. Then we worked together in Dubnica's Škoda works and in the war we were ..." he breathed out a little, "we were together in the uprising."

"Well ... Is it true that comrade Dubček a member of the party in forty-five had a wedding in church?"

"Yes, in the Evangelical church in Kochanovce. It's a "dedina" near Trenčín. "

"What is a dedina?" he asked Kulifaj, as he could not remember.

"Village," Štrougal readily replied.

"Fine ... And those armoury works in Dubnica were under the control of the Nazis ..." Novotný said.

"Yes, it was military production."

"So not just anybody could work there ..."

"No."

"His wife working there ..."

"Yes ... But Dubček was a highly qualified toolmaker and turner."

"I didn't mean that ... Those who worked there had to be checked ... as reliable ... Do you understand Comrade Colonel?!"

"Probably, yes ..." Kulifaj was worried, wondering where Novotný was leading.

"So you see, Comrade ... sorry what was your name?"

"Kulifaj."

"Comrade Kulifaj. Find out something about how Dubček really was ... Even in the uprising!" He thought for a moment, then glanced at Kulifaj with a mysterious smile. "Excuse me if I understand correctly ... You're said to have been a member of the secret security services of the Slovak state ..."

"It was a long time ago, I explained it, I regretted, and I think, Comrade First Secretary that ..." he realized that he had spoken in Slovak and quickly switched to Czech. "I believe that through my actions I have sufficiently demonstrated fidelity to our Party and socialism!"

"That's all right, Comrade Lieutenant Colonel, I'm just asking if you remember why Comrade Dubček does not communicate with you anymore more actively ... You ought to know ... He was in the same section as the commander ... who confessed to helping the Germans ... was he called Trójan?"

"Trójan was accused of sabotaging the five-year plan," Kulifaj's throat began to go dry.

"You know how it's done!" Novotný stood up offered his hand. "We don't have much time ... Comrade Minister here will create all the conditions for you to be successful ... Thank you, Comrades." Novotný made a deliberate gesture that the interview was ended.

CHAPTER 10

DONE, I RESIGNED

After returning from Prague, the Dubčeks moved to a villa on Mišíkova Street. Dubček's personal driver and confidant was again "Brinzíček", as called Jozef Brinzík. He sincerely loved this devoted Záhorák, who never deceived him and never said no. The Brinzík family became friends with the Dubčeks. They went to Prague twice a week, which on the cracked roads was physically very demanding. They usually travelled at night. When Jožko Brinzík's eyes were tired, Dubček ordered him to take a smoker's break or he sang to him. Červené jabĺčko, Trenčín dolinečka and Pieseň frontového šoféra belonged among his most favourite songs.

On 14th October, 1964, Dubček was in his living room with his boys watching a recording of the Czechoslovakia - South Korea football match at the Tokyo Olympics. They were in a good mood. The new Ametyst TV was working and Czechoslovakia was winning with by a high score.

In the afternoon shortly after fifteen o'clock, when Ivan Mráz put one of six goals in the South Korean net, Nikita Sergeyevich Khrushchev came home to his villa in the Lenin hills much earlier than usual. His son, Sergei, welcomed him. His father put his black briefcase into his hand.

"Done. I resigned," he said, the previous day one of the most powerful men of the globe. After a short pause, he added. "I didn't go to lunch with them. But I'm happy. The style of governing and relations in the top echelons has changed fundamentally. Was it possible for someone to come to a meeting and tell Stalin that he didn't meet our requirements and suggest that he resign? He would have let hardly a stain of fat remain from us. It is to my credit that they dared to suggest it to me now."

"Who did they propose instead of you?" Sergei asked.

"Brezhnev."

When Dubček learned the next day that Khrushchev had been recalled, he remembered his meeting with him during a recent celebration of the 20th anniversary of the Slovak National Uprising in Banská Bystrica. At the airport in Sliač they put the Soviet and Czechoslovak delegation in the limousines and set off to the Bystrica amphitheatre for the celebration. Khrushchev was driven with Novotný in one of the first cars with Dubček seated at the end of the convoy according to Novotný's protocol organisers. As the column approached the city, where an excited crowd was waiting, it stopped. The Soviet ambassador, Zimjanin, jumped out of the second car and suddenly ran from one car to the other and looked inside each one. The panting ambassador came up to Dubček's limousine, pushed his head in and cried out, "Alexander Stepanovitch, come with me quickly. Nikita Sergeyevich wants you to be next to him when we head to the city!" Dubček stepped hesitantly, following Zimjanin and passing along almost the entire convoy until they arrived at Khrushchev's car. Nikita Sergeyevich welcomed him with a big smile. He openly praised Dubček's attempt to correct the mistakes of the past caused by the post-war Communist leadership and underlined the importance of complete rehabilitation of the unjustly convicted. Novotný's blood froze.

During the handing over of state honours on the solemnly decorated podium, Novotný forgot Ján Buchel, a representative of the partisan village Uhrovec. When he was alerted, he invited him to the podium and Novotný handed him the medal with a sour face. Dubček stood in a little way off, watching the scene with a smile.

After the celebration, the whole company took off to a nearby spa at Sliač. In the afternoon, Dubček noticed that Khrushchev had slipped through the side doors of the hotel and was strolling along the edge of the forest. He was thoughtful and gloomy. Dubček was worried about him. Khrushchev looked at him sadly and thanked him for worrying. "Everything's all right," he forced himself to smile. Shortly after visiting Czechoslovakia, Khrushchev left for a holiday in the Crimea. From there he returned to Moscow as a prisoner of the KGB, who, along with the Brezhnev clique, dropped him.

Dubček didn't understand why Khrushchev had to leave. He didn't understand that he had finished with Stalin but didn't finish with Stalinism. He himself acted as an autocrat. His historical condemnation of the cult of personality meant the end of mass terror, but nothing had changed in the totalitarian structure of the Leninist state with the absolute monopoly of power by the party. The narrow elite layer of Communists continued to remain intact and with the help of the army and the police remained in power. Its strength Dubček was soon to experience himself at the cost of his own hide.

CHAPTER 11

ŠAŇO, GIVE A DAMN!

President Novotný declared "We were one nation and we will be again!" He was convinced that the Czechs and Slovaks would merge into one nation in the communist society, which in practice meant the total absorption of the Slovaks into Bohemia. While there was investment in Slovakia it was only in primary production and its share of manufacturing industry wasn't even a fifth. Only four percent of Slovaks worked in central organisations in Prague. When the representatives of Slovakia, especially Dubček and Biľak, supported by the overwhelming majority of the Slovaks, strongly opposed the centralizing efforts of Prague, they encountered resistance. "We have stuffed so much money into the Slovaks and they still don't like it," the average Czech citizen did not understand the demands of the Slovaks. In the hockey match Spartak Praha Sokolov - Slovan Bratislava, however, one could hear from the fans "the Slovak losers" or "Big-Ears Golonka", when the defenders Tikal and Bünther incited the spectators. Novotný began to worry about a new wave of Slovak nationalism, and considered Dubček the leader.

"Give a damn," Dubček was told by his close friend, District Secretary of the party in Trenčín, Július Turček. "The ŠtB is coming after you. Even after Anička. They descended on us in Dubnica and, as far as I know, in Uhrovec as well."

"Where do get this from?"

"At the end of April, two Czech-speaking men dragged Engineer Navrátil into a car as they left the Dubnica factory. He told this to Mrs. Konská, and she, as she's from your home town and likes you, came to see me. Similarly I was told by men from Velčice and Topoľčany. They asked whether or not you had cooperated with the Hlinka Guard and the Gestapo and whether Anička had not worn a red armband with a swastika in the Dubnica armoury. The men say that the ŠtB have told them to keep silent about the conversations under the threat of severe punishment. But you see, our people won't give you away," Turček explained excitedly during a walk over Slavín. From that moment onwards Dubček didn't discuss confidential matters on the phone or at his house. This included even the office of the first secretary of the Central Committee.

"Novotný is behind this. Well, if he declares war, we'll fight!" he snapped.

"I think a lot of people are looking forward to a fight with the Novotný gang," Turček smiled. "You have full support in the counties and districts. Even in many of the Czech districts," he said, encouraging Dubček.

"Novotný is a truly man without character," he said, shaking his head disbelievingly. "What can you do with these people? Tell them straight into their eyes!"

Novotný took the sheet from his desk, which his secretary had brought him in the morning. When he read it, he immediately summoned his son, Antonín and his friend, the 41-year-old cossetted favourite, General Šejna, the Party Chief at the Ministry of Defence. "Read it!" Novotný ordered Šejna briskly. He took the paper in his hand and read it aloud, so that the younger Novotný could hear. "Comrade Novotný, I have verified information that the security authorities have carried out an investigation and may still be investigating my person and my wife. In addition, an investigation was carried out at SMZ Dubnica nad Váhom (former Škodove závody), where my wife and I worked for the Slovak state ... I have solid information about the matter in question from honourable people who informed me of this matter. After verifying this, I confirmed the matter. I am a member of the CPC Central Committee and its Chairman and I cannot agree with such a procedure by the security authorities. I write this letter with a request for a personal interview. With a comradely greeting. Dubček. "

"These Slovaks stick together. Even Biľak and Husák are with Dubček," Novotný said thinking aloud. "In the 1950s they spoke cautiously about the Slovak people, now it's all at once a nation and god knows what else they'll want."

"So he knows everything. I suspect that Kulifaj told him personally. This is just like them. Even during Tiso they all stuck together. Communists with the Ľudaks and Catholics!" the young Novotný was furious.

"We are soldiers, and if Dubček declares war, let him have it!" Šejna said resolutely.

"I think, Honza, that you're right. There is a time when we can't afford to hesitate," Novotný said ominously.

CHAPTER 12

YOU SCREWED UP EVERYTHING

From the 27th to 29th June 1967 the fourth Congress of the Union of Czechoslovak writers took place in Prague which at the time symbolized the summit of the meeting of state power with culture and greatly accelerated the coming of the process of revitalization in 1968. "Anyone who, through bigotry, vandalism, lack of culture, unfree tripping up of incipient cultural development, trips up the being of our nation" resounded the brilliant conclusion of Milan Kundera's performance, one the first high points of the writers' meetings. "The main sin of these works was that they exceeded the human horizons of the judges and offended them," Kundera said in defense of banned literature. Alexander Kliment raised the issue of Alexander Solzhenitsyn's letter addressed to the Soviet writer's leadership, in which he protested against censorship making creativity impossible. Pavel Kohout responded, "I've got his Czech translation here. Would the Congress like to get acquainted with it?"

Before Solzhenitsyn's thoughts could be heard in an impatient hall, the angry delegate from the Czech Communist Party, Hendrych, ostentatiously left the meeting and remarked to Kundera and his friends, "You screwed everything." The Slovak Communist delegate, Vasil Biľak, joined him.

Still, Hendrych, who came back on President Novotný's instruction, had no idea that Ludwig Vaculík's speech would be the absolute summit of the meeting. His assertions that "in the space of twenty years, no human question has been resolved with us - from primary needs such as flats, schools, prosperity to a gentler, which non-democratic systems do not know how to solve - such as feeling fully included in society, belief in meaningfulness of a little work or political decision-making subordinated to the criteria of ethics", provoked stormy applause. The three-day sessions had a great response from the public. It was clear that the crisis of political relations extended right to the top. The writers had won the first round the fight for the freedom of speech.

CHAPTER 13

THE SHEPHERD CROSSED THE LINE

The situation was greatly sharpened during Novotný's visit to Martin on 26th and 27th August 1967 on the occasion of the celebration of the 100th anniversary of the foundation of the Martin Gymnasium. At first he refused to include Dubček in his party, who sat angrily in his office and ate his favorite cottage cheese dumplings brought to him by Milan, his youngest son. His wife would sometimes surprise him especially in the evening when the works canteen was closed.

Novotný sat fuming in the dining of ZTS enterprise's Trstená chalet at the Oravská dam, where he had stayed overnight before visiting Martin. The tables were a mess and he didn't have breakfast because the staff and comrades from Prague had drunk until the morning and hadn't woken up. He wasn't cheered up by the visit to Tesla Nižná either, as one of the workers had asked him, "Which one of these is the president?"

At the National Cemetery in Martin, where Novotný had to lay a wreath, thousands of people were waiting for him. He spurned them and went to visit a JRD. He spent the night at the recreation centre of Martin's engineering works in the Gaderská valley, but on the pretext of an assassination attempt he was taken to Turčianske Teplice. On his way, he and his entourage were to pay homage in Mošovce at the monument to the great Slovak poet, a native of Mošovce, Ján Kollár. To the surprise of the waiting Mošovce citizens the presidential column accelerated through the village. While laying wreaths to the Soviet soldiers' memorial in Martin the President sharply and insensitively refused expressions of sympathy by ordinary citizens. At the official ceremony at Matica Slovenská (Slovakia's historical cultural centre) they wanted to hand over a copy of the Pittsburgh agreement of 1918 which irritated Novotný, who with unconcealed anger refused to accept. His wife also did not accept a gift – a Slovak sheepskin coat and embroidery. Novotný firmly ordered her, "Boženko, don't take it, we're going home!" He had previously argued with the director, Paško, of Matica Slovenská, but that was an obvious pretext. The delegation returned to Prague. Surprised Slovak officials have packed the gifts into a neat package and sent them to the presidential office. After a few days the package was returned to Martin with the stamp "Office of the President of the Republic, Prague Castle" with the note, "Returned to sender, the addressee does not accept." Novotný's unprecedented arrogance was considered a national insult in Slovakia.

Dubček's answer was not long in coming. On 30th October, at the plenary session of the Central Committee of the Czech Communist Party in Prague, he made a speech, with at the time an unprecedentedly critical tone. "We must assume that many will not be able to transcend in due time the border to which we have matured ... it is also necessary to create an atmosphere in which maximum unity of intellectual knowledge with unity of conscience in each of us will be achieved and with unity in concrete actions ... It is necessary to take an opinion on the accumulation of functions in the Party's supreme bodies ..."

At these words from Dubček, Novotný stabbed his pencil so hard that it broke in his hands. The Slovak "shepherd" had crossed the line. The challenge to take a position on the accumulation of functions attacked him directly. He was also the first secretary of the UV KSČ as well as the President of the Republic. It was a clear call to remove Novotný from one of the functions. Which one was not hard to guess.

From the cautious at first, but then strong applause after Dubček's speech Novotný was not left in doubt that Dubček was beginning to gain supporters among Czech colleagues in the Central Party Committee. The deep internal crisis, which has changed to an historic struggle of reformers and conservatives, had blown wide open. Novotný decided to react. In his speech he demagogically shifted Dubček's criticism to a position of "Czechs against Slovaks", in the hope of leaning on Czech members of the Central Committee. Once again he embarked on hunting for the Slovak bourgeois nationalism. After the plenary session, he summoned Dubček to a party interview. He requested him to revoke his words and in the December and January plenaries to perform an act of self-criticism. But Dubček would not be intimidated. He called a session of the Central Committee of the Slovak Communist Party, which on 8th December 1967 rejected all Novotný's accusations. On the contrary, it adopted a resolution in which Dubček was instructed to interpret the anti-Novotný opinion of the Central Committee of the KSČ.

CHAPTER 14

THIS IS YOUR BUSINESS

War had been declared. Novotný summoned the first Soviet Communist, Brezhnev, to Prague to help. He looked at the situation, squinting between the four eyes with Novotný and Dubček, with whom he spent four and a half hours. The dispute ended with the familiar words - "this is your business" - "that's your thing". He declared that the dispute was a matter for the Czechoslovak communists, and he returned to Moscow on the same day. It was a severe blow for Novotný. It was clear that the decision on his further being or non-being would fall on the December 19th session of the UV KSČ on 19th – 21st December. On 17th December, the presidium of the UV KSČ met, during which a sharp and controversial debate was held, after which the secretary of the UV KSČ, Koucký, proposed a division of functions of the first secretary of the UV KSČ and the President of the Republic. This new surprise was enhanced by his long-time friend Hendrych, who supported the suggestion of Koucký. Novotný did not know that Dubček had been talking to Hendrych for a long time the day before.

Novotný decided to use a last option. Remove Dubček by force. The threat of the possible fall of his protector was also acknowledged by the supreme party leader at the Ministry of National Defense, General Šejna, whom Lomský promoted to the general post of the Minister of Defense following threats from Novotný. In party circles, the property frauds and wheeler-dealing of Šejna with military material, clover seeds and other goods were known. Since he was a friend of Novotný's son Antonín, no-one dared to speak out against him. It was clear to Šejna that when Novotný fell, he would go to prison for his financial machinations. It was also clear that his protege, head of the all-powerful 8th Department of the UV KSČ for Defense and Security, Miroslav Mamula, would be finished. Together with Deputy Defense Minister, Vladimír Janko, Chief of the General Staff, General Otakar Rytíř, Air Force Commander Vosáhl, Chief of Intelligence, General Kučer from the general staff and Mamula's people a list of more than a thousand names of reform politicians, army and security commanders, writers and journalists was prepared that ŠtB had to isolate immediately after the start of the putsch. First on the list was Alexander Dubček. In Mladá Boleslav, the mobilization of a tank regiment was carried out. Miroslav Mamula wondered if the people's militia and the ŠtB would also join at a critical juncture.

Novotný was trying to gain time for his supporters and so the pre-Christmas session of the UV KSČ, which began on 19th December, was interrupted after two days with the justification that "our lady comrades must cook Christmas dinner". The continuation was set for 3rd January, 1968. The chief organizer of the anti-Dubček coup, General Šejna, spoke at a secret meeting in the younger Antonín Novotný's apartment: "This is excellent. We have a plenary interruption, we have time, no decision has been taken." Spokesmen informed them about the measures of the 8th Department of the Communist Party of the Czechoslovak Communist Party, of Miroslav Mamula about the People's Militia and the creation of an emergency group at the Ministry of the Interior. At the end of the meeting, he resolutely encouraged everybody, ".. we mustn't delay even for a day, otherwise the old man is in the shit and we too. Those who go against must be taken care of!" Every member of the Central Committee of the Communist Party, who had criticized Novotný, was watched by the Ministry of Interior. Orders were given that a desant (a military manoeuvre where infantry rides into action on tanks) would be carried out in the event of immobility in Prague with a tank regiment pulled out from the base in Mladá Boleslav.

CHAPTER 15

I DON'T DARE TAKE ON SUCH RESPONSIBILITY

Alexander Dubček spent Christmas with family and friends not discounting the possibility of an early banging on the door by the proverbial men in leather coats. He didn't know then how intensely this option was being worked on. However the chief of political administration of the Eastern Military District, based in Trenčín, General Samuel Kodaj, said that "if they attempted to arrest several members of the presidium of the UV KSS, he'd declare a mobilization of the eastern circuit and the comrades under threat will be defended by force. In the event that an order was given to arrest them, the Slovak security forces would refuse to obey." The situation mainly due to General Šejna's instinct for self-preservation threatened to escalate into the actual use of force. Dubček informed the Soviet Ambassador Chervonenko about his concerns, which was probably forwarded to Brezhnev in Moscow. At that time the young Slovak politician had full confidence from Moscow. It is likely that Brezhnev telephoned Novotný with whom he left a message for the impatiently waiting Šejna, whose "old man" directed the Ministry of National Defence, to do nothing and categorically ordered him to "not to be silly." Meanwhile Christmas passed and the stormy plenary session of the UV KSČ continued on 3ʳᵈ January 1968. Šejna once more mobilized the party apparatus in the Ministry of Defence and forced it to adopt a resolution supporting Antonín Novotný. Only General Martin Dzúr voted against the resolution.

On 4ᵗʰ January, 1968, on the second day of the continuing plenary session of the UV KSČ, Novotný had already signalled that he was reconciled to withdrawing from the position of the First Secretary of the Communist Party of Czechoslovakia, but retaining the position of the President of the Republic. But he entertained the thought that the post of the first man of the Communist party and thus the first man in the country would be given to a person loyal to him. The individual attitudes of presidium members had clearly polarized as conservatives versus reformists. On 4ᵗʰ January, 1968, Novotný invited those present to write the name of the candidate who they would support in the election of the first secretary. As Jozef Lenárt was the Prime Minister, it was expected that Oldřich Černík would receive the most votes. Dubček himself, who proposed him, had initially refused to consider himself at all.

He reasoned that he still didn't feel sufficiently prepared and experienced for such a high function. "I can say honestly and openly that I do not dare to take on such a huge responsibility - to lead the party and the people in this extremely complex period. Please understand me, I think honestly. There are also those more capable among us, so they have better prerequisites. Let us choose one of them." After counting the test ballots, Černík had got four voices, Lenárt six and Dubček seven. At length, the presidium of the UV KSČ proposed on 5ᵗʰ January at 8 o'clock in the morning a vote for two candidates, classmates from Moscow - Jozef Lenárt and Alexander Dubček, older by two years. Dubček sincerely had never wanted a career as power had never attracted him. But in a situation where the major rivals tried throw each other off the chess board, a third consideration arose for someone, neutral, if possible temporary, someone who didn't have great ambitions. And moreover, a Slovak would be someone who would stop the mouths of dissatisfied Slovaks. Those who sympathized with Dubček convinced him that they would "help him and he should take it for at least two years until the reforms are underway." So the presidium on that morning of 5th January at eight o'clock approved the recommendation to the plenary session of the UV KSČ to elect Alexander Dubček as its first Secretary. On that day Dubček was elected as the first man of the Communist Party. Since Article 4 of the Constitution of the ČSSR in 1960 provided the Communist Party with a leading role in society, its First Secretary was in fact more than the President of the Republic. Just after his election they received by hand Šejna's resolution from the Ministry of Defence. It was too late.

"Lads, it's good," Novotný said after Dubček's election. "Dubček is weak, I know him, he's not up to the job. And the new secretaries are gutless. We'll be back! This is not the end!" Indeed, many old warhorses thought of Dubček as a simple Slovak "Janko', who was a good person down his bones. His election was only considered a transitional solution until a more powerful personality had emerged. The name of Gustáv Husák, which panicked Novotný and his people, was frequently mentioned. But they didn't know that Dubček would surprise them.

After his election as the first secretary of the Communist Party, Dubček traveled to Bratislava to celebrate at an evening hockey match of his favourite Slovan, where the spectators welcomed him with a rowdy ovation. When he was asked before he left when he would be officially in office, he said with a smile, "I've just started. Don't make a fuss, fanfares aren't necessary ..."

CHAPTER 16

A MAN WITH SOUL AND HEART

People didn't pay attention at first to the new, inconspicuous leader. To them he was just another one like his Communist forbears who always promised bright tomorrows after their arrival. They expected this from Dubček. However, the celebratory rants didn't come. On the contrary, in his conversations with the citizens he called on them to cooperate, he listened and didn't lecture. He wasn't the owner but a truth-seeker. He never forgot to thank people and add his enchanting smile.

He never took offence and didn't know how to hate, rather he listened as he spoke. After all the Bacíleks, the Širokýs, the Novotnýs here was the image of a man. Humble, tolerant, patient, calm, trustworthy. He didn't command, but convinced. He didn't demand, but requested. He didn't judge, but understood. He spoke of "the universal liberation of the working man." Words which until then hadn't been heard from a Communist official. Before the astonished eyes of the public, this uncertain, unimposing unknown man, who refused security, sang and danced, went to football and ice hockey games and was an active athlete. He was forty-seven years old and was the youngest of all the then communist leaders.

At first glance, he didn't attract attention with anything exceptional. He didn't stand out from the others, he toed the line, didn't push himself to the front. Despite this one had to notice him. What emanated from him was the charm of his personality. He enchanted people with an unprecedented interest in them and with his pure, diffident smile. His eyes beamed with selflessness and good nature. He wasn't ashamed to admit that he didn't know something. He was not a convincing speaker, on the contrary, but what was amazing about him was that people believed him. For the first time, a Communist leader, who was literally felt from his heart, stood before his citizens.

"If we succeed in furthering the work of socialist democracy, opening up a wider space for the versatile activity of people, removing the barriers that have stood in the way, literally to move the creative effort of people, all the physical and moral forces of society, if every honest citizen for whom the cause of socialism, the homeland and the unity of our peoples and nations lies in their heart feel that it is necessary, that it is taken into account, it will be very much a beginning and difficult to estimate today how much energy will be brought to the full self-realization of mankind ... the party wants to claim your trust. It does not want to rule, it wants to serve."

People did not come out of astonishment when listening to Dubček. They had never heard the words of service, understanding, tolerance, honor, democracy and correction of errors from the mouth of a high-ranking Communist Party official. His speech to farmers ended with something unprecedented from his former arrogant officials, "Honour and appreciation of your tremendous work to which I pay the deepest tribute."

Soon it was clear to the Czechoslovak citizen that they had new hope. It was called Alexander Dubček.

CHAPTER 17

GRADUATION IN THE KREMLIN

Less than a month after his election, Dubček entered the Moscow Kremlin for the first time as the first man in Czechoslovakia. He had never been in working room of the General Secretary of the USSR Central Committee. The dimensions of about twelve by eight metres were dominated by a T-shaped long table. It was covered with a green cloth. On the table were a carafe of water, fruit and ashtrays. Brezhnev was a strong smoker. Dubček came alone, only with one of the administrative staff of the UV KSČ. There was no protocol, no minutes of the conversations. The new party boss from Prague first met eye to eye with Brezhnev and then explained to Brezhnev, Podgorny, Kosygin, Suslov, Kirilenko and Shelest the intentions of the new Czechoslovak leadership. To suspicious questions about the deflection of Prague from the common line of socialist countries, he patiently replied that in Czechoslovakia there were different conditions for building socialism than in the Soviet Union. Although he spoke perfectly in Russian, under the strict eyes of the patrons of Moscow, he faltered a little. "When introducing socialism to a country that was at the time at a technical high-level, at least in its western part, we must use other methods of working and persuading people than in countries where there was not such a strong labour," Dubček said eagerly and became more nervous . On the faces of Stalin's heirs he saw that their thoughts were not very much in agreement with his. Despite this, he continued vigorously. "The existing way of exercising the leading role of the party has led to stagnation and the current crisis. If the socialist system in Czechoslovakia is to function, changes and redress are necessary!" "What should these changes be?" Brezhnev asked, looking significantly at his colleagues at the table.

Dubček stared at the paper from which he read and felt that some passages would have to be dropped, especially words such as "reform", "revision" or "rehabilitation". He tried to replace them with the words "renewal" and "revival." "Our party will in whatever case design solutions which entail that the friendship and alliance with the Soviet Union is a stumbling block to any of our actions." At these words the grim looks eased a little and Dubček felt a little glimpse of humanity in the faces of genetic apparatchiks raised in Stalin's way of thinking, "whoever is not with us is our enemy."

"Our attitude to the socialist community, the organization of the Warsaw Pact, the cooperation of the socialist countries in the Mutual Economic Aid Council is clear and we have a unified opinion in which nothing changes. The new conditions that have arisen in our country build a communist party ahead of qualitatively new tasks. In their solution, we will naturally be guided by the principle of the leading role of the Communist Party."

"Isn't there a fear of weakening its leading role?" asked Suslov, the chief of ideology.

"I want to assure our Soviet friends categorically that if anyone thinks that the leading role of the party can be ceded to someone, they would be making a serious miscalculation!" Dubček responded vigorously, watching the venerable nodding of Soviet leaders. Then he spoke passionately, explaining and answering. All at once he felt as though he were back in Gorky when he stood as a nervous student before the graduation board. His throat had dried a little, but he was determined to persuade the teachers further. The comrades asked him several more questions checking him and although he had a bad feeling that he had not fully convinced the Commission, he passed through his party graduation. He had no idea that he would be back in the Kremlin in a few months, but in a completely different position.

CHAPTER 18

EXPLOSION OF FREEDOM

The ideological secretary, Hendrych, in February joyfully announced to Zdeněk Mlynář, "I just agreed with Eda Goldstücker – I've allowed "Literárky!" " Literární noviny" was a weekly from the

Czechoslovak Union of Writers banned by Novotný in the fall of 1967. Their re-authorization actually meant the cancellation of censorship. Mlynář expressed concern that ceding the censorship before publishing the Communist Party of Czechoslovakia Action Program would mean that the media would write much more radically and then it would be much harder to impose the political framework of the programme.

That won't happen," Hendrych assured Mlynář. "I discussed everything with Goldstücker they won't write against us!" Inside a month, Hendrych was dismissed. Public criticism begun by Literární noviny, blew him out of his position. Although censorship was only abolished by Law 84/1968 of 26th June 1968, it had ceased to be functional after the reopening of the literary press. On 21st January, Josef Smrkovský published an article in the daily, Práca, Oč dnes jde (The Theme of Today) which caused rapture in Czechoslovakia. In Moscow they were wary. There was an unimaginable information explosion. Czechoslovakia embarked on an unprecedented movement. People took gulps of an unidentified or long-forgotten air of freedom. The borders were opened for the first time in twenty years and people could look west. In the theatres plays previously banned began to be performed and the books of writers which previously were only smuggled in were sold. In the cinemas Oswalt Kolle's Das Wunder der Liebe was shown, Bonnie and Clyde with Faye Dunaway and Warren Beatty, Dolce Vita with Anita Ekberg and Dance of the Vampires directed by Roman Polanski. Discotheques were ruled by the Rolling Stones, the Beatles, the Bee Gees, Scott McKenzie, the Kinks, the Who, the Animals, the Hollies, Tom Jones, and others. In Bratislava the Beach Boys, the Tremeloes, Manfred Mann performed in university clubs. Cliff Richard and the Shadows, the Rubettes, Boney M, Smokie, Amanda Lear, Billy Preston and John Mayall appeared at a festival. Musical groups took English names - Golden Kids, Greenhorns, Rangers, Buttons, Beatmen. Young people from the surrounding socialist countries looked at their Czech and Slovak counterparts with envy. The boys wore their hair longer than the girls' skirts. Betka Štrkulová was the first Czechoslovak representative to participate in the Miss World Finals in London. There was an unofficial nudist beach on the lake at Jarovce, and none of the naked people were forced to leave. In the bar of the Perugia restaurant in Bratislava, Striptease performances began, and even tours for members of the Revolutionary Trade Union were organized. The humourists Lasica and Satinský had a permanent show at the "Theater Na Korze" and poked fun at big shots so that people laughed till they cried.

The more cheerful they were in Prague and Bratislava, the more those in power in Moscow, Warsaw, East Berlin, Sofia, and Budapest scowled.

CHAPTER 19

ALEXANDER, TAKE CARE!

On 7th February, 1968, a cold wind blew in Ostrava. On the pavements and roads there had been a weak falloff snow. "Shall we go for a little stroll?" Gomulka asked after dinner on the first day of their meeting.

"Good idea." Dubček made his excuses to the Secretary of the UV KSČ, Vladimír Koucký, who was sitting next to him and took his coat. They walked for about an hour around the football stadium, escorted at an appropriate but safe distance from the civilian staff of the Ministry of the Interior.

"I fully understand you," Gomulka said, "but you should be more careful. More control of the printed word."

"We rely very much on you and Comrade Kadár," Dubček began to explain to him with his heart on his sleeve. "We haven't yet made a decision on rehabilitation, but what I'm telling you has been in my head for a long time. I'm determined to make the most of my efforts to mitigate the consequences of all crimes of the 1950s. We have to correct all the injustices that have affected communists, non-communists, soldiers, civilians, priests, partisans, soldiers, men, women, Czechs and Slovaks. I'm convinced that this is the first necessary step towards reform and democratization. There is no other way to get people to trust us again," Dubček gestured passionately.

"Everything's in order, you just have to be more tactical," Gomulka said slowly, thinking of every word, not to make Dubček feel like he was speaking on the orders of Brezhnev. Though he suspected that Dubček knew it, he did his best to appear as though he was the sovereign master of his decisions. But his life experience spoke wholly otherwise. He tried to convey to Dubček matters so he could understand what he was saying without his well-meaning words being used against him. The Communist leaders knew that Brezhnev invited them to eye to eye interviews and were never able to know how things might go in Moscow under the influence of vodka. "Twelve years ago I tried with my friends in Poland substantially what you want now. I warn you, Alexander, take care! We ended up in Stalin's prison," he was almost persuaded by the sixteen years older paternal Gomulka. "If by any chance you think that you can leave the Warsaw Pact, forget it. The division of the world after Yalta is valid and the Americans fully respect this. That is why you must have in mind socialism in the first place. I know what I'm saying. When we started to reform, people stuck to us who wanted to destroy it under the pretext of reforms."

"Of course we won't permit this."

"How many people should this rehabilitation involve?"

"Many thousands. In the first stage, we would involve prosecutors, the courts, parliamentary committees, party bodies and national committees. In the second, extra-judicial rehabilitation would follow," said Dubček.

"What do you mean?"

"I mean those people who were never in court, but persecuted in unlawful ways." Gomulka was silent for a moment, nodding his head.

"I understand morally and humanly, but I'm afraid you're bringing about an uncontrolled political move. It can have very serious consequences that could undermine the party's position. "

"On the contrary, I think that we would be renewing confidence in a socialist society and putting the party on a new, democratic basis."

170

"Hm ..." Gomulka smiled and grasped Dubček's arm in a friendly way. "When I was voted in as first secretary of our party in October fifty-six, we started exactly like you. Remedying errors. Immediately Khrushchev flew in. We hadn't even invited him. Due to his unexpected arrival, we interrupted the meeting of the Central Committee. I'll never forget that image. We stood at the airport, and he cordially greeted the Soviet generals. But when he noticed me, instead of offering me his hand, he shook his fist in front of my face. Do you understand? He literally bellowed at me as if I were a snotty kid! The First Secretary of the Polish United Labour Party," Gomulka said with a voice in which sadness was mixed with hatred." And this was after his criticism of Stalin. Hah ... reforms are allowed, but only with the consent of Moscow!"

"That was twelve years ago. Times have changed since then," said Dubček.

Gomulka smiled bitterly. "Did you hear about Novocherkassk?" Dubček shook his head. "It was in July 1962. The Supreme Soviet issued a decree to increase meat prices. The Russians were not accustomed to price rises and even after Stalin food prices had fallen several times. But this time, in the iron and steel plants and locomotive works in Novocerkassk, Ukraine, they had also cut wages by thirty percent. The workers stopped production and organized a meeting. The Chief Director told them that they were already full of meat pies so they should eat only pasta. At midday there was a strike in the whole enterprise."

"There was a strike in the Soviet Union?" an astonished Dubček asked.

"A strike in the Soviet Union. To this day it's a strictly guarded mystery. On the second day, thousands of women with children in their arms went to protest in the town in front of the City Soviet building. Portraits of Lenin were carried over their heads. When the commander received an order from Moscow to fire on the crowd, he preferred to commit suicide. His successor, however, gave the order. The soldiers shot mothers and children and even shot children from the trees, watching the demonstration through curiosity. They killed thirty people. Then there was a trial."

"Did they convict them?" asked an indignant Dubček.

"Yes. The nine organizers of the revolt. They executed them. Nothing happened top those who fired. And it was six years ago ..."

"This was from Khrushchev ..." protested a shocked Dubček.

"Keep your eye on your newspapers, radio and television. That's what irritates Moscow most. I can reveal to you that Brezhnev recently called me about I would say about your press, so I told him that it made me uneasy ..."

"But you're free to get all Western newspapers," Dubček pointed out.

"Well, yes, but they only have an impact on those who know foreign languages. You did very well, too, to allow them. It creates the impression of democracy and openness, but it doesn't have a greater impact. "

"But you shut down the Free Europe."

"We had to block it, something can still be understood," Gomulka said as if making excuses. But he realized he might have pointed out too much to Dubček and turned suddenly ending the conversation quickly. "Comrade Dubček, Alexander, we'll keep our fingers crossed for you, but always keep in mind what they say about your steps in Moscow ..." and he clapped him on the shoulder.

At the time of Gomulka's walk with Dubček, things were heating up in Poland. The staging of the play Dziady (Remembrance) by Mickiewicz at the National Theater in Warsaw became a pretext for a brutal intervention against the intelligentsia and the eruption of a power struggle in the PZRP. The PZRP leadership banned it and declared it anti-Soviet. After the last performance on 16th January, 1968, a student demonstration broke out that the police raided arresting 35 people. A petition against the ban on the play and the "renunciation of the progressive traditions of the Polish nation" was signed by more than 4,000 people. Meetings spread beyond Warsaw. Both students and workers protested against the brutal police intervention and provocations and against conflicts between workers and students. They also expressed sympathy for the reform process in Czechoslovakia.

Gomulka knew that if Dubček's wave of reforms crossed over to Poland, he would be ejected from power as quickly as Novotný had been in Prague.

CHAPTER 20

THIS WON'T BE GOOD

The new leadership of the Communist Party prepared for the celebrations of a major event - the twentieth anniversary of February 1948. During the preparations, Brezhnev called Dubček and suggested that he invite all supreme representatives of fraternal Communist parties to celebration. Dubček was pleased with the proposal as the personal presence of Communist leaders would give Czechoslovak representatives the opportunity to assure their friends that their reforms would not jeopardize the strategic interests of the socialist countries. And this would be seen as a certain support for democratic changes in Czechoslovakia. Indeed, all General Secretaries, except the Yugoslav leader Tito, who sent his representative, Vlahovič, came to Prague.

At the meetings of the top representatives of the Communist parties, it was customary for the speakers to exchange speeches before they were presented. Brezhnev read the design of Dubček's speech and sent it back with objections that Dubček only formally took into account. Although he mostly read his speeches, he supplemented them with some things in his own words that had annoyed Brezhnev. He knew that Brezhnev and the other party leaders would listen carefully to every single word, and he therefore gave special attention to the standard professions of friendship with the Soviet Union and the unity of the socialist camp.

"Whatever solutions our party comes up with the friendship and alliance with the Soviet Union is the cornerstone of every action we have. Our attitude to the ECHR, the organization of the Warsaw Pact in the fight against imperialism does not change," said Dubček to Brezhnev and other socialist leaders in the solemnly decorated Vladislav Hall of Prague Castle. "A true fidelity to 1948 and our revolution does not consist in the repetition of the ideas and the programme of the time ... From the ranks of the workers and the peasants, there have been serious voices for a long time, that on our side and in our society it is not enough just to make things right here and there, but that things have to be fundamentally changed not by words, but by actions ..." Brezhnev held his earphones to his head nervously as if the translation wasn't correct. Dubček's speech had been read in advance, but these words were not there: "We have achieved certain successes, but we feel it does not yet meet our potential."

Brezhnev leaned nervously towards President Novotný sitting next to him. "What certain successes? Is not the construction of socialism a huge success?" Novotný was silent. Dubček continued. "The area where we have to start is with our policy ... It is no coincidence that the passivity and resignation among Communists has recently begun to multiply... In the highest party leadership, a progressive position has prevailed that we must fearlessly look into the eyes of the problems and that we have to deal with them in a new, creative manner ... The action program that we will soon put forward for approval will be primarily the conception of the all-round development of socialism, the transformation of the material and spiritual conditions of society, the real liberation of man!" Dubček finished. The faces of Brezhnev, Zhivkov, Gomulka, Ulbricht and other party bosses frowned slightly. When the applause turned into a hurricane of consent, they had to applaud politely too. "This won't be good," Brezhnev said to Zhivkov in a nervous manner when he lit a cigarette in the lounge during the break.

On the second day, the media reported on the escape of General Jan Šejna and his girlfriend to the US, where his new employer became the CIA. Šejna's desertion was one of the greatest coups of the American intelligence service in her history. His flight provoked horrified talk in the leadership of the Warsaw Pact.

The call for Novotný's departure took on a mass character. Finally, on 22nd March, the president resigned and his son, Antonín, was dismissed as General Manager of the Artia foreign trade company. In Moscow, where the development of the Czechoslovak reform process was watched with great concern, Novotný's departure caused offense. For the first time since Gottwald one of Moscow's satellites had made a major personnel change without their consent.

Novotný settled down into seclusion and spent most of his time outside Prague alone in his cabin in the Vysočina. The fate of an ostracized high party official overtook him. Those who once used to play Mariáš with him in Orlík turned away. They even began to criticize him in a demonstrable manner. No-one took any notice of the ailing once most powerful man of Czechoslovakia. When his health deteriorated, Dubček provided him with the necessary medication and appropriate medical care.

CHAPTER 21

THAT'S HOW COUNTER-REVOLUTION BEGINS!

On 23rd March, 1968, Dubček and Vasil Biľak, Oldrich Černík, Jozef Lenárt, and Drahomír Kolder in Dresden were given the opportunity to listen to Brezhnev and his satraps in person on the second day after Novotný's resignation. Following a demand from Moscow the first secretary of the East German Communists Walter Ulbricht had invited them to this historic German city. The invitation contained information that negotiations would deal with the economic cooperation of the countries of the Mutual Economic Aid Council. Dubček, of course, knew and felt that a barrier of mistrust was beginning to form between him and other high-ranking representatives of brotherly countries, but he assumed that if something else would be spoken about besides the economy, it would be the Romanian leader, Nicolae Ceausescu, who, since the end of the six-day Israeli-Arab War had begun to exercise greater independence from Moscow. Czechoslovakia was the first country after the Soviet Union to break off diplomatic relations with Israel, which was considered as a manifestation of Novotný's servility. However to the surprise of the Czechoslovak delegation they saw, after entering the Chamber Hall in the Dresden City Hall, that in the second row around the negotiating table twenty generals of the Soviet and East German army were sitting. Brezhnev, Kosygin, Ulbricht, Kadar, Gomulka and Stanko Todorov, who represented the sick Bulgarian leader Zhivkov, were sitting in the front row. Their accompanying personnel were with them. On the table in front of each delegation, besides notepads and carefully sharpened pencils, there were also folders with clippings from Czechoslovak newspapers. Alexander Dubček and his delegation were entering a bleak environment.

Walter Ulbricht had the opening word. The seventy-five year old East German leader who spent the war in the warmth of Paris and in immigration in Moscow was the oldest of all of them. He claimed an unspoken function as the "senior" world communist leader. Sometimes he did not only master and teach Dubček, but also Brezhnev, who was sixty-two, Gomulka a year older Kosygin, two years older, and a relatively young Kadar, who was fifty-six. "We hope that the head of the Delegation of the Communist Party of Czechoslovakia, Dubček, will report on the plans of the Central Committee of the Communist Party and the preparation of the Action Program ... I recall that no one lives in the world alone and imperialism, our enemy for life and death, does not sleep. We must be uncompromising especially against the attacks of West German imperialism ... I believe that our discussion will contribute to the clarification of our positions." Then Ulbricht handed over to of Todorov, who gave the floor to Brezhnev.

"Because our discussion will be very serious, I suggest that we don't follow protocol and make stenographic recordings. I therefore ask the technical assistants to leave the hall." (The meeting was preserved due to the Stasi East German Secret Service, who recorded the whole session.) After Brezhnev's opening sally, Todorov gave the floor to Dubček. He appeared visibly nervous. His speech was unconvincing because he had prepared to talk about economic issues. In this way he had to improvise and this was not his strong point.

"In connection with the preparation of the plenary session of our party with the conclusions and resolutions of the October, December and January meetings of the Central Committee of our Party, we are preparing the development of some internal issues ... What are the questions? ... It is a question of the work of the Central Committee and the relationship of the party's leadership to the management of the economy ... the truth ... of the culture and the individual sectors of our economy. In drafting our program, as we have already said, we are preparing for a plenary debate, based on the basic principle that in this and the next stage of socialist construction the leading role of the party in building a developed socialist society will be ... truth. ..to consolidate ..."

"Excuse me, Comrade Dubček, for interrupting you," Gomulka said to Dubček without asking the presiding chair's approval, "but I do not think there is time in this situation for the general theories about building socialism, which ultimately dominate here. We would like to hear your comment on the current situation in Czechoslovakia and on the Communist Party as suggested by Comrade Brezhnev!"

Brezhnev, Ulbricht and the others with earphones nodded their agreement with Gomulka. Biľak, Lenárt and Kolder also nodded. Černík looked at the table and nervously played with some paper.

"Well ... sorry, our delegation was ready for economic questions ..." the harassed Dubček explained.

"I guess it shouldn't be a problem for you to inform us of the situation in the country and the party, although, I acknowledge, we had a different program originally," Gomulka broke in before Brezhnev.

"I just want to get there ... As I said, at this stage of building ... a developed socialist society, we start from the principle that the party is working in new conditions. What are these new conditions when the socialist social establishment has triumphed? We start from the fact that there are no antagonistic classes in our country, that there is a class that will play a leading role in the future" said Dubček, visibly nervous.

"Sasha ... we will deal with future issues at other meetings, please, as Comrade Gomulka said, be more specific. We want to hear your analysis with an account of contemporary developments with you. Thank you," Brezhnev abruptly said to Dubček.

"Well ... yes, Leonid Ilyich, I'm getting there ... so ... as I said, the main class is the labour class, but also the class of agricultural workers who came from the triumph of collectivization in our country, the workers of the agricultural cooperatives who are standing at such a degree of economic development with its position in production towards the republic and the socialist society and its political position ... the truth ... " stammered Dubček. The atmosphere in the hall was tense, no one understood what he was actually saying.

"Comrade Dubček, can you tell us something about the upcoming action program?" Ulbricht interrupted him, disrespectfully familiar. Members of the Czechoslovak delegation stared silently in front of them, and Dubček occasionally looked at them as if seeking support.

"... and I wanted to say about the upcoming action program of our party ... It is about making as many members of the party as possible, as well as non-party members, simply interested in the whole of the role of the central committee of our party. If, for example, I talk about the situation and the work of the Communist Party, I come from the situation that was created within the party and our Central Committee and it is therefore real for us. That is why we have a question - how can the leadership of the party be strengthened under these conditions?"

"Alexander Stepanovitch, can you say something about your prepared action program?" Brezhnev repeated with an angry tone.

"We think there is no need to clarify in detail here ... In particular, for us it's about democratization. Some say what lies behind democratization? What is democracy? It's our opinion that the most democracy that can be provided in the party is if the members of the parties elect those in the regional committee or in the district leadership or in the basic organizations that they enjoy great confidence and they'll cooperate with these comrades. Our Comrades and Communists are good comrades such as the Chairman of the Union of Writers, Goldstücker, or Comrade Smrkovský, who has been a member of the party since 1934 and was the chairman and member of the Party's illegal Central Committee in the Czechoslovak Socialist Republic and the initiator of the Prague uprising, and this programme translate the main principles ..." When Dubček saw how Brezhnev glanced angrily at Kosygin at the mention of Smrkovský and Goldstücker and whispered something, he felt his heart miss a beat. "I do not know whether any further questions will be raised in the course of our consultation. Perhaps the comrades themselves have questions about us that they are interested in and about which we should explain ..." It was difficult for him to sit down.

There was a deep silence. Brezhnev indicated he wished to speak. He turned to the Czechoslovak delegation.

Dear comrades, sorry, Alexander Stepanovich, if I have a different opinion than you do, but I think it is necessary to say this because the Soviet Union and our Communist Party are interested in Czechoslovakia being better... Your words are at odds with your actions. You talk about democracy, but there is no democracy and no order. On the one hand, you say that you are consolidating the leadership role of the party and in your second breath you talk about some secret elections ... There are attacks against your closest allies and on the other the bourgeois republic, Masarykism, are glorified. There is an attempt to create new political parties ... The wave that is growing in your country is heading for counter-revolution! Yes, that's how counter-revolution begins!" Dubček looked with astonishment at his colleagues who were silent and gazing straight ahead. He wanted to object, but the chairman, Todorov, urged with a gesture not to interrupt Brezhnev. Dubček's jaws clenched. Brezhnev's words were an unexpected shower of ice. "Yes, I'm talking about counter-revolution. Its manifestations are present not only among your citizens but also among your communists. It even seems to us that the Communists are at the forefront of anti-communist exploitation. Who actually directs Rudé právo? Are they still the newspapers of the Central Committee? You are renewing the social-democratic party, the question of the effectiveness of the Warsaw Pact is raised and whether it is necessary for Czechoslovakia at all! You have questions of neutrality!" At that moment, Brezhnev's voice leaped into a falsetto and he poured a glass of water and drank. He put it down and looked at his generals as if waiting for their approval. Then he continued with passion. "You talk about the democratization of society. You have been building socialism for twenty-five years and you haven't had any democracy yet? How are we to understand that? How are we to understand your newspapers?" he indignantly banged Rudé právo down. "Every day there's a new attack against the party leaders! You say there are major economic difficulties in your country. And who is guilty? Your newspaper writes that the guilt is the socialist system and friendship with the socialist states! You are looking for a solution in the

West, you want financial credits from the West! This is because the leadership of your party is in name only and in fact the party and the country are led by a self-appointed such as Procházka, Goldstücker, Černý, Smrkovský, Kosík and others. If you praise Smrkovský, then I understand that he and not the central committee directs the course of events! Sasha, comrade Dubček, I say to you clearly – the way Smrkovský speaks, only a counter-revolutionary speaks! And on top of it he presents what's happening in your country as an example to others! He gives an interview to the West German imperialists and Rudé právo instead of condemning it, publishes it all! Smrkovský, Šik, Procházka, Pelikán, Goldstücker have created a fifth column behind your back! They run the Writers' Union, radio, television and printing presses! Goldstücker sees a way out of the crisis, quoting "in changing the current police dictatorship to a real socialist democracy!" Somebody called Holeček in Rudé pravo writes that "the leading role of the party is defeated!" So such things are written and said in your country! I appeal to you, comrades, deliver a deadly blow to the counter-revolution! Discover Communist courage! If you need help, openly tell us and we'll help! We are mandated by our Central Committees to tell you that you, led by Dubček, are in a position to stop this dangerous development. We will not stand idly by at further developments in Czechoslovakia!" Brezhnev's sat down red in the face. There was a strong applause.

"Attention for the Chairman of the Polish Unified Labor Party, Comrade Gomulka." I would endorse the words of our dear Leonid Ilyich. The Polish delegation fully agrees with his assessment of the situation!" He looked at Brezhnev, who gave him a look of approval, then looked directly at Dubček. "Why haven't you learned from events in Hungary and in our country? It always begins with writers and journalists. Polish students are just waiting for it to develop in your country they can cause unrest! They're spreading a password among themselves, 'Poland waits for Dubček!' We've come so far! They give us your Communist Party as an example! But from our experience, I say to you that the enemy has a cross in one hand and in the second a knife!" Gomulka became so agitated that he did not realize that he had raised his index finger as if threatening the Czechoslovak delegation. "You are lucky that you are not as strong Catholics as in Poland! Your new type of socialism is inspired by Free Europe. You have nothing in your hands, your government or the means of communication. Someone else rules you, you are just like a company. You drove out Novotný! Please do not talk about democracy! People are afraid to tell you their opinion. You have a counter-revolution! And you do not want to see it! Terror will come to you! What you suffer is deviation! You're dismantling the party, the army, discipline, you have no democracy! You are spreading nationalism! Don't you see the threat of the disintegration of the Czechoslovak Socialist Republic as a state? Understand that your whole model is zero! In ten weeks you've made more mistakes than Novotný in ten years! Comrade, I warn you, consider!"

Dubček was slowly losing the ability to listen. Before his eyes, he had the images of the meeting with Gomulka in Ostrava two weeks before, where Gomulka grasped him under this armpit in a friendly way and gave him a good-natured talking to. There was no hint of criticism so, on the contrary, Dubček felt that he was enjoying the Czechoslovak reforms. Gomulka, of course, enjoyed the trouble that Dubček produced in Moscow. He himself had huge problems in Poland. On March 9, 20,000 students led by Kuron, Modzelewski, and Michnik demonstrated in Warsaw. The cops brutally beat them with batons. Worst, the initiators of the new, unprecedented movement were children of the Communist elite. On March 11, from the balcony of the PZRS building Gomulka personally watched a brutal police action against the students. "Polish Gestapo" and "Poland is waiting for Dubček" were slogans on banners brandished over their heads. Dubček was horrified to realize that Moscow was probably waiting for the situation to develop in Poland or Czechoslovakia before striking. Brezhnev could not allow the spark to spread to other Eastern European countries, not to mention into the Soviet Union. Czechoslovakia was more dangerous for Moscow, Soviet troops were located in Poland, Hungary, and the German Democratic Republic. However, they were not in Czechoslovakia.

The Czechoslovak leader did not even realize that another prosecutor, the Hungarian leader János Kádár, had already spoken. At least he did not threaten, he did not yell, he spoke to the point. "The Hungarian Socialist Party had a bitter experience in 1956. Learn from it!"

"I categorically refuse to compare Hungary in nineteen fifty-six with us. Then it was about dismantling socialism, we are trying to strengthen it!" Dubček interrupted Kádár's speech.

Kádár paused for a moment, but calmly, almost as if with some sympathy, he continued. "Imre Nagy played a big role in the Hungarian counter-revolution. We've studied his life in detail. Nagy was neither agent nor counter-revolutionary in the sense that he wanted to remove socialism in Hungary. He was an old member of the party, living for a while in the Soviet Union, not an enemy of socialism. It was 25th and 26th October 1956, when the logic of development led him to the enemy camp when there was no way back for him ... I do not mean to compare some of the Czechoslovak comrades with Imre Nagy ..." Kádár looked for a long time at Dubček, who did not understand. He'd walked with this man on discreet hunting trips, during which time Kádár gave him fervent support for his reformist intentions. There was a short pause and Ulbricht took the floor. He spoke an unusually arrogant and offensive tone. In his own country, as in Gomulka's Poland, the Communists there were stirrings of rebellion and so he tried to use Dubček's unfavourable situation to distract attention from the problems in the German Democratic Republic.

"I have to say that I have always considered the Communist Party of Czechoslovakia to be under-prepared in theory. You have declared in the sixties a transition to socialism without respect for reality. Because you are weak in theory, the crucial elements of managing a national economy have been given to bad theorists and not good politicians. You have permitted Šik not the Central Committee to speak on your behalf. You are re-creating a Masaryk democracy and Smrkovský shamelessly proclaims the password, "Citizens will decide for themselves!" He's organizing counter-revolution and you can't see it. There will be no order in your country in this situation. Young people have to learn to work and not to listen to Goldstücker's nonsense and others like him! Your media achieve the summit of arrogance when they criticize the German Democratic Republic for informing you incorrectly of developments in your country! The same is repeated six times a day by propaganda from West Germany. You don't have to invent arguments against socialism at all, it's enough to take articles from your newspapers! But you are not alone here!"

bawled Ulbricht in his high-pitched, squeaky voice. For Dubček scene inadvertently flashed before his eyes when he trembled with fear buried underneath leaves in a hole during the times of the Slovak National Uprising and clearly heard orders issued by German commanders in just such a screeching voice. He almost had the urge to jump up and shout at Ulbricht as he desired, but he managed to keep himself under control. At that moment, Gomulka who'd had a thought, raised his hand, but Ulbricht had stopped him vigorously. "Comrade Gomulka, now I have the floor!" He turned back to Dubček and continued his assault. "Comrade Dubček, I ask you to think with great care about the road which you have taken!"

There was a moment of silence. Todorov did not join in the criticism. Those present looked at the Czechoslovak delegation and waited for its reaction. Gradually Lenárt, Kolder, Černík took the floor. The last one to speak was Vasil Biľak.

"It was hard for me to listen, not because we were criticized, but because the Communist Party of Czechoslovakia has caused you concern, even though you have enough of your own. In the undertone of the contributions here, which have died away is a feeling of mistrust, history has still to show who has done more evil, Comrade Novotný or us. It is not easy for us because we need to explain to people the mistakes Novotný committed. I see an analogy here with 1956. Even then, we had to explain things at meetings with citizens. People wanted to know the truth. And we have problems now because we have not been consistent since 1956. In 1963, thousands of Communists were in prison, no one wanted to rehabilitate them though it was clear they were innocent. Almost all the partisan commanders of the Slovak National Uprising were unjustly condemned and no one has so far returned honour to them in its entirety. This is in the way like a rock ... What has accumulated over the years is now moving. Comrades, passivity spread through our ranks. Workers have until recently collectively left the party. You understanding of our situation came through Novotný's lying information. Half of our members did not attend the party sessions. The Central Committee was forbidden to speak about it. Now it has turned round. Since the commencement of Comrade Dubček, there has been a 100% participation by members at meetings. We feel huge interest in the people and new, young people have registered in the party. I would like to emphasize the situation in Slovakia which is diametrically different. In our country the main topic is the federal arrangement of the republic. We have to deal with this issue because the relationship between Slovaks and Czechs was not good in the times of Novotný. From the election of Comrade Dubček as the first secretary of the Central Committee of the Communist Party of Slovakia not once did Comrade Novotný attend a plenary in Slovakia. When they invited him to Martin, he refused to lay the wreath on the graves of prominent Slovak historical figures. What would the Comrades in Ukraine think if, for example, Comrade Kosygin was invited to Kiev and refused to lay a wreath on the Shevchenko monument? Yet now the relationship between the Czechs and the Slovaks has improved ..."

Biľak finished speaking and Dubček cast him a grateful glance. Finally Brezhnev took the floor. He expressed the conviction that all the tasks the Czechoslovak comrades had spoken of would be filled to the satisfaction of the entire socialist camp.

After returning to Moscow, he met with Minister of Defense, Marshal Grechko and the ideological Secretary, Suslov. Informally, they considered how the Soviet army would react if the situation in Czechoslovakia had escaped Moscow's grasp.

CHAPTER 22

UNTIL THEY SHUT US UP

From Dresden, Dubček returned home like a whipped dog. During one of the long night sessions with those closest to him - Smrkovský and Černík, Smrkovský looked out of the window and said sharply, "We have to hurry up the preparation of the action program. Let's get down to work until they shut us up and as long as people support us."

On the twenty-eighth of March, Dubček prepared a presentation that he was supposed to have on the reception of teachers on the occasion of their holiday. But he couldn't concentrate. He stared at the two ciphers that lay before him on the table. The ambassador to the United States, Karel Duda, had written in a cipher from the previous day, "Stadep (Foreign Affairs) staff in informal talks indicate that the US recognizes the interests of the USSR in Eastern Europe and that they do not want the ČSSR to become the object of an enormous confrontation." When he read the cipher in the evening it didn't improve his mood. Of course, he hadn't expected America engage in Czechoslovakia's problems, the division of power between the great powers at Yalta still held good, but he'd hoped America would at least show an interest in Czechoslovakia. But Washington had other concerns. Millions of Americans were engaged in protests and demonstrations against the American War in Vietnam. The American draft board announced that in 1968 another 302,000 conscripts would be called up for the Vietnam War, 72,000 more than in the previous year. This report caused a storm of student demonstrations. It was clear that the US was stewing in its own juice, which it was boiling in Vietnam. Millions of people sought to stop this aggression and President Johnson had become the most unpopular US president in history.

The second cipher from Ambassador Duda of 24th March, put Dubček even more out of sorts. "According to Soviet Ambassador Dobrynin, the Soviet Embassy is assured by American administration officials that the US will not take any action that can be interpreted as interference with the internal affairs of the ČSSR. According to the head of the NSR, Knepstein similarly echoed the NATO Ambassador at Stadepe with regard to developments in the ČSSR. "

A week after Novotný's resignation, General Ludvík Svoboda was elected as the new president of the Czechoslovak Socialist Republic. After the election, he placed a wreath at the tomb of the first Czechoslovak president Tomáš Garrigue Masaryk, which had been unprecedented since 1948.

On 6th April, the government of Jozef Lenárt resigned and President Svoboda ordered the formation of the new government under Oldrich Černík. One of its vice-chairmen was Gustáv Husák. On 18th April they chose Josef Smrkovský, as chairman of the National Assembly. However, the main event was the adoption of the Action Programme at the meeting of the CPC Central Committee on 1st – 5th April, 1968. On 7th April, Soviet Ambassador Chervonenko sent a secret message of alarm to Brezhnev on the sessions of the Central Committee of the Communist Party. A large group of translators provided an operational translation of the literal wording of the Action Program for the Soviet leadership. 9 - 10 April, the Central Committee of the KSSZ met in Moscow with a single item on the agenda - the situation in Czechoslovakia. In the evening, after the end of the plenary, Brezhnev invited his working minister of defence, Grechko, Prime Minister Kosygin, the ideological secretary of the Central Committee of the KSSZ, Suslov, Chief of General Staff Marshal, Zacharov and the Chief of General Political Administration of the Soviet Army, General Jepishev. He offered cigarettes from a crystal box, he himself smoking one cigarette after another. He sat down, blew out smoke violently threw the documents on the table. "This is awful. Dubček has deceived us and so he mocks us and insinuates that he's still ahead of us. In Dresden, we clearly told him what we think of Smrkovský, Ulbricht even described him as a counter-revolutionary and they elected him as chairman of parliament and as a member of the party's presidium! It's a scandal! It's provocation! From the presidium, the party has removed all our loyal comrades; Hendrych, Chudík, Laštovička, Šimunka and Dolanský. Lenárt is fired from the position of Prime Minister! At least, they've given the Mnister of the Interior, Pavlov, to our man, Šalgovič as the Deputy Director of the ŠtB. And this pamphlet? They called this an action programme! In fact it's a counter-revolution programme! And they promised us in Dresden to correct this! So this is his remedy," shouted Brezhnev. "Read it out!" and he threw the translated Action Program to Jepishev.

"The basic idea and specific content of the action programme is to promote socialist democracy in managing all aspects of life in Czechoslovak society and to assure all the democratic rights for every individual citizen; freedom of expression, freedom of the press, assembly, association, residence, freedom of religion, federalization. In the economy it will promote decentralization and the independence of business management. A private sector will develop in services. There will be the possibility of leaving the republic without criminal consequences! The Communist Party does not perform its leading role by ruling over society, but by devoting itself to its free socialist development. To monopolize socialist state power, neither a single party nor a coalition of political parties can have access to all the political organizations of the people. "

"This is a counter-revolution!", Suslov joined in the criticism." It's a direct appeal to liquidate the party's leading role! They propose to separate the ŠtB from public security. Without enterprise, socialism does not survive! Hell," he said. "As if I hadn't mentioned that profiteer Baťa to him? Introducing the self-standing business and business clusters! It's a proposal to abolish the party's leading role in the economy. It's a programme that opens up the possibility of the restoration of capitalism!" Brezhnev listened to him, nodded, and wrapped himself round a cigarette.

"This is a deadly danger to socialism. If this spark passes to other socialist countries, a serious situation may arise," Grechko said coldly.

"Comrades, I think that if a group of loyal Czechoslovak Communists turn to the Soviet Union for assistance, the Soviet army will be ready to fulfill its international duty ..." Jepishev said in a significant manner.

"We've talked about it with Leonid Ilyich. Chief of General Staff Marshal Zacharov has prepared a strictly secret directive for the immediate commencement of preparation for the Danube military operation," Grechko informed those present.

"Is it a preparation for a possible military intervention as we concluded?" Suslov asked.

"Exactly. Comrade Shelest was charged with confiding in Comrade Biľak," said Brezhnev lighting up another cigarette.

CHAPTER 23

STOP DUBČEK!

On 24th April, Marshal Jakubovsky, chief of the Warsaw Pact, visited Czechoslovakia. He asked the Czechoslovak representatives to bring forward the tactical manoeuvres of the Warsaw Pact, scheduled for October, to June. The Czechoslovak side did not like this idea because a military exercise would cause unnecessary upheaval in the population. When Jakubovsky was rigidly insistent, Dubček told him directly that his request was unacceptable. At length, Jakubovsky proposed a "small workout" to which Prague agreed. The Czechoslovak leadership, however, was not astonished on 20th June to see a "small staff" in Czechoslovakia of almost thirty thousand soldiers with appropriate combat techniques, whose exercise in Šumava became a demonstration of military force against the reforms. At the same time, Polish-Soviet exercises took place in Poland with the participation of 80,000 soldiers and 2,600 tanks. The goal was to practise an attacking manoeuvre towards the Czechoslovak border. Simultaneously, 60,000 soldiers from the USSR and the GDR with 1,800 tanks trained in the southern regions of the GDR. In both cases, the training troops remained in the border areas and did not return to their bases. Under the pressure of public opinion and after interventions by Czechoslovak officials, the troops of the Warsaw Pact finally pulled out.

On 4th May, at the invitation of Brezhnev a Czechoslovak delegation of Dubček, Černík, Smrkovský and Biľak went to Moscow. Brezhnev, together with Kosygin, Podgorny, Katushev and Rusakov, reiterated the Dresden criticism, but this time significantly more in terms of an ultimatum. The Soviet High Representative noted that the Communist Party was losing control of the media and the Czechoslovak economic reform could lead to the revival of capitalism.

Dubček protested at this. "The Communist Party of Czechoslovakia is not only not losing support in society but it's strong as never before in its history. With regard to the media, censorship has been abolished and yet the press mostly supports the policy of the Communist party ... We are solving the political problems, but they can only be managed if we improve the economic situation," said Dubček. "The Prime Minister will explain this in more detail," and he handed over to Černík.

"Comrades, there is a huge amount of financial resource accumulated among our populations which is necessary to invest or spend. Since private business is not yet possible, we need to boost consumption. We need to improve market supply. Our deliberations - to buy consumer goods from the West will lead to an increase in confidence of the citizens of our country."

"Do you need a gold ruble loan for that?" Brezhnev asked menacingly.

"Leonid Ilyich, comrades, we do need the loan," Dubček stressed.

"Fundamentally, we have no problem lending it to you, but we can't lend to you in a situation where you don't address basic political issues. The supply of consumer goods is a secondary issue," Brezhnev puffed at his cigarette. "Don't you see comrades, what's happening to you? What positions have your anti-socialist powers got you into? How many NATO officers and various staff at your checkpoints are coming through as tourists? Do you want to know how many beds in the hotels in Karlovy Vary were ordered by a West German revanchist organization for their trip to Czechoslovakia?"

"Excuse me, Leonid Ilyich, but this is the first time I've heard this. It's possible that there was some information buzz among your people in Prague. We would have known that," protested Dubček.

"And the flow of people at your borders? People are walking across your borders with West Germany and Austria as if on a Sunday afternoon stroll! Do you know how many are agents and saboteurs?" Kosygin said coldly. "And if you don't get a loan from us?" he asked abruptly changing the theme of the discussion.

"If we don't get it, we'll be forced to turn to financial institutions in the West," Dubček said quietly.

"But that would mean selling out the capitalists! Be aware of the political implications. It would be a gift to counter-revolution!" Kosygin exploded.

"Forty-five to five million dollars is insignificant in comparison with the volume of our cooperation with the Soviet Union and other socialist countries," Černík objected. "We, unlike you, have no gold reserves to draw on. But if you give us a hard currency loan, we won't need it from the West." The negotiations ended without result. On the second day after breakfast before the delegation flew back to Czechoslovakia, Brezhnev praised Biľak in a private interview confidentially murmuring to him: "Dubček is a hopeless case!"

Three days later Brezhnev called a secret meeting of the leaders of the Soviet Union, Hungary, Poland, Bulgaria and the GDR. The participants were told that Moscow was already losing patience. The Communist leaders from the four countries of the Warsaw Pact nodded earnestly. The most aggressive, Ulbricht, sensed what Moscow meant and urged Brezhnev: "Leonid Ilyich, if the spark from Prague skips to Berlin, Warsaw or Moscow, socialism will be seriously threatened. That's why I strongly ask you to stop Dubček! At any cost!"

CHAPTER 24

MR. DUBČEK, WE LOVE YOU!

While Dubček was a hopeless case for Moscow, his popularity in Czechoslovakia and the world grew in unprecedented ways. In his honour rolls were baked, masses were said for him, the people voluntarily donated money, jewelry and gold for the success of the republic. The Communist Party had changed so much that people spoke increasingly of a "Dubček party". The actress, Iva Janžurová and singer, Marta Kubišová, were waiting for Dubček in front of the entrance to the Central Committee building so that they could publicly acknowledge his lustre. Marta Kubišová gave him her talisman for luck. "Thank you very much, Mr. Dubček, and we love you very much," Janžurová applauded the upbeat Dubček and embraced him.

The Czechoslovak film "Closely Observed Trains" won an Oscar. The dramatist and dissident, Václav Havel, was among half a million Czechoslovak citizens who enjoyed freedom for the first time in capitalist foreign parts. He visited the USA. The vast majority of citizens returned home; the borders were open.

During the May Day celebration in 1968, citizens witnessed scenes they had never experienced before. For the first time, parades were not obligatory and yet thousands of people came. The tone of the parades was the same - clear support for Dubček's leadership. Even Mother Nature has blessed the occasion. It was a wonderful day and a kind of national happening took place in Czechoslovakia. In Bratislava, students held their own portraits over their heads instead of conventional portraits of political figures. They summoned up an excellent atmosphere full of laughter and humour.

Dubček stood on the lowest step of the podium in Prague. The people walking below the podium gave him flowers. His fame was also acknowledged by representatives from the Committed Non-Party Club and the Association of Former Political Prisoners. American and Israeli flags even appeared in the parade. Over people's heads, instead of the usual slogans, Long Live the Communist Party and The Plan Will Be Fulfilled there were fewer routine slogans and more thoughts, Make Love Not War, Democracy At Any Price, Let Israel Exist, I want to contribute to population growth, but I have nowhere to live. The Hippy Soul Club held their placards over their heads. Hundreds of people wanted to shake Dubček's hand and so he had to have police protection. He took the microphone and apologized that too many people wanted to talk to him than he could manage. People understood and smiled. The ambassadors of the Warsaw Five countries were shocked by the incredible popularity of the Czechoslovak leader. The official guests of the First of May Parade began to be disturbed. The Bulgarian ambassador was angry with the podium when he saw a banner where Macedonia, claimed by Bulgaria, belonged to Yugoslavia. That evening, students gathered in front of the Polish embassy in Prague to protest police attacks against their Polish colleagues.

Dubček waved at the enthusiastic people and was obviously moved when a whole group of Prague citizens called out slogans in Slovak. Not until 1968 had the unity of Czechs and Slovaks been so strong as it was then. People enjoyed a new, long-forgotten freedom, travelled, discussed, asserted and agreed without compulsion, spontaneously, from the heart. Anna Dubček stood on the side of the podium and although unknown to the public when the group of Prague people discovered that she was Dubček's wife, she was inundated with a flood of flowers. She couldn't hold back tears of emotion. She loved Prague. It seemed that this time they had settled in the capital for longer. Even though she knew that the post of the First Secretary of the Communist Party was not the securest place, she believed that her husband would remain in place until the Prague Spring, as they had in the meantime named this new era in Czechoslovakia, had become irreversible.

In May in Velehrad, the nationwide constituent assembly of Catholic organizations held a conference of Conciliar Renewal with the participation of 2500 priests and laity in which a rebirth began in the Catholic Church. The Assembly was also attended by secretly ordained bishops who even served mass with legally ordained bishops broadcast directly by Czechoslovak Television. As well as the Catholic Church, representatives of Protestant churches and the banned Greek-Catholic Church were increasingly allowed a voice.

From the period May to July about one hundred prisoners were released.

The commemorative celebration on the occasion of the 49th anniversary of the death of General Milan Rastislav Štefánik in Bradlo was transformed into mass support of Alexander Dubček's political direction. The participants of the ceremony openly demanded a return to the values of Masaryk's democratic Czechoslovak Republic. KAN was formed – the Club for Non-Party Activists and Club 231. Number 231 was the number of the 1948 law, under which political prisoners were arrested and imprisoned. Under this law, players of the 1950 ice hockey team were also convicted. In just a few weeks, the club's membership base rose to fifty thousand former political prisoners. A Slovak organization for human rights protection was established with a similar focus to K 231. A commission, led by Gustáv Husák, worked diligently on the preparation of a federal arrangement for the republic.

In May, selected enterprises began an experiment with free Saturdays, which was applied to the whole country from September. Despite this industrial production increased. In the summer of 1968, the Communist Party reached a peak of popularity with young, educated people entering it, but the reformers were in a difficult situation. From below they were pressed by a mass of citizens enchanted by restored liberty. From above a post-Stalinist clique in Moscow was in a panic that Czechoslovakia would abandon the Warsaw Pact and initiate the final breakdown of the socialist bloc. Moscow was determined not to lose Czechoslovakia at any cost.

CHAPTER 25

JUDAS ARRIVES ON THE SCENE

In May, the second man in the USSR, Kosygin came with his granddaughter on the pretext of a cure in Karlovy Vary. Citizens recognized him and greeted him warmly at the Colonnade. They expressed sympathy and support for friendship with the Soviet Union. Kosygin first thought that these events were organized, but after all, he realized that their number and intensity could not be organized. After individual meetings with Dubček, Černík, Biľak and Kolder, Kosygin after returning to Moscow said at the politburo meeting: "The analysis of my interviews, meetings and materials suggests that currently there are no people in the country and state with more authority than Dubček, Černík, Smrkovský, Svoboda. For citizens, they are the natural and respected representatives. Therefore, we have to formulate our policy in accordance with these facts." When Kosygin's report was read, members of the politburo more or less agreed with his view that reliance on "healthy power" around Biľak would not be productive at this stage, and that they must work with the current Czechoslovak leadership. At that moment, however, Brezhnev received an emergency call from the Ukrainian First Secretary, Piotr Šelest.

"Comrade General Secretary, I've met Comrade Biľak."

"I hope nobody knows about it," Brezhnev smiled.

"Only the first secretary of the Transcarpathian Regional Committee, Yuri Vasilyevich Ilicnickij, who is his personal friend and to whom he turned with a request to meet me. We met in Kamjanyc village in the Uzhgorod district near the Czechoslovak border. "

"What does this Vasil say?"

"The situation in Czechoslovakia is catastrophic. According to him, Dubček is unable and unwilling to reveal the role of right-wing elements. He pointed to the different situation in Slovakia, and he literally said that "it is clear that we Slovaks will have to liberate Czechoslovakia with you."

"What does Comrade Biľak recommend?" Brezhnev asked nervously.

"He has clearly recommended that manoeuvres be held in Czechoslovakia. He told me that "When the Russian soldiers show up here, all the political rats will disappear into their holes. He also informed me that there had been a great number of suicides and harassment of party activists, secretaries of party organizations in companies, and in JRDs. If things come to the worst, he would ask for asylum to protect their families in Uzhgorod. "

"Whose families?" Brezhnev was interested.

"According to the words of Comrade Biľak, Kolder, Lenárt, Janík, Kapek, Švestka, Indra are the most threatened."

"All our people. Who, according to Comrade Biľak, are the leading rightists?"

"Smrkovský, Šik, Kriegel, Císař, Slavík, Prchlík, Vaculík and Šimon."

"Is it possible for Comrade Biľak to count on Dubček?"

"No."

"Good, Comrade Shelest. Thank you. You've done a good job. I will inform the politburo."

Biľak's information had a major impact on the change in Soviet politburo thinking. Kosygin's suggestion to communicate with Dubček was taken off the table. If Shelest hadn't come with such gloomy information, the politburo might have hesitated over the use of force. Brezhnev analyzed the situation in Czechoslovakia by saying that "Biľak is more sensitive to the situation than Dubček and it is necessary to maintain a relationship with "healthy forces". The most prominent representative of these "healthy forces", Biľak, was their connection in Prague. His Soviet contact was Piotr Šelest.

CHAPTER 26

WAR OF NERVES

From the from the moment he assumed office of First Secretary, Dubček took a room in the party hotel in Prague. He actually slept there, for it was typical for him to leave his work as one of the last and in the morning to be in his office among the first. According to the lights, Pražaks (people from Prague) knew that Dubček was still working. The hotel room was small and could not accommodate visitors. Finally, officials of the ÚV KSČ suggested that he move to an empty villa in the Trója district where Viliam Široký used to be. In April, he brought his wife and sons, Petr and

Milan, there. Pavol stayed in their Bratislava home with Dubček's mother, who still enjoyed health good enough to take good care of him.

It was the last Sunday of June, and Dubček had come home after a long time. His eager wife and mother, Pavlína, did not regret the fact that after a long time, the family was back together. The master of the house, inside walls hung with work by Hložník, Sokol and other Slovak painters, among many flowers and especially with his family and friends felt good. In the living room, Jozef Zrak, Anton Ťažký, Viktor Pavlend, Hvezdoň Kočtúch and Teodor Baník sat around the large dining table. They drank Dubček's Irsay wine and passionately debated.

"I defended Goldstücker from Brezhnev as far as possible and they do this to me. I begged him to curb the writers at this stage. Moscow is in a frenzy, Gomulka and Ulbricht are adding fuel to the flames and if that's not enough ... "

"OK, Šaňo, you know, these Prague intellectuals have always thought they were the navel of the universe. But with this manifesto, they've gone too far," Ťažký became serious.

"Why is it two thousand words?" Baník did not understand.

"Because it has two thousand words. They were very creative. For Vaculík calls directly for a struggle against the party," Dubček rubbed his head, reading Literární noviny aloud. "The Communist Party has turned into a power organization that has become appealing to power-hungry egoists, calculating cowards, and people with bad consciences ... The initiative and effort of democratic communists is therefore only for the repayment of the debt which the party has to non-communists." He put the paper on the table.

"We had to condemn it on the day it came out in the presidium. Even Pepik Smrkovský called it a call for anarchy."

"Well, not for anarchy, it's just says that if necessary, the country will stand for you, with weapons, too," Klokoč corrected him.

"If we had left Literárky banned as Novotný did, there would be calm, but we do not want that," exclaimed Dubček.

"They've also published it in Zemědelky, Práca and elsewhere ... The problem is this, Vaculík is right, only publishing it is absolutely misjudged at the worst possible time," explained Ťažký.

"If that hero Vaculík were in Dresden or Moscow, he wouldn't have done this ... I'll meet the writers and try to convince them ... to explain to them how we are in danger ... The strange provocations are taking on absurd dimensions. Our Berlin ambassador has informed us that the Ulbricht Berliner Zeitung newspaper reported that eight US tanks appeared in Prague. These were the tanks that the American director filmed at Davle, a short way from Prague, for the Bridge at Remagen film ... Our people in the ŠtB informed us that they had discovered a group of thirty tourists with West German passports. When they sounded them a bit, they turned out to be Soviet agents speaking broken German with a strong Russian accent. In Karlovy Vary, a legal group of KGB officers was in one hotel. The ŠtB commander in Vary was taking care of them, someone called Bohunek."

"They're putting pressure on you, but there's no way back. Surely you don't want to stop everything that we've started here? And how? It's no longer just about party reform. It's the power of the nation that is drawing water to the mill. My dear Šaňo, Brezhnev is right. We don't have things under control. But Goldstücker and Pelikán aren't controlling it, but the people. The people's enthusiasm is an energy that no one can stop ... Only with brutal force," Kočtuch considered.

"I absolutely exclude the use of force. Brezhnev would never allow it. And we're keeping our promises carefully. They have to see it. I talk to the journalists almost every day. I try to explain, I beg them, so that the media is more disciplined. We have abolished censorship and so they are like this."

"We also guided them to this point. Well, then, not us ... but it was here ... No one was able to put our point of view even in times when we were in leading positions ... Truly, we are only correcting what we have brought about ... and for some Czech writers that seems to be slow, but they are afraid the whole thing can be stopped," Ťažký stated.

"It's all very well for them to say. They've got me watching their back, but I've got Moscow on my back. Don't you see that Russians don't want to go home any more, even if the military exercise is over! ... Here's Moscow Pravda of 19th July. "In the area of the famous baths of Karlovy Vary, on the road to Cheb, near the border with Western Germany, the Czechoslovak security authorities discovered a secret warehouse of weapons of unknown origin. As reported to journalists by eyewitnesses from the local population, all the discovered guns, machine guns, guns were of American descent and were apparently supplied from West Germany for Sudeten revanchists and adherents of an old-fashioned restoration in the ČSSR. According to a security officer, the weapons are suitable for use by large rebel groups. Similarly, the Bulgarian press office writes. Rudé Právo took from Neues Deutschland the report that a cache of weapons and ammunition was discovered in the Sokolov region between the villages of Mýtina and Arnoldov." he put down the newspaper. "The Minister of the Interior, Pavel, informed the Central Committee that, according to a recent investigation, these weapons came from the German Democratic Republic. The lubricating oil on the machine guns is of Soviet origin. Our experts considered that the weapons originated from Soviet war material in the GDR and were placed there by Soviet agents. The Soviet government has sent us a sharp protest asking us to have allied troops deployed on our western border. They accuse us of wanting to regain Zakarpatian Ukraine. They say we are organizing support activities among local citizens there. This non-existent problem has been deliberately inflated into enormous proportions."

"That's what's going on. They need to get us at any cost. They urged Gottwald and Novotný to consent to the deployment of their troops with us. We are the only country in the socialist camp that borders NATO countries without Soviet troops present ..." Dubček sighed.

"How is it possible that Soviet Pravda reported on these weapons sooner than our newspapers? Zrak was annoyed.

"I have the feeling they're looking for any excuse just to come here," said Ťažký thoughtfully.

There was silence. Dubček smiled and, as he used to in critical moments, he imitated Brezhnev's contorted Russian. "Well, Alexander Stepanovich, what do you want to do?" And immediately after he replied in Slovak, "Tovarisch Brezhnev, I won't let you in here!" He turned abruptly to his friends. "So! I won't let them in! As much as I like them, I won't let them in!"

CHAPTER 27

THE COUNTDOWN BEGINS

On 11th July, Brezhnev read the Czechoslovak press analysis sent by the Soviet embassy in Prague. "From 30th June to 10th July, a survey was conducted in Czechoslovakia to find out whether people want to continue living in socialism or want a return to capitalism. 89 percent decided to live in socialism. Only 7 percent of citizens said they were dissatisfied with Dubček's policy. East and West European youth, as well as from North America, are moving to Prague to see how true freedom looks. Students in revolt in Western Europe take Dubček as a model, as well as founding clubs in his name. He has become a darling of hippies, the hope for many who did not see a way out of capitalism. They sing about him in songs and students wear badges bearing his portrait. He is unquestionably the most popular politician in the world and the Pope has declared that he was praying for him. "

Brezhnev laid the analysis aside, lit a cigarette and thought for a long time. It was not the first time that he had caught himself thinking that he was not entirely convinced that Dubček wanted to leave the socialist camp and deceive Moscow. His practices were marked by his youth and naivety, which were used by the experienced right-wing around him. Kosygin had a similar opinion. Ulbricht and Gomulka, however, were pushing for Moscow to be decisive. He said he would give Dubček one last chance. He tried to persuade him to make fundamental personnel changes and stop expression of anti-Soviet and anti-socialist opinion. He first consulted with Kosygin, who supported his idea. After calling the other communist leaders, Dubček was invited to a council of six people in Warsaw on 14th and 15th July. Dubček was clear what would be the subject of the council; condemnation of reforms in Czechoslovakia. He called the presidium of the ÚV KSČ and, with its blessing, told the Soviets that it would come only if the leaders of all the socialist states, including Tito and Ceausescu, were to take part in the deliberations, and if the issues had been previously discussed at bilateral meetings. Of course, Brezhnev did not accept this request. They sent a letter of ultimatum from Warsaw to the Czechoslovak authorities, which the ÚV KSČ refused.

Czechoslovakia was the third socialist country in history, after Yugoslavia and Hungary, to oppose the all-powerful Soviet dictatorship. She declined the invitation to Warsaw. On 20th July, the troops of the five Warsaw Pact troops were put on alert.

On that day, Piotr Shelest stayed in Kadar's private cabin just off the shores of Lake Balaton until dusk. The weather was unbearable; a strong wind blew up a high wave on the lake. Šelest went to the shore in the hope that he would meet Biľak, who, according to information from Hungarian comrades, was staying in a club nearby. With the Hungarian assigned to him, he told Biľak he was waiting for him in the cabin. Biľak, however, asked to meet on the shore of the lake at 22:00. Shelest went to the shore of the lake. It was dark and even over a short distance it was hard to make out a person and even harder to hear. At the appointed time a man appeared in front of Shelest. He had wanted to call Vasil, but he was pre-empted. It transpired that it was someone whom Biľak had sent out to reconnoitre. After a short while Biľak himself appeared. They went to the cabin and talked from eleven to five in the morning.

"It is of the utmost importance that a bilateral meeting be held in the near future at all costs. If he doesn't come, it can lead to a final split and departure of the KSČ from our common line. You have the right not to want to come to such a meeting in Prague. These "Svejks" would think they had won. Černík, Dubček, Smrkovský and Kriegel are afraid to travel to the Soviet Union, they are afraid they wouldn't return," said Biľak.

"What is your opinion on Smrkovský?" asked Shelest.

"He's a political prostitute."

"And Černík?"

"He is fully under the influence of the Yugoslav ambassador, without him having to do anything."

Tell me, Vasil, who can be relied upon to organize a strong block of healthy forces?"

"Indre, Kolder, Švestka, Rigo, Barbírek, Piller, Kapek ... me ..." Biľak slowly recited twenty names.

"Why haven't you made more effort?"

"We were afraid we'd be accused of treason. We're ready to support you by all means, but we don't know what to do. "

He whispered, slowly sipping tea, and then it came out. "We need a request for help from you. We can give you full assurance that the letter or its authors won't be published. "

"You must understand our position. We're ashamed to beg for help when we haven't done anything in our country. What do you think of us? "

"Wouldn't it be better if your group now wrote a letter asking for help? Would your positions be strengthened? "

"Yes, it would strengthen our cohesion."

"Couldn't we act through Slovakia?" Shelest asked unexpectedly.

"We will see. If absolutely unavoidable, we can proceed without the Czechs in order to save Czechoslovakia," Biľak said.

"So can we count on your invitation?"

"Yes."

"When?"

"I'll talk to my comrades. Very quickly."

Then they shook hands. It was 21st July, 1968. Dubček had breathing space for another month.

CHAPTER 28

YOU WON'T BE CHEERING HIM FOR LONG

Although Vasil Biľak was First Secretary of CC KSS, as a member of the ÚV KSČ in Prague he had a Secretariat and offices. That night he was in an extremely good mood. The Soviet comrades had so far agreed to all that he had proposed. With Indra and Kapek, he discussed the steps to take after the Soviet invasion. A conversation between Vladimír Škutin and Jan Werich was taking place on the TV screen.

"I'm in constant contact with Chervonenko. He informs me that very recently in Moscow they definitely approved military assistance. Comrades, we must be ready and everybody must know what they have to do," Biľak conspiratorially informed in his Czech-Rusyn-Slovak language.

"Karel Hoffmann will gain control of radio and television," said Indra.

"Who can we one hundred percent rely on in Prague?"

"I have written here, Lenárt, Kolder, Jakeš, Hoffmann, Korčák, Fojtík, me, Štoll, David, Švestka, Dolanský, Laštovička, Havlín, Zavadil and some others," said Indra. "And in Bratislava?"

"Comrade Šalgovič is in constant contact with the KGB. He's leaving for a holiday for Bulgaria, but he can come back immediately. If necessary, he will ensure a smooth Soviet arrival. In this regard this line, cooperation with healthy forces in state security is ensured. I spoke to Janík, Pezlar, Boďo, Martinak, my assistant Cheben and they added even more.

"Wait ..." he checked Kapek. "Look at Werich. And we'll give that to Škutina soon too." On the TV screen, Jan Werich was explaining his opinion on Alexander Dubček in his "What do you think of it, Mr. Werich ".

"So look, we'll make a diagnosis. The pressure on our chests has been relieved. That's clear. I ran to the TV to look at the news. Alexander Dubček spoke. You know, that's a wonderful person. Truly a wonderful person. The inscription "Es lebe Dubček" has appeared in Prague. It's as if the Germans are suggesting they want their Dubček. Perhaps it was written by some endeerak (inhabitant of the NDR, the German Democratic Republic) because he knew he couldn't write it on a wall back home. I'm going to bet you anything you like if Dubček were to run for some job anywhere today, perhaps to take over from U Thant, so he'd win in the first round. There's great enthusiasm for him ... The world is full of phrases. And those faces that interpret them ... they can't be trusted ... And among these faces comes a smiling gentleman from Slovakia, he smiles, talks like everyone, when he stutters just to correct himself, he does not pretend. .. Dubček's optimism is contagious ..." Well, you won't have that optimism for long," Biľak threatened the screen. But Werich was not intimidated and continued. "He's an ordinary man, one of us ... And people like to favour this man ... And he also has a sense of humor ... Such a man is worth favouring ... He speaks in his mother tongue, he can flawlessly change accents when saying comrades and Comrades ... " At these words, Indra and Kapek chuckled a little, staring at the shaking Biľak." And when he reads and reverts to himself, he corrects himself. He does not pretend not to have said something. He behaves like an ordinary person. He is an ordinary person. And people love a man like that."

"You won't be cheering him for long," muttered Kapek.

"We've given him a national honour. He's like a pig in clover and he's like that ..." Indra nodded uncomprehendingly. He stood up and switched off the television so that nothing would disturb them as they prepared the greatest treachery in post-war Czech-Slovak history.

CHAPTER 29

MEETING IN A TOILET

It was clear that a bilateral meeting of the highest Soviet and Czechoslovak leadership, which Dubček proposed, was essential. Hawks, led by the chief of the KGB, Andropov, didn't support a meeting. However, Kosygin, supported by Brezhnev, advocated the meeting.

"I think," said Andropov accusingly to Kosygin at the politburo meeting, "that in fact this meeting won't achieve anything, and you, Alexei Nikolayevich, are pushing me unnecessarily. They are now fighting for their skins and fighting fiercely. The right-wingers, headed by Dubček, stand firmly in their positions. Not only are we, but they are preparing very carefully. They are currently preparing a worker class and a worker militia. Everything is directed against us. "

Kosygin rejected his reproach. "Comrade Andropov, I would like to say that I'm not pressing you, on the contrary - you are pushing us. In my judgement, the Czechoslovaks aren't fighting for their own skins but for a social-democratic program. That is the essence of their struggle. They fight fiercely, but for the goals that are quite clear to them that Czechoslovakia should first change to

Yugoslavia and then to something similar to Austria. We know that at the beginning as First Secretary in Slovakia Dubček met Tito."

After haggling over the venue, Brezhnev suggested to Dubček that they meet in the border town of Čierna nad Tisou. Dubček objected that they were unable to provide decent conditions for the negotiations, accommodation and other technical requirements. Brezhnev informed him that they were arriving in their own train, which had everything necessary. For security reasons, after the negotiations, the Soviet authorities always travelled back to the Soviet side of the border. The talks began on 29th July at the railroad club at the station in Čierna nad Tisou. The Presidium of the ÚV KSČ, before the meeting, was given an expert assessment on the West's relation to Czechoslovakia, which stated clearly: "Western governments in support of Czechoslovakia are doing nothing and the international labour movement, and the world democratic public cannot intervene effectively in favour of Czechoslovakia."

The Soviet leadership came to Čierna with the suggestion that the Czechoslovak party fulfill what was dictated to it in Warsaw, complemented by the request to remove from leading positions of Kriegel, Špaček, Císař, Slavík, Šika, Pavel, Pelikán and Prchlík. Opposed to this, the KSČ leadership came to Čierna with the request that the Soviets should distance themselves from the Warsaw Letter, which meant that its assessment of the situation in Czechoslovakia as counter-revolutionary was wrong.

The interviews soon reached a blind alley. Both sides' views on the issues in question did not come close. Some Soviet leaders were unusually arrogant. Kosygin took a swipe at Franz Kriegel's membership of the presidium as a "Galician Jew", which Dubček had strictly rejected.

The Czechoslovak public watched the negotiations in Čierna nad Tisou with great concern and hope. There were thousands of greetings and encouraging letters, resolutions, telegrams to Čierna. The motto of the day was, "We are with you, be with us." The solidarity of the citizens with their leadership was touching and all-embracing. On this civic spontaneity, Brezhnev said laconically, "When I give instructions, I have tons of supporting letters and thousands of supporters."

Dubček could not sleep after the first day and walked on the railway station. He was surrounded by railway men, coming to the morning shift. He could not give them much optimism. "I'm afraid that Moscow will actually stop us. But someone had to make a start."

On the third day, it was clear that the negotiation was a dead end. They told Dubček that Brezhnev was sick and lying in his wagon. He went to see him. He found him in the dark pajamas in his bed, but it was clear he was pretending to be ill. He complained of fatigue and headaches, but after a while he abandoned playacting and returned to the matter in hand. He wanted to hold a meeting with other members of the Warsaw Pact. Dubček knew that such a meeting could blunt the edge of the controversy and bring matters after the Warsaw Letter back to normal. He counted on the XIV Congress of the KSČ scheduled for 9th September, still forty days away, which was expected to confirm the Dubček line and finally eliminate the conservatives. He agreed with Brezhnev's proposal to hold a new, multilateral meeting, which would accept a document on the new relationships. There were to be no representatives from Yugoslavia or Romania. They agreed to hold a meeting in Bratislava in two days.

The new hotel for trade unions, Sorea, on a slope above the Danube, opposite the Bratislava Park of Culture and Relaxation, had not yet experienced any security measures. After the presentation of the Soviet draft, Dubček was appalled. The Czechoslovak party drew up a counter-proposal in which the possibility of the specific path and internal development of each socialist country was anchored. It was a direct rejection of what Brezhnev had tried to dictate in the Warsaw Letter. A furious debate began. Ulbricht and Gomulka did not consider such a sentence as necessary. Dubček argued that such a principle had also been adopted by the international communist movement, and that the demand stemmed directly from the fundamental principle of interstate relations – non-interference in the internal affairs of other countries. It happened that he did not sign the document proposed by Brezhnev. Kosygin solved the problem by proposing a compromise formulation which said that "the support, protection and consolidation of the successful achievements of the block states are a common international obligation." This very phrase, which came into history as the Brezhnev doctrine, was later interpreted by Moscow as Czechoslovak agreement to military intervention.

During the Bratislava meeting, however, one major event did not take place in the large dining room of the union, but in the toilet. On the second day of the meeting, Piotr Shelest went to the toilet. He stood at the urinal and pulled a face that he was peeing. He stared nervously at the clock. There was no one in the toilet. After a moment, the door opened and the even more nervous Vasil Biľak peeped inside. When he saw Shelest he was relieved. He placed himself beside Shelest and, besides his worker-smallholder natural feature, pulled out something far more significant. An envelope. He handed it to Shelest. "Spasibo, Comrade Biľak" and put the long-awaited invitation letter into his pocket. With this valuable prize he immediately hurried to Leonid Iljič. When the Soviet leader read it in the bowels of his room, he smiled contentedly. The aim of the Bratislava meeting had been achieved.

CHAPTER 30

SASHA, YOU'RE DECEIVING US

Six days after the end of the Bratislava meeting, the popular Yugoslav leader Josip Broz Tito came on an official three-day visit to Czechoslovakia. Wherever he went, he was greeted by enthusiastic crowds. He had the reputation of a hero who'd fought not only against fascism, but also against Stalin. Moscow regarded his visit to Czechoslovakia as provocation, just as they regarded the visit of the Romanian leader, Nicolae Ceausescu, who came to Prague on 15th August.

Two days before, Dubček had called a meeting of the presidium of the ÚV KSČ. At about 5:35 p.m. Dubček was called out of the session. After a while he returned and excused himself for an urgent call from Soviet ambassador, Chervonenko. He instructed Oldřich Černík to lead the meeting and requested Josef Smrkovský to go with him. Biľak both watched with a smile. He had from Chervonenko information that Brezhnev would call Dubček at 17.35. Chervonenko had asked him to see who would be accompanying Dubček. When he phoned his request, he remarked pointedly, "I bet it's Smrkovský." He was right. On the other end of the line in Brezhnev's office in Soviet politburo resort in Yalta were Podgorny and Kosygin. On a nearby beach was János Kádár, whom Brezhnev had invited for a few days to Yalta. The conversation had been switched to loudspeaker output. In the course of the interview Brezhnev learned that Smrkovský was with Dubček who also switched the phone to the loudspeaker. He spoke to Brezhnev in Russian. Brezhnev addressed Dubček in familiar terms, Dubček, on the contrary, addressed Brezhnev formally. After the initial courtesy phrases, Brezhnev came on the attack without wasting time. Instead of the friendly Sasha, he began addressing him as Alexander Stepanovitch which presaged nothing good.

"Alexander Stepanovitch, we have little time and therefore let us get straight to the point. In our politburo, we are assessing the situation as forming a breach of the agreement from Čierna nad Tisou. Your mass media has not stopped attacking the Soviet Union!"

"As far as I know, there has been nothing like this recently."

"How has it not happened when literally every newspaper publishes anti-Soviet articles? I want to ask you what it means...! ... I can tell you frankly that delays in fulfilling commitments are nothing but cheating and the open sabotage of jointly accepted solutions! How will you solve the agreement on cadre questions? In Čierna, we shook our hands as friends and promised to solve this question in the coming days! "

"I haven't promised to solve this question in two or three days ..."

"But these questions cannot be solved in an indefinite time period! You promised to call the presidium to address them. You've already had one, now you have another. Will you solve these questions today?"

"These questions can only be discussed by the plenum of the Central Committee ..." Brezhnev turned his head to Podgorny and Kosygin, who shook their heads even more obtusely.

"When are you calling a plenary?"

"By the end of the month ... But it may be early September."

"And in this plenum, will you deal with cadre questions as we agreed in Čierna?" Brezhnev added.

"They will be dealt with as the plenary decides," Dubček replied quietly.

"It's a pity," Brezhnev breathed deeply. "I will tell you honestly that what you promised us in Čierna was taken as twenty-four carat. I don't understand why you're still postponing the solution to these questions? If you raise these questions today in the presidium, it would be a last chance to rescue the matter without bigger losses!"

"Comrade Brezhnev, I said that these questions will be solved by the plenary."

"Sasha, I want to ask you right away, what does it mean? Even over this matter, you are deceiving us! "

"I don't see any deception here. We're fulfilling our commitments as much as possible in the given situation. "

"You're creating a new situation that forces us to adopt new, different measures."

"Comrade Brezhnev, you take the measures that your politburo deems right."

"Your answer is not serious."

"I can't answer otherwise. Comrade Brezhnev I'm telling you with every responsibility if you consider us to be cheats, take the measures that your politburo deems necessary! "

"Sasha, I understand that you're nervous, I know that getting back control of the mass media is not easy. Right wingers direct everything through Pelikán, Císař, Kriegler and other bad hats. Questions for their recall may be dealt with in the first presidium."

"Is it easy, Comrade Brezhnev, to solve such questions?"

"Sasha, it can't be said as irritatingly as you are saying it now! Let me ask you one more question. Do you personally stand in the positions of fulfilling the commitments you undertook at Čierna or not? "

"There will be a plenary, Leonid Ilyich, the plenary will decide. We now have a different agenda for the Bureau. From what we agreed at Čierna, we will discuss today only a question about the ministry of the interior," said Dubček.

"Alexander Stepanovitch, I regret that you speak so irritably to me!"

Dubček fell silent for a moment. He looked at Smrkovský, who was smoking nervously. Both were clear that they needed time.

"I'd rather leave everything. Why am I annoyed? We undertake matters, we work, and you only accuse me of doing the wrong thing and being deceptive! Comrade Brezhnev, it can't be solved only in this way. The whole party, the whole nation stands united behind the leadership of the party! People are enthusiastic!"

"If I give instructions, people will show enthusiasm in ten minutes! You call it liberalization, we call it counter-revolution!" Brezhnev shouted.

"Another first secretary of the ÚV KSČ will be elected at the next plenary," Dubček said with resignation. Smrkovský began indicate sharply that he was crazy.

"Sasha, don't go to extremes. I don't know where you're speaking, if you can talk to me openly. At the end of your presidium, ambassador Chervonenko will come to you and you will tell him openly when and how you intend to resolve the issues we have agreed upon." Dubček looked at Smrkovský as if seeking support. Smrkovský resolutely shook his head.

"I've said everything, Comrade Brezhnev, and I can't say more to Comrade Chervonenko." Dubček realized his back was sweating. "If you think we're deceiving you, take what measures you think are right. It's your affair."

"Look, Sasha, we will undoubtedly take the measures we consider to be right. But I ask you when do you intend to solve what we have agreed on?"

"You don't ask me! You order! I can work anywhere, I don't care for this function. Let anyone deal with it. I can't work anymore in a situation of ceaseless assaults."

"All these troubles you have brought on yourself."

"Leonid Ilyich, tell me what to do?"

Brezhnev thought. "It'll be like this, we'll come to an agreement with you and we'll take what measures we consider necessary."

When, after an eighty minute telephone call, Dubček and Smrkovský returned to the presidium hall, they were pale as a sheet. Bil'ak smiled contentedly.

On that day, 16th August, the Moscow Politburo took a definitive decision on "Brotherly military assistance to the Czechoslovak people." The Defence Minister, Marshal Grechko, issued the relevant instructions to the commander of the Western Soviet Army Group in the GDR to General Piotr Kirilovic Koshev, Commander of the Northern Soviet Army Group in Poland, Ivan Nikolayevich Shkadov, Commander of the Southern group of Soviet troops in Hungary, Konstantin Ivanovich Provalov, commander of the Carpathian military District Lieutenant General Vasil Zinovjevovich Bisjarin, Commanders of Airborne forces Generals Vasily Filipovich Margelov, Air force commander, Marshal Konstantin Andrejevich Vershinin, Rocket troop commander, Marshal Nikolai Ivanovich Krylov, Air Defence Commander Marshal Batich and Commander of the Naval forces Admiral Sergej Georgijevich Gorsk.

Soviet intelligence had mapped the Czechoslovak army. It was the second strongest in the Warsaw Pact. They had calculated all the alternatives, including armed resistance.

CHAPTER 31

DETAILS ON MONDAY EVENING

On 18th August, the first secretaries of the Communist parties held a meeting in the Kremlin in Moscow, where the only thing they did was to approve the invasion of Czechoslovakia formally. Brezhnev, Podgorny, Kosygin, Suslov, Ulbricht, Zhivkov, Gomulka, and Kadár sat in Brezhnev's office at a long table. They were not as usual in the official reception lounge. The meeting had been called quickly. It was only a formal confirmation of what everybody present knew. So that he could preserve a facade, Brezhnev looked worried and responsible. His voice thundered in a business-like manner. "We will never give up socialist Czechoslovakia to anyone. It is a strategic point in Central Europe. To lose it would mean annulling the results of the Second World War. Two hundred thousand of our soldiers died there so that Dubček can now give it to the imperialists! We have to act together! Even before their extraordinary XIV Congress. Otherwise it will be difficult for us and for the healthy forces in Czechoslovakia. Dubček has really provoked us. He doesn't come to Warsaw, but he invites Tito and Ceausescu to Prague! It is the renewal of the pre-war little entente! We asked him to recall Krieger, Císař a Pelikán within fifteen days. We also agreed that the National Assembly would adopt a resolution according to which State Security would be placed under the authority of the Interior Ministry, and Šalgovič would become the head of the ŠtB. Nothing like that happened. That's why I telephoned Dubček on 13th August. It was during the time of their presidium. Comrade Biľak informed us that Dubček left the presidium with Smrkovský, who was the only one in our call, even though I expressly asked Dubček to call Comrades Černík and Biľak. The face of Comrade Dubček is revealed! I asked Dubček to inform the Presidium about our call, but he kept it secret. Today I talked to Comrade Indra. He told me that a group of trusted and loyal comrades are ready to help us adopt a resolution in which they express their distrust of the right wing and will take over the leadership of the party and the state. Comrade Indra guarantees in the course of the night at least another fifty comrades from the presidium and government who will support our action. Taking into account the self-regard and cowardice of Comrade Černík, we assume that after the entry of the troops, he would become the Prime Minister and cooperate with the troops. Comrade Šalgovič will issue an order to close the western border. Last night, we received a document from Comrade Kapek, a member of the healthy kernel of the party, informing us that, at a meeting of the presidium and the secretariat with selected journalists, Císař announced that in the coming days and even hours the situation would escalate. You see, they sense it! I want to show you the document I received in Bratislava when I left the meeting. This is an invitation letter that was handed to Comrade Shelest by Comrade Biľak." Brezhnev smiled bitterly. "Matters have gone so far that it had to be handed over to him in the toilet ... The letter begins with the words, 'Dear Leonid Ilyich'. We asked the writers of the letter not to come back to me personally, but to the Central Committees of the Communist and Workers' Parties and governments of the USSR, Poland, Hungary, Bulgaria and the GDR. So I'm going get you a modified letter. "Dear comrades, members of the Central Communist and Workers' Committees and Governments of the Soviet Union, Poland, Hungary, Bulgaria and the German Democratic Republic. We are aware of our full responsibility for our decision and we turn to you with this statement. Our fundamentally sound democratic process, the correction of the mistakes and shortcomings of the past, as well as the overall political leadership of society have gradually slipped from the hands of the party's central committee. The party leadership is no longer able to resist attacks on socialism successfully whose existence is threatened in our state. Right-wing forces have created the conditions for a counter-revolutionary coup. In this difficult situation we turn to you for help with all the means at your disposal." Brezhnev took his glasses off for a moment and added, "We understand this as military as well." He didn't tell his listeners that he had added this formula to the letter himself. Then he put his glasses back on and continued. "In connection with the complex and dangerous developments in our state, we ask for the maximum concealment of our statement. Signed by Indra, Kolder, Kapek, Švestka, Biľak."

There was silence in the chamber. "Comrades, what do you have to say? After a profound analysis, we have concluded that Dubček's commitments will not be fulfilled that has moved totally to the right. Therefore there is only one option. Stop Dubček at all costs! Minister Grechko has informed us that armed resistance could also be expected. We will avoid this worse alternative. Troops have been ordered not to hinder Czechoslovak citizens who will flee to the west. It is not the role of our soldiers to detain refugees, but to fight. In the light of the Hungarian experience, there will be very many refugees and we won't know what to do with them. Will we bring them to court, will we hang them or let them go free? And if he's a counter-revolutionary, let him go!"

"The soldiers of the German Democratic Republic testify to the highest level of military morality!" Ulbricht swore.

"I wanted to tell you, Comrade Ulbricht, that the supreme command of the troops had already agreed that the GDR troops would fulfill important roles, but for understandable reasons it would not be appropriate for them to enter the territory of Czechoslovakia." Ulbricht went pale. "I still want to ask you to make your embassy available to healthy forces in the event of their being in danger. Please prepare enough secret accommodation in your embassies. Comrade Kapek, for example, wrote that he would be staying in a certain factory. The troops will begin Operation Danube on the night of 20th – 21st August. We have discussed all the details with our comrades in Prague. For security reasons, we now send only a brief telegram of the following wording: "We agree with your plan, help comes, details on Monday evening.""

CHAPTER 32

MOSCOW COULD HAVE DONE NOTHING BETTER

It was a warm afternoon on 20th August, 1968, 17:00 hours Washington time. US President Lyndon Baines Johnson was drinking Scotch whisky, Cutty Sark, while watching a Western Conference basketball match between his favourite team, newcomers the San Diego Rockets and the Los Angeles Lakers. The match was extraordinarily dramatic, but the San Diego boys were leading narrowly after the half-time, so the president was in a good mood. He was a little bit put out that the Soviet ambassador was announced at this time, but he had to give preference to state duties over his basketball fan's passions.

His secretary ushered Dobrynin into the Oval Office, with which he was intimately familiar. He'd already served as Ambassador of the Soviet Union in the United States for six years. The President walked up to him with a broad smile. Then the Ambassador greeted the President and his aides. In San Diego, the second half of the match had begun and Dobrynin noticed the president's nervousness which he didn't control as occasionally he looked at the screen against protocol. Dobrynin knew about Johnson's weakness for basketball and cigarettes. Nevertheless, the President seemed to him to be smoking somewhat too much.

"You must excuse me, I'm a little nervous, our team has a chance to beat the Lakers. It looks like Lakers are winning the West Conference that year, but we're going to spoil it for them. But work is work," the president stood and finally turned off the television with a little sigh. "My colleagues - Walt Rostow, the head of the National Security Council and Jack Valetti, my personal assistant – I don't need to introduce you."

Dobrynin didn't know that a few hours ago, the President's working lunch with his security and foreign policy advisers hadn't spoken at all on a possible Soviet invasion of Czechoslovakia. The Americans had rated the potential invasion of minimal importance. Their main security concerns were the war in Vietnam and the tense situation in the Middle East only a year after the six-day war. They had discussed in detail the progress of the negotiations with the Soviet Union on the bilateral strategic defence agreement SALT 1.

The Soviet ambassador entered the presidential office at eleven o'clock in the evening Central European Time on 20th August, 1968. He was acting exactly according to the instructions of Moscow, who wished to inform the President of the United States of the "action" in Czechoslovakia at that time. According to their strategic plans, they'd calculated that by this time Soviet tanks would be in Prague. They would be welcomed enthusiastically by Czechoslovak citizens and perhaps soon a temporary, worker-smallholder government led by Alois Indra.

After introductory courtesy phrases and heartfelt greetings from the Soviet leaders, Dobrynin presented the president with a diplomatic note.

"Thank you for your information, Excellency," he obligingly thanked the President when he read the note in which President of the Presidium of the Supreme Soviet of the USSR, Nikolai Podgorny, informed the President of the United States of America that Warsaw Pact troops had taken military action to support socialism in Czechoslovakia the night of 20th – 21st August 1968.

The President offered the ambassador a cigarette. The Ambassador thanked him politely. "Jack, I hope everything that the ambassador has said to us is accurately noted ..." the President turned to Valetti. Jack's hand was shaking slightly. He nodded. The President thought for a moment, looked at Rostow and stared ahead. Dobrynin's face puckered in anticipation of a violent reaction. In case of vigorous criticism from the highest American representative, Moscow's headquarters had agreed to the possibility of using the unofficial position of the Soviet Union. Its main content was a counter-argument pointing to the American invasion of Vietnam. Of course, the ambassador's opinion was to be used only in the case of a truly unsatisfactory reaction by the President. Otherwise, Moscow recommended restraint and didn't want to provoke irritation.

Johnson took some candies. Dobrynin watched his unusually large, meaty ears swing from side to side.

"Is this at the invitation of the Czechoslovak government?"

"Yes."

"Is there a threat to Romania?" Johnson asked.

"No."

"Events in Czechoslovakia must not block negotiations on the restriction of nuclear weapons. This is the priority of our foreign policy, and I think the world will understand it ... "he nodded his head and nodded in agreement." Tomorrow morning we will discuss your information with Dean Rusk and my advisers. We'll give you a reply." He downed his whisky and Jack poured him another. He noticed that Dobrynin had drunk up. The Soviet Ambassador agreed with his view with another glass.

The president lit a cigarette, exhaled and smiled. "Tomorrow morning, I intend to notify the public of my intention to visit the Soviet Union. I have invited several friends to have breakfast so that I can announce this joyful message. I would be very pleased, Excellency, if I could get your government's position on my visit before my appearance before the public. I think this visit would be extremely important for our countries. Let's drink to the development of relations between our great and powerful countries." Dobrynin's eyes almost jumped out of their sockets. He didn't understand. The entire staff of the best Soviet-American relations experts had worked in Moscow on a sheaf of arguments that he had prepared in his pocket. It wasn't needed. The President toasted him for the second time. Dobrynin sensed surprise on Rostow and Valetti's faces. He was almost disappointed with the President. He had already been looking forward to a laudatory cipher from the "highest" for his stout defense of "the action". Now nothing.

"Certainly, sir, I will do everything to put my country's position on your desk tomorrow by nine o'clock. However, I can almost certainly assure you that it will be positive," he replied to the president's interest in Moscow's position on the planned visit. Then the president began to tell funny stories from Texas. Dobrynin had another shot of whisky. Another was poured for him by the President in person. Johnson was obviously unable to conceal his good mood. Though aware that the Soviet invasion threatened to withdraw from an arms control treaty, the president was almost beside himself with joy. Dobrynin, like an experienced diplomat, was in the same mind. He was out of the stables of Soviet diplomacy, a disciplined Soviet soldier in the Soviet foreign, who never spoke his mind, even though he had one. He was looking at a satisfied president and he knew they were thinking the same thing. There was nothing better the fools in the Kremlin could do for their principal enemy. He smiled in his mind when he thought that at the moment he learned about the final decision of the Politburo to invade, it awoke in him a healthy sedentary sense and he wanted to resign. Now he is pleased with the show of praise he receives from Moscow. He writes about the acceptance of the dramatic cipher by the president and he retells how he defended the brave "action" in Czechoslovakia.

"I am very pleased to recall my recent meeting with your honorable Prime Minister Kosygin in Glassboro. Greet him warmly ... "Johnson continued. Rostow's face was becoming more despondent and he mastered himself not to interrupt the President. As he said his farewells to the Soviet ambassador, the President repeatedly asked for a quick response from Moscow and stressed that he was looking forward to a visit to Moscow. When the Soviet Ambassador left the Oval Office, Johnson quickly switched on the TV. The match was just ending and the Lakers were winning by a clear margin. Still, he smiled. He poured for both his aides. "From tomorrow, the

Soviet invasion of Czechoslovakia will replace our actions in Vietnam in the headlines of the world's media. Moscow couldn't have done anything better for us. Cheers, gentlemen!"

After returning to the Soviet Embassy, Dobrynin immediately wrote a cipher telling Moscow about the reaction of the President and advising a positive opinion on his planned visit. The positive position actually took only a few hours. He summoned his secretary and instructed him to connect him with Secretary of State, Dean Rusk. He waited for the phone and poured pure Moscow vodka out of happiness. In Moscow, they hadn't expected such a pleasant reaction from the president. The ambassador became as nervous as his assistant didn't connect him with the Foreign Office for some time. The secretary entered the room personally. "What is it?" Dobrynin asked nervously." Comrade Ambassador, you must go to the Department of State immediately. They've just brought us a note signed by Secretary Rusk." Dobrynin knew at State department professionals would take a different opinion from the president. Johnson was an inexperienced farmer from Texas and Congress had traditionally ruled foreign policy in the United States. He hoped that Rusk under the president's influence would not have a negative effect on the declaration. It was certain that he took an unofficial position that he didn't use with the president.

Rusk received the ambassador in his office late at night. He told Dobrynin that he had just returned from the White House with a mandate to transmit the statement of the United States government. Rusk calmly read to him a statement saying that the United States had no information about any invitation to the Warsaw Pact troops from official representatives of Czechoslovakia. In conclusion, he recommended to the ambassador that both sides should carefully consider the early public announcement of a visit by the US President to the USSR. Dobrynin was clear that the President's visit would be delayed.

Lyndon Baines Johnson met US Army Chiefs of Staff within a few days. They agreed not to use force against the USSR. In addition, Johnson ordered that there be no public condemnation of the invasion. He added, "Let's hope that Moscow will appreciate that we are not violent here in the United States."

CHAPTER 33

THEY DID IT TO ME AFTER ALL

The morning of 20th August began just like all the mornings of the then Czechoslovakia. A beautiful day, people went to work smiling and Czechoslovak radio broadcast the hit parade. People no longer read the newspapers backwards from the last page as with Novotný, when the only thing they were interested in were the sports pages, but they eagerly scanned every line. Not even the slightest hint on television or from radio announcers or a line in print media, suggested that the night of this day would go into the history of Czechoslovakia as one of its blackest. Prague was full of tourists, whole families strolled through the city parks and the lovers embraced each other on the benches. Trnava football fans were preparing for the afternoon match of the Central European Cup against Red Star Belgrade.

The deputy Prime Minister, Gustáv Husák, who was the most prominent protagonist of the rebirth process in Slovakia in the pre-August era, met workers in the aliminium works in Žiar nad Hronom on that day. Dubček told a joke about him that when he made a move, Husák would make two. In his most radical speech so far, he talked about the benefits of the democratization process for Czechoslovak society. He resisted efforts to stop him. "There are people who want to shut the door through which fresh air flows into our political life." It was obvious that he meant the unpopular Vasil Biľak, whom he would replace with himself as the head of the Slovak Communists.

In the afternoon, Belgian journalists asked their colleagues in Czechoslovak Radio if they were afraid as the Czechoslovak border with Poland and the GDR was experiencing large-scale manoeuvres of troops and pointed at Hungarian events. "Don't you see the gigantic difference between what happened in Hungary in 1956 and what is happening in our country?" Czech journalists answered. "In Hungary there was an attempt to change the regime, while here we're improving the regime. What's happening is a revival of socialism! "

At that time, a reporter of the Czechoslovak Press Office in Budapest received a confidential report from his Hungarian colleague that Hungarian troops would cross the border on the night of 20th

August. Ambassador Púčik immediately encrypted this message. But recently such reports often appeared in domestic and foreign media. Dubček, like everyone else, felt that Brezhnev was bluffing and wouldn't dare to give the army that had been on the Czechoslovak border since spring, the order to march.

Rudé pravo's printers prepared the edition for 21st August. On the front page, there was a great deal of information about the fact that workers had collected nearly 200 million crowns for the fund of the republic and donated 60,808 kilos of gold to the Golden Fund of the Czech Republic.

On 20th August from two in the afternoon the last meeting of the ÚV KSČ took place before the 14th Congress which was due to begin on 9th September. Present were all the members and candidates for the presidium, except for Jozef Lenárt, who was allegedly ill. His illness does not seem to have been serious, because after midnight he was already on duty in the Soviet embassy. The eleven members of the presidium, who could decide on the main political issues, sat in the first row: Dubček, Kolder, Biľak, Švestka, Barbírek, Rigo, Piller, Smrkovský, Černík, Kriegel and Špaček. In the second row were the secretaries of the ÚV KSČ – Císař, Indra, Mlynář, Slavík, Sádovský and Voleník. Documents, mineral water, coffee, sandwiches were placed on the tables. The ashtrays, full of holes, were occasionally changed for clean ones by Dubček's personal guard, Jozef Brinzík. A light evening meal was served during a meeting. Dubček presided over the meeting and occasionally looked uneasily towards the sky under which was nighttime Prague. There was an obvious drone of aircraft engines. He was a little nervous, his wife, Anna, had been hospitalized in the morning with a gall bladder attack. When he was saying farewell to her at the hospital, he told her that the day's session of the presidium was going to be a long one. Then, he had no inkling that it would be the longest day and longest night of his life.

"Is there a military exercise?" Voleník opened the window a little. In the sky, the lights of unknown aircraft could be seen.

"I don't know ..." a slightly perturbed Dubček reacted. He didn't know that a special AN-24 from Moscow had landed at nearby Ruzyně airport. Shortly afterwards a second AN-24 arrived this time from Lvov. Civilians disembarked from the aeroplanes who were cordially welcomed by unknown people at customs. Among those welcoming them was the commander of the government squadron, Colonel Elias and the Chief of Customs Administration at Ruzyně, Stachovský. There were unusual staff at the airport who nobody knew. Then, an AN-12 landed on the airport tarmac. On board were paratroopers, whose boots were shortly to trample through the building of the KSČ at Nábreží Kyjevskej brigády.

The meeting of the Bureau had taken a long time. Indra, Biľak and Kolder insisted on him discussing the political situation in the country, which most of the members of the presidency rejected. "Comrades, we have been sitting for nine hours, I know you're tired, but it's our last meeting before the congress. A successful course of the congress is key to the consolidation of our reforms. The cadre composition of party bodies will change markedly. Therefore, if we have refused to include the report of Comrade Kolder on the political situation in our country, it is the right decision," Dubček said to Biľak.

At that moment, a white-faced Černík entered the room, from where he had been called a moment before by a call from the Minister of Defence. He could hardly catch his breath. Dubček and everyone else looked at him in anticipation.

"I've just spoken to the Minister of Defence. They're here ... The Soviets and the other four have crossed the border. The Ministry of Defence is occupied, they've interned Minister Dzúr."

Černík looked to Zdeněk Mlynář as if he had come from another planet. His first, uncontrolled feelings resembled the shock he had experienced years ago in a car accident.

"They did it to me after all," a stunned Dubček reacted. He felt as though he had died. Images of his father, mother, the Kirgiz of the thirties, where the Dubčeks had volunteered to help the young Soviet Union. He thought of the Russian partisans he'd fought with in the Slovak national uprising, his brother Julko, who perished in the uprising. His entire life had been connected to Communism, the idea of social justice and the belief that the Soviet Union would achieve it. His faith had now been destroyed by those in whom he believed.

CHAPTER 34

SO LYNCH ME!

After that it continued. At one-minute intervals, one military AN 12 after another. arrived They brought tanks, armoured transports, technical support, soldiers. By 25th August, 27 divisions in full battle array had arrived in Czechoslovakia, including 12 tank units, 13 motorised units and two parachute units, a completely airborne army including missiles, 6,300 tanks, 2,000 units, 550 combat planes and 250 air transport. A total of about 500,000 soldiers. A half million army against defenseless citizens. So much was Moscow afraid of Dubček's socialism. Czechoslovakia had 10 divisions, which was 3:1. But if it had been necessary, the ratio could have been changed to 6:1 eventually even more. "We were ready to attack if your army, security or militia were to stand in our way. We were aware that our action could be the beginning of the Third World War," Grechko said later.

"Minister Dzúr was actually arrested in his office by two Soviet officers! The only thing allowed him was a call to me," Černík spoke as if from another planet.

"I swear on my honour that not even I knew ... I have the last letter from Brezhnev in my bag ... Here it is ... He suggested nothing ..." Dubček began to read the letter in an agitated voice. He was so nervous that he stammered. No one listened to him. Absurd theatre. On one side there were people sitting in the room who, with anxiety, considered what would happen to the people and to them personally in the next few hours and days who, although they hadn't spoken out, could count on arrest and deportation. On the other side there were people who would rather they were at the Soviet Embassy setting up a worker-smallholder government. They sat together in silence, busy with themselves and somewhere, as if from a distance the phrases of the letter sank in, the author of which had already decided on a military invasion when he wrote them.

"That's betrayal!" Kriegel looked at Biľak.

"Then lynch me! Lynch me! Why don't you kill me" the little summoner of the Soviets gestured hysterically.

"Comrade I have decided to resign my secretariat position," Mlynář said laconically.

"Everything's finished ... I'm leaving," Dubček added.

"Don't babble, Sasha. You should call Brezhnev," urged Špaček.

"They'll get to us themselves..." Dubček waved his hand.

"It is necessary to keep calm. I talked to the President of the Republic. He's on his way here," Smrkovský said calmly. They hadn't even noticed when he'd gone out and come back in again.

"If they had something against me, why didn't they deal with me? If they hang me out to dry I'll take the responsibility!" he sat down in resignation, tugging at his shirt with tears running down his cheeks.

"Comrade, no one is allowed to resign! We were legally established, the organizations expect us to lead them!" said the old Spanish veteran, Kriegel.

"Connect me with Chervonenko," Dubček asked.

"We tried before, he isn't answering," someone said.

At that moment the door opened. President Svoboda entered. He didn't seem shocked at all.

"So they're here ..." he said completely calmly, so peacefully that he aroused Smrkovský's suspicion.

"You invited them? Are you aware of this?" the chairman of parliament asked him.

"I did not call them!" Svoboda cooled things down seeing that the mood there was dramatic.

"Sit down, Comrade President," Dubček requested having recollected himself after the initial shock.

"At 23.30 the Soviet ambassador called me that he had something important to tell me and asked for an immediate audience. As soon as I was dressed, he was already in the castle. He told me that the army of five had crossed our borders and we would be occupied by six o'clock in the morning," the president declared.

"They told us otherwise we wouldn't have noticed it," Smrkovský said with typical sarcasm.

"He said it wouldn't take long. I replied that we hadn't asked for it and that this was completely disgraceful of their part. We were all very marked by this and that things would have been solved without troops. Now they are here, and I think we should all remain in our positions as it's the people we're responsible for. "

"What can we say to the people?" asked Smrkovský.

"We must draw up a position for the presidency on this situation!" Dubček decided.

"An opinion in which we emphasize that all this happened without the knowledge of the president, the government and the central committee!" Smrkovský began to formulate the first draft of his opinion.

"I commission Comrades Mlynář and Císař to draw up an opinion. It must be short and clear. Zdeněk, Česťo, please prepare a proposal. But quickly," said Dubček, who took over the meeting again. Mlynář and Císař went to a neighbouring room.

"Comrades how is it going to make sense if we say that nobody knew about it? If we say this, the Bureau of the Central Committee will be at the forefront of the counter-revolution!" Biľak attempted to protest.

"Comrade Biľak, finally stop talking about some counter-revolution," Kriegel quashed him.

"If we don't, people will think that we knew about it and that we were lying to them," Smrkovský argued. "Or did you know about that?" he turned tauntingly to Biľak.

"Or that we even invited them. Wasn't it you who invited them by chance ?" Kriegel intensified Smrkovský's question. Biľak pretended he was writing a note.

"There should be no strong words in this statement," Svoboda suggested cautiously.

"Can't we even protest?" Kriegel said. "Our people know it's an act of rape. Every word that goes there will go into history. "

"It is very important to consider carefully what is going on so from the beginning we don't call on hatred down on the Soviet soldiers. We apparently have to cooperate with them," Biľak attempted to weaken the proposals that had been put.

"I'm sorry to say to you that I call hatred down on the Soviet soldiers. Perhaps they called it down on themselves!" Kriegel stammered. After a while Mlynář and Císař returned." Comrades we have a draft announcement."

"Read it," said Dubček.

Mlynář read the draft announcement. There was a stormy debate about it that turned into an open argument. Biľak's people objected to some passages of statements, but not even they claimed that the intervention was in accordance with international law. They constantly disputed that it was the Czechoslovak government's fault to underestimate the danger. Not one out of Biľak, Švestka, Rigo, Kolder, Kapek, Jakeš and Indra spoke the words about international aid or the protection of socialism in Czechoslovakia which they later used. Kriegel and Smrkovský first identified as a traitor to the nation anyone who identified with the intervention. Dubček hesitated over the words "denial of international law." Finally, he terminated his hesitation by concluding, "But so what, it is true!" President Svoboda followed the argument, but did not enter the debate. The passage on why armed resistance was not possible was omitted. Then Dubček closed the discussion. "Read it again in its definitive form," he requested Mlynář.

"To all the people of the Czechoslovak Socialist Republic! Yesterday, on 20th August, troops from the USSR, the Polish People's Republic, the German Democratic Republic, the Hungarian People's Republic and the People's Republic of Bulgaria crossed the borders of the Czechoslovak Socialist Republic at 23:00. This happened without the knowledge of the President of the Republic, the Chairman of the National Assembly, the Prime Minister and the First Secretary of the Central Committee of the KSČ and these bodies. The presidium of the KSČ Central Committee was meeting and discussing preparations for the XIVth Congress of the party. The Presidium appeals to all citizens of our republic to keep the peace and not to resist the armed forces that are entering, because the defence of our national borders is now impossible. This is why neither our army, security forces nor the people's militia have received a command to defend the country.

The Presidency is convinced that this act contradicts not only all the principles of relations between socialist states but also the fundamental norms of international law. All the leaders of the state, the Communist Party and the National Front remain in the positions to which they were elected by representatives of the people and members of their organizations according to the laws and other provisions in force in the Czechoslovak Socialist Republic. Constitutional officials will immediately convene a session of the National Assembly, the Government of the Republic. the Presidium of the ÚV KSČ will convene a plenary meeting of the Central Committee of the KSČ to discuss the situation. Signed: The Presidium of the ÚV KSČ."

Mlynář in a sombre voice, read this draft statement. "Comrades, we should first ... I'm afraid that such a formulation will cause citizens to resist and arrive at unpredictable actions", Biľak attempted to argue.

"The discussion was during the creation of the document," Dubček stopped him. "We are voting now. Who votes for this?" Dubček, Smrkovský, Kriegel, Barbírek, Piller, Špaček and Černík raised their hands. From those who didn't have voting rights they were supported by Mlynář, Šimon, Císař, Slavík and Sadovský. Is anyone against?"

Biľak, Kolder, Švestka and Rigo looked ahead. Slowly they raised their hands. From those without voting rights Indra, Kapek and Jakeš were against.

"Thank you. The presidium has accepted the statement by seven to four." Dubček took the paper and handed it to Soják. "Deliver it so that the press agency broadcasts it at once. Comrades, thank you. I'm ending the presidium consultation. Whoever wants to can stay, whoever wants to can go." Biľak, Kolder, Švestka and Rigo quickly left the room. Of those remaining, from the pro-Moscow group Jakeš joined those remaining. Perhaps he had received the role from an unknown director in overseeing the others.

At 1.30 am on 21st August, Czechoslovak Radio began to broadcast the statement from the presidium of the ÚV KSČ, but after the first sentences radio broadcast was silenced. On the orders of the Director of Central News, Karel Hoffmann, the medium-wave transmitter was shut down.

But he forgot to shut down the radio over the wire. After the occupation of Czechoslovak Radio at Vinohrady, a broadcast soon began from a spare studio in the Karlín barracks, installed with the support of the Czechoslovak Army and the Prague city Communist Party Committee. The editor-in-Chief of Rudé Právo, Oldřich Švestka, forbade publishing the statement. Meanwhile, the Soviet press agency TASS had sent a false message to the world that Soviet troops had come to Czechoslovakia at the invitation of "party and state bodies."

CHAPTER 35

I'M ARRESTING YOU!

Dubček, Smrkovský, Kriegler, Špaček, Šimon, Sádovský, Slavík, Barbírek and Mlynář left for his office. Surprisingly, Kapek and Jakeš came with them. Biľak, Kolder, Voleník, Indra and Švestka have got lost somewhere. Prime Minister Černík returned to his government office and President Svoboda to the castle where he had been previously, leaving those present to their fate. "Sasha, listen," said Smrkovský, "this is bad. You have the responsibility. If they arrest the Minister of Defence, we'll have just minutes remaining."

"I understand you, but because I have a responsibility, I have to stay." He searched for the phone on the desk and waited for the phone to ring and for someone to explain to him that it was just an enormous misunderstanding. The room was thick with cigarette smoke and someone opened the window. They came to him and looked at the people on the river bank at the seafront. Over the muddy waters of the Vltava went the words of "Kde domov můj" (Where My Home Is) and " Nad Tatrou sa blýska" (Over the Tatra Lightning Flashes). When the anthems finished, some people began singing the anthem of the proletariat - the Internationale. Dubček was telephoned by his wife, who was lying in hospital after her gall bladder procedure. Peter was luckily with friends in Egypt and Pavol was staying with karate club friends that night. Just in case he didn't go home that night, but stayed with Fero Šebej.

"Never mind my gall bladder, you take care Alex," she said with tears in her words.

"Everything has been destroyed, everything was thrown off the table. They've cut my whole life to pieces. Why did we help them in the thirties? Why did I fight with them in the Uprising? Why did Julo die? It was unnecessary ... They've buried Socialism for years if not indefinitely ... I shouldn't have taken this function. I shouldn't have."

"Alex, it's bad, but you have to endure."

"Sure, but there's nothing to fight for."

"Right now there is! First of all stay calm. Was it a good situation after the Uprising was crushed and after your wound? And you believed things would change. And you must believe that now."

"What about Paľo and Mama?"

"They're fine ... Peťko is in Egypt and what else has happened I don't know yet. At least he's safe. And you and Miško? "

"I'm fine ... so far ... In the same state as we all are ... And Miško? Dear God, I'll send Jožko immediately so he can take care of him. You can rely on that!" Through the open window, the gathered crowd had begun to chant, " Dubček, Svoboda ", "Russians Go Home. .

"So hold on," his wife encouraged.

"You too. I hope we'll see each other soon..." Dubček put down the phone and immediately ran to the secretariat. His secretary informed him that Brinzík was already on his way to Trója. Dubček thanked God for having such a devoted friend. Jožko walked on foot to make it less noticeable. As he drew near Dubček's house, Russian soldiers stopped him, pulled him under threat of a machine gun to the wall and searched him. When they discovered he had no weapon, they let him go. He came to the house in Trója where it was already dawn. The cook told him that Miško had been taken by a lady with a man unknown to her whom she knew by sight. Sweat started on Brinzík's forehead. It occurred to him that they could be family friends, the Bortels. He hid his own and Miško's papers so that they couldn't be found by accident during a search and he hurried to the Bortels. Through the youngest son, the occupiers could easily strike at his father. Miško was actually with the Bortels and he spent the next few days with them. When they started to run trains again, Brinzík took him and travelled to Bratislava. The train stopped in unexpected places and the journey had no end stopping constantly because of Russian tanks trundling over crossing points. They couldn't know that shortly after Miško had been taken out of the house in Trója, Soviet commandos had raided the house opposite the Dubčeks and completely searched it. After they'd left the shocked homeowners understood that they were probably mistaken, as home numbers and street names had been dragged down.

Dubček asked Špaček to call the Prime Minister's office. Špaček called Černík, but his phone slowly dropped to his desk. "Soviet soldiers have just taken Oldřich away." As soon as he had finished, the phone rang on Dubček's desk. Smrkovský answered.

"Sasha, Husák is calling you from Bratislava."

"I'm listening, Comrade Husák."

"Šaňo," began the disturbed Husák. "I want to tell you that I've prevented the worst. The presidium led by Hruškovič on Bilʹak's behalf finished a moment ago. By a vote of six to four, the entry of allied troops was approved. Someone sent them a telegram that you had approved it in Prague. Nevertheless, Falťan, Daubner, Turček and Ťažký were against. When a later note appeared with the actual position of the presidium, Pavlenda and Zrak called me. I immediately came to the meeting and sharply condemned their approved text. I have noted their behaviour for the dagger they have stuck in your back! What have they done to you? The document was revoked immediately and we received a new one supporting your opinion. Šaňo, Comrade Dubček, I want to tell you that I'm with you, I stand and fall with you! "

"Thank you, Gusto, thank you ..." Dubček put down the handset and walked along with the others to the window. Dawn had begun. The Black Volga of the Soviet Embassy had brought armoured transporters and tanks to the front of the building. Soviet parachutists from the special Taman Division with their wine-coloured berets, marina striped t-shirts under their tunics and machine guns in their hands. A number of officers and skydiving parachutists ran into the building.

Smrkovský came to Dubček. "Sasha, when they arrest you, it's over. You're not just first secretary. You're a symbol, you understand? Criminals always destroy symbols first!"

"Pepík, I understand you, but I'll wait for them here." Smrkovský understood, nodding at Dubček that he was right. They embraced, standing by the window, looking at the crowd that was standing apart, but for one Soviet soldier seemed too slow. He fired from a machine gun directly at one young man standing ten metres from him. In front of Dubček, Smrkovský and others, the young student died. Smrkovský dialed the phone of the Soviet embassy and furiously shouted at somebody, "You are responsible for the bleeding! Stop killing!" He didn't manage to say what he intended as a soldier dashed in and smashed the phone with all his strength. The device exploded into pieces. There were eight paratroopers in the Dubček's office commanded by a junior officer. They blocked the windows and connecting doors. To Dubček it seemed like an armed burglary.

"Excuse me, I'm sorry but I'd like to make a call." One of the soldiers with ginger curls at the bottom of his cap responded handing him the phone with an almost apologetic gesture. Then another, aiming at Dubček with a machine gun, snatched the device out of his hand and pulled the cord from the wall. Dubček went rigid, holding the handset with the cord looping from it. The curly-haired soldier shuffled back.

"What does this mean?!"

"No speak, no speak Czech!" the officer ordered them in broken Czech.

"Where do you think you are?" Mlynář shouted at him in Russian. "You are in the office of the First Secretary of the Communist Party, so behave as though you were!" In a moment the main doors swung open. Senior KGB officers entered. They were led by a Lieutenant-Colonel with a number of Soviet badges on his uniform. He was accompanied by a Soviet interpreter and a few Czech-speaking people in civilian clothes. Dubček knew the interpreter who had interpreted for Marshal Jakubovsky a few weeks before during the visit of the chief commander of the armed forces of the Warsaw Pact. The lieutenant-colonel approached Dubček and offered his hand. Dubček refused and so he grabbed his hand anyway. Then he quickly checked a list of the high-level members of the Czech Communist party present.

"I'm taking you under my protection," he said laconically. The protection was truly superb. Each of them had an unlocked dismantled machine gun over their backs. Soldiers waited when three Czech-speaking civilians wearing the tweed jackets and open-necked shirts entered. One of them was Kulifaj. Dubček's eyes almost popped out in surprise. "I'm arresting you in the name of the worker-smallholder government led by Comrade Indra."

"You?", a shocked Dubček looked at him.

"Yeah and what are you?" Smrkovský asked.

"We are members of the Revolutionary Committee at the Ministry of the Interior. We are operating his work under the direction of Šalgovič" Kulifaj responded.

"The Ministry of Interior is still run by the government!" objected Dubček.

"Yes, he'll be running it as soon as he's appointed," Kulifaj said coldly. "Within two hours, you will stand before the revolutionary tribunal presided over by Chairman Comrade Indra ..."

"What is the authority for this the workers' government? That I know nothing about it as the Chairman of the National Assembly ..." Smrkovský looked surprised.

"Pepik leave it alone, it makes no sense," said Dubček.

"Does that mean you're arresting us?" asked Smrkovský.

"Yes. Please surrender your weapons!" the ŠtB officer ordered, instructing Kulifaj to collect their weapons. Smrkovský theatrically pulled a handkerchief and a knife from his pocket and placed them on a table. "We didn't need any weapons against our own people." Kulifaj approached Dubček who, with a disarming smile, raised his hands above his head and said, "So go on, search!"

The Soviet officer understood the inappropriateness of the situation and ordered the ŠtB officers to leave the room. The soldiers closed the windows and pulled down the shutters. The members of the presidium, silently, with the machine guns at their backs, sat behind the long table. Time passed and nothing happened. It was five o'clock in the morning.

"I'm assuming it won't be until at least eight o'clock that they put it all together. We're all sleepless and I advise everyone to sleep. We'll need clear heads." With these words, František Kriegel got up from his desk, found a vacant space on the floor behind Dubček's table, lay on the carpet and, under the astonished eyes of the Soviet soldiers, slipped his briefcase under his head. In about ten minutes he began to snore aloud. He snored so peacefully and in such different tones that even the Soviet soldiers realized he was asleep and stopped pointing their machine guns at him.

CHAPTER 36

CAPTIVES OF THE KREMLIN

Biľak, Indra, Švestka, Rigo, Lenárt and some others left for the Soviet embassy to try to clear up what they'd made a mess of. It was clear that there would be nothing coming out of their worker-smallholder government. On the morning of 21st August, Brezhnev summoned Biľak to the phone at the Soviet Embassy. He did not conceal his deep disappointment with the inability of the putsch to organize a worker-smallholder government. Even if this puppet government had been put together quickly, President Svoboda told the main organizer of the conspiracy, the Soviet Ambassador, Chervonenko, that he would not appoint any government with Indra as leader. Indra and Chervonenko had even given the President a fake abdication letter from the legal Prime Minister Černík. Brezhnev understood that he would have to negotiate with Dubček.

The Soviet Colonel called on all to leave the room. Smrkovský still managed to put some pieces of sugar into his pocket. "Take it too, you'll need it. I have experience from Ruzyně." When they walked, somebody remarked on - "It's starting to get hot here". After a few steps, an officer told Dubček to follow him. They came to the rear exit from the building of ÚV KSČ into the courtyard, where tanks and armored transporters were drawn up. They ordered him to climb on a rack-up vehicle whose engine was running. A soldier sat on its hull, nervously smoking and gazing at the ground. For a moment, their eyes met. It was the ginger-haired soldier who wanted to give him the phone. He was crying. He was thinking of his students, as now there was no-one who teach them to play the violin back in Lvov.

"Do not worry, everything will be fine," he patted the soldier on his shoulder.

Part of an arm, through a round opening, brusquely shoved Dubček into the floor. Before the armoured hatch closed, bellowing began as if someone were quarrelling. The bellowing increased. Then there was a shot. He shoved himself back through the hole and saw the curly-headed soldier lying on the ground shot through the head. At that moment, the hatch closed abruptly and the vehicle moved. Dubček tried to work out where they were going and somehow needed to let the community know that they were driving him away. He pretended that he had difficulty breathing so they opened the hatch and allowed him to stick his head through the opening. He recognized a street which led to Ruzyně airport. At Letná, his eyes met those of a random pedestrian in which he could see shock at seeing Dubček's head in the opening of a transporter. Maybe he didn't want to believe it was Dubček, but a moment was enough for him to be seen. The soldiers shut the hatch again. Shortly after midday they arrived at Ruzyně Airport. They waited until the evening in a separate room. Dubček didn't know that Smrkovský, Šimon, Kriegel and Špaček, later joined by Černík, who was arrested in his office at the Office of the Presidium of the Government, were in an adjoining room. As darkness fell they drove Dubček to an Antonov aircraft, pushed him inside, but after a while they pulled him out again and moved to a Tupolev.

It was obvious that the occupants were confused. Eventually, the plane took off and landed at Legnica Airport in southern Poland after two hours. Dubček was brought to a wooden barracks, where the Soviet officer who had arrested him in Prague was already waiting. After a short stop the aircraft continued to Uzhgorod. Both Černík and Šimon were already there. Several KGB officers in civilians handed them over to jeeps on the landing surface. Černík refused to get into the vehicle, so they pushed him there. Dubček said loudly in Russian, "What are you doing? This is the prime minister of a sovereign state!" The officers froze for a moment and let Černík get in himself. After an hour's ride through wooded terrain, they came to a complex of mountain chalets.

Everyone stayed in a separate chalet. They gave him warm slops and threw a blanket on the bed. Two officers entered the room before midnight.

"Get dressed, you're coming with us!" He didn't have to dress, he lay on the bed in the suit he'd gone to work in the previous day. Even though it was August, it was cold in the Carpathian forests at night.

"Where are we going?" The officers kept silent. One started the vehicle, a Major sat in the back seat beside Dubček. The moon shone, the car climbed the forest road until it came to something like the works of a gravel pit.

"Get out!" the Major ordered abruptly.

"What is it? Where are we going?" Dubček asked. He thought of the photographs of the unknown victims of Stalin's terror, which had fallen into his hands during his studies in Moscow. The victims had disappeared, they were lost, and no one ever found them. It's over, he thought.

"March," the Major ordered. They walked toward part of the gravel pit, the slope of which descended to the water. No machines or buildings could be seen, but the gravel has long since been removed. The other soldier walked two steps behind them. At that moment, the radio in the major's pocket buzzed. He pulled it out nervously and left them so they couldn't hear him. After a long while he returned. His face was completely different, he smiled.

"Well, we've had some fresh air, I'm sure it made you feel better," he almost apologized. They got into the jeep and returned to the room. He lay down, but he couldn't sleep. He never knew what might have happened at the gravel pit that night and he never would. The next, 23rd August, they put dark glasses on him and, after an hour's drive, he was dropped off at the office of a local party official. After a while, the phone rang. Dubček's guard told him it was for him. He picked up the handset. At the other end, was Podgorny, Chairman of the Presidium of the Supreme Soviet. He told him coldly that they would have to talk.

"Where and where?" Dubček asked sharply.

"In Moscow."

"How do you want me to get there?" As a prisoner? First, I need to know where the others arrested with me are. I'm not willing to think about your proposal unless there are all of us!" Podgorny said he would do it. Dubček knew that Soviet plans were collapsing. While they'd threatened him with a "revolutionary tribunal" two days before, they were now ready to talk.

CHAPTER 37

"Es lebe Dubček! Vive Dubček"

The plans of the invaders began to go awry from the first hours of occupation. The Soviets quickly came to the conclusion that Biľak's claims that citizens would welcome them with bouquets were not going to happen. Quite the opposite. In Czechoslovak towns and villages there was an unprecedented wave of resistance to the occupiers. At the President's call for peace, people responded with understanding. Mottoes in people's exhibition halls were transformed where posters challenged the invaders with "Ivan go home, Natasha is waiting", "Lenin wake up, Brezhnev is crazy", "Kosygin – son of a bitch", "Dubček - Svoboda, that is Our Freedom","We are with you, be with us! ", " Go away!" and many others. Never before had so many tricolors appeared on Czech and Slovak clothes. People stripped away the names of the towns and streets and the names of enterprises, which made it considerably more difficult for the invaders to find their way. Flags were pulled down to half-mast.The Soviet soldiers took transistor radios away from the people. Students ironicallly put coal briquettes, shaped like the radios, to their ear, which infuriated them. People debated with the soldiers and put to them a single, insistent question: "WHY?" The invaders occupied the building of Czechoslovak Radio in Prague on Vinohrady, where there were also bloody armed clashes. Radio workers broadcast from various locations - factories, garages - moving as they operated the transmitters, so by the time Soviet soldiers found the original locations they were in another place. The Czechoslovak army liberated dozens of its transmitters. Radio became a key tool for broadcasting information. It named collaborators. It warned of betrayers and provocateurs.

Similarly, newspaper vendors handed out editorial packs of extraordinary newspaper releases that people instantly seized hold of. Citizens did not stand obstacles or repeated calls for peace. Soviet tanks became more and more the target of amateur-made Molotov cocktails, paving blocks or just rocks thrown by hand. Nervous and stressed young Soviet troops reacted with irritation. There were shots in the air, as well as shots at human beings. In front of Comenius University in Bratislava, a Soviet soldier's shot killed fifteen-year-old Danka Košanová. At the post office they shot Peter Legner and the captain of a ship, Ján Holík. During the week when Soviet tanks were on the streets, about thirty people died in Slovakia and about seventy citizens in the Czech lands. On 22nd August the extraordinary XIV session of the Communist Party of Czechoslovakia was held in Prague's Vysočany, which confirmed Dubček in his leadership in various functions. On the other hand, potential representatives of the workers and the standing government were not elected to any position.

In defence of Czechoslovakia, practically all Communist and Labour parties, many official governmental and non-governmental representatives and international organizations stood against the intervention. At the request of the Danish government, an immediate meeting of the UN Security Council was convened to discuss the situation in Czechoslovakia. On the night of 21st – 22nd August, the Security Council condemned the intervention, except for the votes of Hungary and the USSR, and described it as a gross violation of international law. Personalities such as Louis Aragon, Bertrand Russel, Jean-Paul Sartre, and others protested with vehemence against the invasion. In Europe's capital cities, people organized protest meetings. The governments of Yugoslavia, Romania, Cuba, China and the governments of democratic countries also protested. The Soviet poet, Yevgeny Jevtušenko, sent Brezhnev a telegram in which he strongly protested the invasion. He wrote a poem: "Tanks go to Prague, tanks go to the truth". On 21st August a 20-year-old Leningrad student, Boguslavsky, raised a banner over the statues of Klodt's horses on the Anichkov Bridge with the message, "Brezhnev out of Czechoslovakia." He was sentenced to five years in jail. On Red Square in Moscow a worker, Vladimir Dremľug, the poet, Vadim Delone, the physicist, Pavel Litvinov, the philologist, Larisa Bogorazov, the linguist, Konstantin Babicki, the historian, Viktor Fajnberg, the poet, Natalija Gorbanevska and a student,Tatiana Bajevová protested. They sat in the square and looked in silence at the building of the historical museum with the flag of the Brotherhood with Czechoslovakia and its banner. When a crowd influenced by the Soviet media, began to beat them, Fajnberg lost four teeth. Eventually, the militia vehicles rescued them them from the riot and took them away. They were condemned them to prison, forced labour or sent to an asylum.

On 21st August, young people in the capital of the German Democratic Republic, chanted "Es lebe Dubček ". ("Dubček! Freedom!") Two sons of Professor Haveman, who condemned the invasion and participation of the GDR army, were arrested. Bernd Eisenfeld handed out anti-occupation leaflets.

The world at this time had been shaken by the decolonization of African countries the six-day Israeli-Arab war, and the March massacre of over four-hundred civilians in the Vietnamese village of My Lai by American soldiers. Military aggression by the USA against Vietnam had pushed the United States into a moral blind alley. The USA was dismayed by a civilian revolt, and the Soviet invasion had brought it to an end. The invasion was a blow to the anti-war movement, consolidating American public opinion about the Communists aspiring to world domination, which provided renewed justification for the war in Vietnam.

The position of the strong Communist parties of Italy, France and other countries was greatly diminished. After the Soviet invasion, the label Communist became a worldwide badge of shame. For more than a year, the West German government had fought an unprecedented student revolt led by the Berliner, Rudy Dutschke, a charismatic leader. However, the Soviet invasion offered more to chew on for the German media and for the Bonn government a quarrel with its Moscow counterparts.

In May 1968 students in Paris wrote to the faculty of medicine: "Vive Dubček - Vivat Dubček!" When President Pompidou sent tanks against French students in revolt led by Daniel Cohen

Bendit, portraits of Che Guevarra and Dubček were carried overhead. The youth of Western European countries loved Dubček as did their peers in the countries of so-called real socialism. The powers-that-be in the East and the West were aware that if Dubček's reforms were implemented, their positions would be jeopardized. The invasion favoured the mighty East and West blocs. The soldiers caused fear, and fear instilled obedience into citizens.

CHAPTER 38

A BUNCH OF GANGSTERS

A dirty, dusty, humiliated Dubček was brought to the Kremlin on Friday, 23rd August, at 11 a.m. Moscow time. He was led through several rooms before entering a large office with a rectangular table, where Brezhnev, Podgorny, Kosygin and Voronov sat. He entered silently, alone, naked among wolves. A long silence. They didn't greet him, they didn't offer their hands.

"Sit down," said Podgorny. Dubček sat on a chair opposite them. Again there was a long silence. They watched. "They're crooks. After Khrushchev, the Kremlin is occupied by a bunch of gangsters", came into his mind.

"How does Comrade Černík feel?" Brezhnev asked, looking at him sideways.

"Bad. Bad as we all do." Dubček wondered what was going on at home. He wasn't to know at that very moment President Svoboda was on his way to Moscow, to enable Brezhnev to find a way out of a difficult situation for the five countries after Moscow and the "invitors" had struggled to establish a worker-smallholder government.

"We do not want and we will not interfere with your internal affairs, leaving the government to work on the basis of January and May plans," Brezhnev continued. Dubček smiled bitterly at this sentence. "Because of the failure to meet the commitments we agreed on, five countries were forced into extreme measures. The current course of events fully confirms that behind your back right-wing forces were preparing anti-socialist actions. We aren't claiming that you were at their head! We aren't occupying Czechoslovakia and we won't occupy; we only want to implement socialist cooperation freely. We won't dictate to you, but find a solution together. Tell us your design on how you should proceed."

"Fine, Comrade Brezhnev, I will say a few words, even though I am in a difficult mental situation. I haven't been home for three days and I have no information what's happening to us," Dubček began slowly. But all of a sudden he burst out with an accusation. "Comrades, I don't understand at all why five countries have undertaken this military operation. I would be lying if I didn't tell you that sending troops was a huge political mistake that has tragic consequences! I'm convinced that this act will be seen not only in Czechoslovakia, but in the entire Communist movement as a huge defeat. I don't know how this act has been accepted by our working class, but certainly badly. Both I and my family have devoted their whole lives to socialism and now ... As far as I'm concerned, I am ready for the worst. I'm already reconciled to it. "

"Why are you saying that?" Brezhnev frowned.

"The Communist Party in Czechoslovakia has never had such support and trust in history as in recent times. But this obviously was not important to you in your process against. It is something that our citizens don't understand because there was no threat of counter-revolution in our country for you to take such measures. I can't give you any suggestions, comrades, as the last images from Prague that I have before my eyes of you are your soldiers who invaded my office with machine guns and pulled out the phone line!"

"We don't have time, Alexander Stepanovich, for great analyzes. The truth is that at the time our troops arrived large masses of citizens were organized against them. Radio stations instead of welcoming us, they scolded them! In Bratislava, young hooligans tossed a car to the Danube with two of our citizens! You organized a congress of illegal parties in some factory. Slovaks weren't even at this congress!" He waved some documents indignantly. "They chose a sort of central party committee composed of right-wingers. Neither Comrade Indra nor Comrade Biľak is there!" Brezhnev thought for a moment and continued. "Ludvik Ivanovič Svoboda has a number of times spoken out well in public urging people to maintain peace. On his own initiative Ludvik Ivanovič announced to us that he is flying here. I have also assured your president that we aren't occupiers, on the contrary, we've come to protect your sovereignty and, after a while, good relations will be established again. President Svoboda informed us that he would be bringing some Klusák from Bratislava. "

"Klusák? That's his son-in-law and he lives in Prague ... It could be Husák ..."

"We aren't going to talk to you about the composition of the delegation of your president," Brezhnev shrugged. "And Comrade Indra and your friend Comrade Biľak will come with him. You should consult him. Comrade Bil'ak is a man completely devoted to socialism. He'll tell you how it was. "

"When your soldiers came in front of the building of the central committee, masses of people stood under our windows and sang the Internationale ..." Dubček thought aloud, full of impressions from the latest events. Brezhnev and his cronies muttered. "Our people will never understand this."

"A conference of Sudeten Germans took place in your town of Cheb. How are we to understand that? And you call this right!" Kosygin convinced himself more than Dubček.

"That is not possible."

"How isn't it possible? Twenty-five thousand Sudetes gathered in Cheb and had a conference for three days! "

"When?"

"Three days ago," Kosygin said uncertainly. He couldn't quite remember the information that Ulbricht had given him.

"That was in Western Germany," said Dubček.

"In your country. Fortunately our troops came. "

"Will Černík come in?" Dubček paid no further attention to Kosygin's conspiracies.

"Right now," Brezhnev said.

"And Smrkovský?"

"It'll be about two hours. Everyone is all right and healthy. "

"I couldn't get out of the car for seven hours, they aimed machine guns at me from both sides..."

"Your safety depended on it," Brezhnev said cynically.

"When I was recently in Karlovy Vary, you also gave me people who protected me," his boss Kosygin added.

"That was voluntary, but you were protecting me against my will, with violence!"

"You're responsible for what happened! You made mistakes so now think how to get out of them. Comrade Biľak is coming and you'll find a solution along with Černík. There are two options - find a solution to be found or war. With the power at our disposal we can defeat the devil and not just some Goldstücker. We've heard that your Minister of Defence, Dzúr, is under pressure to begin armed resistance. If that starts ... we'll just leave his shoulder tabs!" Kosygin threatened.

CHAPTER 39

GUSTÁV NIKODEMOVIC, I TRUST YOU

At Brezhnev's request, President Svoboda also brought Biľak and Indra, as well as the Minister of Defence, Dzúr, a member of the presidium of the ÚV KSČ, Piller, and the Minister of Justice, Kučera. In Bratislava, Svoboda's favorite, Gustáv Husák, joined them. Shortly before his flight Svoboda in a broadcast requested support from the Czechoslovak nation, assured the continuation of post-January politics and expressed the conviction that everybody would return from Moscow in the evening. To the surprise of the improvised Czechoslovak delegation, after the Soviet aircraft that had brought them landed, they were greeted by an honorary unit of several types of troops, including the navy, thousands of Muscovites waving Czechoslovak and Soviet flags, almost the whole politburo, the playing of national anthems and the firing of a twenty-four gun salute. On the way to the Kremlin, the Czechoslovak president praised the enthusiastic ranks of the Muscovites. Soviet television broadcast images of Svoboda's "triumphal" arrival to the world as evidence of the continuing fraternal relations between the USSR and the ČSSR.

The Soviet leadership discussed separately with various groups of their Czechoslovak counterparts which had gradually come to Moscow. Negotiations were an absurd theatre that consisted mainly of circular discussions. Brezhnev was looking for a potential future successor to Dubček. Upon their arrival in the Kremlin, Brezhnev invited Svoboda and Husák to his office. He wanted to personally meet the recently rehabilitated lawyer who was so popular especially in Slovakia.

"Ludvik Ivanovič, I am glad you brought Comrade Husák to Moscow. We've heard a lot about you," Brezhnev said to Husák.

"Comrade Husák is the Vice Chairman of the federal government. He isn't a member of the Supreme Party yet," smiled Svoboda.

"What is your opinion of the events?" Husák was serious in a moment.

"After the meetings in Čierna and Bratislava, when I spoke to Comrades Dubček and Černík, both of them said they understood the seriousness of the situation. I also saw that our leaders were maintaining the friendship with the Soviet Union and other brother countries. I have also been watching tendencies consistently and gradually to get rid of the rightist orientation. I personally consider that our Soviet comrades that you …. have rushed into the situation … and exaggerated the danger. We are also Communists, I've been in this movement since I was sixteen, almost four decades. For us, that is, for those who are in the Communist movement, being a member of the party and being a friend of the Soviet Union is one and the same thing. I fully understand that Soviet comrades want to have a complete guarantee that Czechoslovakia won't develop outside of the socialist camp, but I'm convinced that it could have been achieved without military intervention. To ease the situation, the most important is that the troops leave as soon as possible."

Brezhnev thought for a moment, then scolded Husák, "I have been listening to you carefully … I understand that your words about the misunderstanding of our international assistance and your proposal for the earliest departure of our troops come out of your current psychological situation and perhaps you don't have enough information. .. "

"Please excuse my openness, but I said what most of our people feel. I have the power of leadership of the party bodies in Slovakia and the Czechoslovak Government to submit the request - to release the interned comrades and to enable the work of state and party bodies. If it is no longer possible to talk about the immediate departure of troops, it is necessary to deploy them outside towns and villages. As far as the party Congress in Prague is concerned, I wasn't there. I only learned from the radio that they'd chosen me as a member of the presidium. We can't just say that the congress was illegal"

"That congress was illegal! You yourself said you didn't participate in it and there were no other Slovaks. Of the Slovaks there were only Kolder, Simon, Piller and Sádovský! How can a congress be held when the whole leadership of the party is absent?"

"Excuse me, Kolder, Piller and Simon are Czechs."

Svoboda broken into the conversation, "We've already spoken to Comrade Brezhnev that Comrade Dubček will resign as Secretary of the Chamber of Deputies shortly after the return of the delegation. I told Comrade Brezhnev, too, that I won't return home without our arrested comrades. I am also of the opinion that Comrades Černík and Smrkovský will gradually resign on their return."

"Frankly, Comrade Indra is a great disappointment for us. Likewise Comrade Biľak. They didn't control matters. It was probably too demanding for them. Dubček became a national hero, Biľak a national traitor. We need a third, somebody new to top politics, a good name, a communist past ... As far as possible, Slovak ..." Brezhnev looked significantly at Husák, Svoboda smiled secretly. "We are say openly that Alexander Stepanovich is not enough for the post, but he himself has told me a number of times that he would like to leave the position of the first secretary ... I'm glad to meet you, but manner in which you've gone about things today makes it hard to find positive starting points ... " Husák wanted to say something, but Brezhnev didn't let him get a word in. "We haven't redeemed the danger of right-wing forces, you've underestimated them."

"I agree with you that we have made a lot of mistakes since January. I understand that the Soviet Union is a world power and wants its rights in Central Europe to be respected! That's why we need to talk about these questions and we want to talk." Brezhnev listened attentively and it was obvious that Husák's words appealed to him.

"Your president has a great deal of trust in Soviet and my personal leadership. Together we fought against Hitler," he tapped Svoboda's shoulder in a friendly way. Then he turned to Husák. "You were in the Slovak National Uprising. Ludvik Ivanovič has praised you very much," Brezhnev smiled. "Comrade Husák, what was your father's name?" Husák didn't understand. "How was your father addressed? We address our friends with their father's name," Brezhnev smiled.

"Nicodemus."

"Gustáv Nikodemovich," Brezhnev thought, "we would like with Ludvik Ivanovič and Vasil Mikhailovich, to convince your delegation of the illegality of the congress held in Vysočany. This must be in the final protocol! There must also be that the protection of socialism is a common cause of all socialist countries, that cadre exchanges will be broadcast on your mass media and that the Czechoslovak leadership will withdraw the question of the situation in Czechoslovakia from the agenda of the UN Security Council. Here's our suggestion and we'd be happy if it were changed as little as possible. I give it to you with in confidence in advance so that can discreetly convince your comrades about... Mostly, Comrade Dubček," Brezhnev gave Husák the paper kindly, but categorically.

„I understand ... And the question of your troops leaving? We have to bring something back home. There should be a formula about their temporary stay ..."

"Let's see how your comrades take this proposal ..." He paused, and then turned directly to Husák. "You have great influence in Bratislava, we would also like to see the Slovak congress not taking place. Or let's say later so there is enough time to prepare everything... With regard to the new leadership ... Ludvik Ivanovič tells me that he has lost his confidence in Comrade Dubček and he'll have to be replaced as the highest representative of the Communist Party of Czechoslovakia ... " Brezhnev stood up, giving Husák and Svoboda his hand with a wide smile. "If you need anything, contact me directly. I hope that the negotiations that await us will not be very difficult. You are a capable comrade, an excellent Communist. I heard you acted with courage in prison. Believe it or not I also know that you proposed to unite Slovakia with the Soviet Union during the war. You made a great impression on me! I trust you. I believe that also with your help we can find solutions."

They broke up and Brezhnev went to another part of the Kremlin, where Kadar, Gomulka, Ulbricht, and Zhivkov were meeting. On 24th – 27th August, they were in Moscow and consulted with the Soviet leadership. Czechoslovak officials refused to negotiate with them.

CHAPTER 40

ASK THEM WHAT THEY ACTUALLY WANT

"Your extraordinary congress was illegal," Kosygin shouted at Dubček. "It was in the absence of the old presidium."

"The old presidium was not home!" Dubček snapped. "We planned a proper congress on 9th September. Our comrades were forced to summon an extraordinary congress after your intervention!"

"Sasha ... calm ... calm down, please," Brezhnev lit a cigarette nervously. "I'm not blaming you for anything. You did what you could. We think the counter-revolutionaries did it all behind your back ... " Dubček realized what the Soviets wanted drag in him. They needed this because he was a symbol of the Prague Spring and the resistance to invasion. Their plan for a worker-smallholder government headed by Indra hadn't worked. Bil'ak's men had failed to overrun the radio, television or press agencies. The whole world had learned that it was a blockheaded occupation. Deploying direct military rule would confirm the total resistance of Czechs and Slovaks. On the contrary, Bil'ak was trying behind Dubček's back to push into the final draft a protocol on counter-revolution.

"Leonid Ilyich, I want to be able to talk to my colleagues," Dubček ignored Brezhnev's words. One by one the Soviets had sought to persuade Dubček of counter-revolution in Czechoslovakia. Dubček could not respond to such absurdity and lies. When they were done, he repeated his request. Prime Minister Černík was allowed into the room. After two hours of meetings without result, the Soviet potentates went to their premises, and Dubček and Černík were brought into a room where the President Svoboda and the other supreme representatives of the ČSSR were already waiting. Dubček was surpised by Svoboda's evasive look. Coldly they greeted each other and began a discussion that lasted until three o'clock in the morning. Dubček was tired and did not feel well. Bil'ak watched him and was convinced that he was feigning an indisposition. One thing was clear to all - the Soviets wanted to legalize the invasion.

On Saturday, 24th August, Dubček slept for almost the whole day. He was sick, he'd had a cardiac episode and fallen in the bathroom where he smashed his forehead on the edge of the washbasin. The small wound was glued with leucoplast. He was cared for by the military doctor Mudr. Smrček, whom President Svoboda had brought with him. He literally didn't participate on the preparations of the protocol. In the afternoon, when a third part of the Czechoslovak delegation - Mlynář, Lenárt, Barbírek, Jakeš, Rigo and Švestka - arrived in Moscow they woke him up. Mlynář went straight to Dubček and informed him about the latest developments at home. "There was a general strike across the country yesterday to protest the invasion of troops. In Vysočany, there is the XIVth Party congress held almost constantly. Everyone stands behind us. At home, people light candles, everywhere there are your portraits, people write different slogans on the walls to drive the Russians home. Czechs and Slovaks are united as never before. In southern Slovakia our Hungarians have expelled Hungarian soldiers. The Russian soldiers are confused and several of them have shot themselves. They don't know why they are there. The whole world is on our side. Sasha, we have to fight. The people believe us." Then he sat down, drank some tea, thought and out of nowhere started singing a song. Dubček stared at him. In this incredible situation, Mlynář was singing. "... don't cry, brother, don't waste your tears, swallow your curses and save your strength, you mustn't blame me if we don't arrive. Learn a song, it's not that difficult, lean on me little brother, the road is broken, we'll gallop, we can't go back. It's raining and outside in the dark, this night won't be short, the wolf wants the lamb, little brother close the gate!" Dubček listened attentively. "It's all over the Republic. It was spontaneously composed by some Kryl that night as they invaded us."

The Soviets quickly called for another round of discussions. Dubček was thinking all the time about how to gain time. He knew that the longer the talks, the more the Soviets would be nervous and their troops in Czechoslovakia more helpless. President Svoboda asked him to speak briefly and clearly. He even told him that most of the time he was talking "crap". In the evening, both delegations, led by Dubček and Brezhnev, again sat down at the negotiation table. What Dubček said, froze everyone in the room. "Comrade Bil'ak, ask them what they really want ..." Bil'ak looked at him uncomprehendingly. He knew Dubček's Russian was better than his, and he did not understand what Dubček was pursuing. Slowly, clearly in Russian he repeated Dubček's question. Brezhnev shifted in his seat, but he managed to control himself. He repeated in a slow voice that it was necessary to prepare a joint document that would be solemnly signed as soon as possible. Silence again, looking at Dubček. Bil'ak did not control himself and raised his voice, "Do you understand or do I have to translate it?"

"We can start negotiating at eight in the evening," Dubček said quietly. "Excuse me," and he stood up and left the room. The Soviets left by another door. Gradually, the Czech and Slovak politicians also left. Dubček took no more part in more negotiations which were chaotic and did not lead anywhere. All Sunday, the Soviets and the Czechoslovak leadership talked to each other in different groups. No formal deliberations were held. The Czechoslovak politicians have noticed that a good half of the Soviet leaders were strongly under the influence of alcohol.

CHAPTER 41

YOU HAVE DEEPLY WOUNDED THE SPIRIT OF OUR PEOPLE

Dubček lay in bed on Sunday. A part of the delegation thought he was exhausted, part of the delegation was suspicious that he wanted to avoid responsibility. To facilitate negotiations, he proposed to step down as First Secretary of the ÚV KSČ. All the Czechoslovak politicians rejected this. The Soviets needed Dubček's signature while he was still in office. Moreover, they did not want to make him a national hero and a martyr. Smrkovský, Černík, Špaček, Mlynář and Šimon kept him informed about the negotiations. He lay in bed, his body exposed to the waist. On the left side of his chest was a square handkerchief, a leucoplast on his forehead and he breathed heavily. The negotiations were led by Černík, Smrkovský and Svoboda. In the evening Smrkovský informed Dubček that the Soviets had arrogantly rejected an attempt by the Czechoslovak side to put any proposals in the text. They pointed out that they weren't in a position to lay down conditions. Husák and Dubček against Brezhnev's will inserted a note in the protocol on the "temporary" stay of the Soviet troops. Brezhnev smiled and waved his hand. It was clear to everyone that the term "temporary" would be for the stronger to decide. They simply gave the Czechoslovak side an ultimatum.

On Sunday evening, the Czechoslovak delegation met to take a final position on the Soviet proposal. Husák suggested that everyone speak their mind. He asked that they end the barren discussion adding, "I will sign it." After Husák, who expressed his readiness to sign first, gradually all the others agreed. Mlynář meditated aloud, "It's cruel, I'm not signing." Smrkovský said, "If I didn't have a wife and children, I would not endorse it. In this situation I will sign it." Černík said, "I sign." Then Husák took the floor. He stood firmly against Mlynář, who'd kept silent. Kriegel and Dubček were the only ones left. To convince Dubček was Černík's task.

On Monday morning, Mlynář announced he would sign. In the course of the afternoon Dubček arrived white as a sheet. The leucoplast had gone from his head. He called on the others to come into a meeting room. They looked over the document and agreed to sign it with the exception of Kriegler. A plenary meeting of both delegations took place on Monday 26 August. The Soviet politburo was already sitting behind a long table opposite the Czechoslovak delegation with the exception of Kriegler. Dubček sat opposite Brezhnev as if he were without life. There were flowers on the tables, the Czechoslovak and Soviet flags. Everything was prepared for the celebratory signature of the protocol. The Czechoslovak delegation was serious, the Soviets affected cheerfulness. Through the open door, a number of journalists, photographers and cameras could be seen in the next room, some trying to enter the meeting room with an organizational employee pushing them back.

"Journalists please hold on for a moment, we'll call you back immediately!" echoed in the conference room. Then the door was closed. The floor was taken by Brezhnev. His forced smile stretched to almost those eyebrows, which someone called the continuation of Stalin's moustache at a higher level. "My dear comrades, we have come to the conclusion of our complex but honest and open comradely meetings. I think all of us sitting behind this table are aware of the meaning of the protocol that we will sign in a moment. Its significance for the people of Czechoslovakia, the Soviet Union and the world labour movement. Since everything has been said in our three-day discussions, we won't have long speeches, but I suggest that we sign the protocol."

"The Czechoslovak party is agreed and ready to sign," Svoboda said quickly. At that moment, however, Černík's hand rose. Svoboda, Biľak, as well as the Soviet delegation showed their displeasure. They wanted to have it done with and they were afraid that a new round of debates would start up again. Since the Soviet side wasn't prepared to talk to anyone, they had to get an interpreter quickly.

"I would like to say a few words just before the signing in the name of Comrade Dubček, who does not feel well ..." Dubček sat beside Černík and irritably played with an empty ashtray. "While we are ready to sign the protocol, I must under the authority of the ÚV KSČ emphasize that the occupation of Czechoslovakia by five brotherly armies has gone without its foreknowledge and that the ÚV KSČ did not ask for such assistance." The faces of the Soviets, but also Biľak, Husák and others scowled." The presidium has mandated me to reject comments in the media of the five countries where Comrade Dubček is portrayed as the head of the right-wing. We prepared our own draft protocol, but we received the information that Politburo refused ... To reach agreement, we showed good will and we accept your proposal ..." Černík sat down and a deep silence came. They all looked at Brezhnev.

"Comrades, we should approach ..." he began when Dubček put down ashtray, and interrupted Brezhnev without apology. His gesture was so forceful that the surprised Brezhnev fell silent. Dubček began with perfect Russian: "I saw your document. I ask that both documents be part of the final protocol. Yours and the one we have prepared. I also ask for no names to be present in the documents to avoid possible comparisons with the 1950s. We have information about the situation in our country. It's worse than we thought. Neither the presidium of the party nor the whole party understand the entry of troops ..." There was a visible commotion on the Soviet side and among some members of the Czechoslovak delegation. "The entry of the troops has caused the disagreement between the people, the party bodies and the working class. This incursion has had a destructive effect to the lives of our people. It was a hard blow against the thought and feeling of our nations. We speak openly that we consider this step to be a gross mistake that will bring great harm to our country and the entire Communist movement!"

"Please, let us not discuss and sign," Svoboda interrupted. However, as if in a trance still under the influence of the sedatives he had taken before starting the session Dubček continued. "The entry of troops has never met with a positive response. We are far from giving you advice on what to do. But you count on the fact that the presence of troops has escalated the tension in the party and in society. It is imperative that you think about how you deal with it, because this action has no support in our country! You have wounded the spirit of our people! It will take a long time to put it right." Dubček sat down and a deep silence fell, which Brezhnev interrupted after a moment. He was red-faced and controlled himself with difficulty.

"What Comrades Černík and Dubček have said now liquidates everything that we have done so far and sets us back a long way. If you want to say now at home what you're saying, it will be even worse." Angrily he turned to Dubček. "Sasha, when they were thinking about whom, to have instead of Novotný, it was me who defended you and trusted you. In January, I asked you if his people wouldn't endanger you. I asked if you wanted to replace the Minister of the Interior and the Minister of National Defence. Do you want to replace them? But you just told me no that they were good comrades. And then I learned that you had replaced the Minister of Interior, the Minister of Defense, other ministers and replaced the secretaries of the Central Committee. In February I gave you comments on your presentation at the 20th anniversary of the February revolution. I warned you that some of the formulations were incorrect and asked you to change them. But you didn't change anything. Is it possible to work like this? Nothing was consulted with us. Even when I'm about to act, I consult my comrades. We have collective leadership, that is, you must submit your opinions to others! I assumed with everybody that Sasha was a good comrade. And you've deceived us terribly You consulted nothing with us, you kept nothing you had promised, you promised cadre changes, you claimed that you were fighting against the cult of personality while creating one for yourself. He had celebratory telegrams sent to you, he has organized inspection trips of militia where you had them celebrate you." Brezhnev was almost shouting.

"He dived into a swimming pool in an undignified way just to show off! Everyone as you sit here, you bear responsible for developments in your country in the last seven months. The style of your work was support for the anti-socialist forces!" He turned back to Dubček. "How many times have I reminded you in a friendly way - Sashenka look around, it's counter-revolution! I wrote you letters, I called you and you hid everything from your politburo. When the "2000 words" pamphlet came, you didn't do anything against it. When Indra criticized it, instead of supporting him, you attacked him! Today it seems impossible to accept all this, but look at Gomulka. In 1956 he was also against our troops helping Poland. If I said today that our troops from Poland would be recalled, Gomulka would fly in and ask me not to do it. In the name of the lives of those hundreds of thousands of our soldiers who laid down their lives in the Second World War, we have the right to send to you our soldiers. The results of the Second World War are inviolable for us and we will defend them at the risk of the danger of a new war conflict. I asked President Johnson whether the US government even today still fully recognizes the results of the Yalta and Potsdam conferences. On 18th August, I got an answer. As far as Czechoslovakia and Romania are concerned, they are unconditional, with regard to Yugoslavia, it would be necessary to negotiate. So what do you think will be in your favour? Nothing would happen! Comrade Ceausescu, Comrade Tito or Comrade Berlinguer, and that's all. You're counting on the Communist movement in the West, but it has been meaningless for fifty years!" Brezhnev gave away in a wave of sincerity what he thought of the world communist movement. Then he sat down and Kosygin jumped up.

"We thought you understood why we sent troops to you. We thought we understood each other. The entry of troops is a historical event that saved socialism in Czechoslovakia. I have a bad feeling from this speech of Comrade Dubček. It is not true, Comrade Dubček, when you say the situation is worse in your country. It has substantially improved. However, if you speak at home as you are doing now, it will lead to civil war!" After these words, the chamber was completely disrupted. Without a word Brezhnev put down the pencil with which he had been playing nervously all the time and stood up. He departed through the left door followed with sheep-like obedience by the entire Politburo. Svoboda still tried to say something, but Brezhnev wasn't listening to him.

CHAPTER 42

I'M NOT SIGNING

After a moment of hesitation, the Czechoslovak delegation got up and left by the right door to a smaller side room. The Soviets were standing in the corridor, Brezhnev nervously smoking and gesticulating angrily. There was a smell of alcohol. When the group with Dubček walked around him, he took some steps towards him, but Dubček entered the hall assigned to the Czechoslovak delegation and closed the door firmly. "It doesn't matter whether we sign anything or not. They will just do what they want. I'm not signing it!" He lay down with difficulty on a divan and unbuttoned his sweat-soaked shirt.

Two groups had formed in the chamber, one around Biľak, Jakeš, Piller and Lenárt and the other around Černík, Husák, Smrkovský and Svoboda. Dubček wanted to be alone and they watched him. Leaders are always alone in the most difficult of times. He knew the signatures of all the others were not important. Anybody could sign it ten times over, but if the first secretary didn't sign, it would be clear to the whole world that something was wrong. He wondered how his fellow-citizens, especially the army, would react if they knew he hadn't signed. Instinctively his mind turned to the mysterious death of his former party chief, Gottwald, who died in 1953 just three days after returning from Stalin's funeral in Moscow. He remembered well what was whispered all the time in the narrow confines of the party leadership about his mysterious death. He understood that even though the Communist Party was the leading force in society and he was its highest representative, the supreme commander of the Czechoslovak Armed Forces was President Svoboda. He'd clearly said he would sign. Finally, he himself didn't want bloodshed. No, he couldn't allow even a single life of a Czechoslovak citizen to be squandered. As the others had indicated that they would sign, he would be plainly isolated. He considered and searched for arguments to put to himself. If he signed, he would make room at least for the promise of the Soviets to leave Czechoslovakia. And yet, and yet finally ... whether they signed or not, the Soviets would do what they liked. As he knew them, they would calmly falsify his signature. However, time was passing and Smrkovský, Černík, Svoboda and Husák were coming over to him. Smrkovský, Husák and some others were smoking which was not good for Dubček. In the chambers bottles of vodka, mineral water, caviar, sturgeon and other delicacies on the tables had been allotted to them. Some were nervously eating, but most had no appetite.

Černík surprisingly began to press him to sign. If they didn't sign it, there was a risk that they'd force them to sign something even worse. He firmly believed that the promise that Brezhnev had given him eye to eye that he'd continue to be prime minister would be fulfilled. Smrkovský sadly added that they had no choice. After a brief pause he drew a parallel with the situation of President Hácha in Berlin in 1939. "They managed to slow things down and save many people." It was clear to everyone that the comparison of the German fascists with Soviet communists meant that Smrkovský was wholly resigned to Communism.

Svoboda sent Biľak to Brezhnev to tell him that what Dubček said was not the opinion of the Czechoslovak delegation.

"I'm not signing it! They can do what they want, I'm not signing it! It's just like Joseph Hácha with Hitler!" Dubček clutched at his heart.

"Get the doctor, where's the doctor?" cried Svoboda. His personal physician came. "Comrade Doctor, give Comrade Dubček something to calm him down."

"I don't want anything, don't give me anything!" Dr. Smrček looked at Svoboda, who turned urgently to Dubček. "Sasha, you need to calm down ... That's it ... That's it!" he said paternally as Dubček had an injection.

"Sasha, it makes no sense now. We've all agreed to sign it! I understand you, but if you don't sign, people will leave their homes and go on the streets. The Russians will suppress this by all means. Do you want so much blood?" Smrkovský said.

"If we don't sign it, they'll push us into something even worse," Černík insisted.

"I'm not signing!"

"Šaňo, I was in gaol for nine years ... I know them well ... I don't want to leave you here ... And when we're home, they won't be constantly breathing down our necks ... Your signature is key. If you sign it, there'll be room for negotiations about their departure ... Finally, there is nothing terrible in the protocol. On the contrary! That there is international aid is a commonplace slogan and there is no mention of counter-revolution or the legality of their entry!" Husák convinced.

"Whether I sign or don't sign, they'll do as they please ..."

"You're still babbling and babbling you've babbled us into an occupation. If you carry on babbling, maybe we won't be going back home! And if you don't come home, there will be demonstrations and blood will flow in our streets!" Svoboda lost his temper. Then he recollected himself and almost begged Dubček, who listened carefully. "Sašo believe me, I know what I'm saying. The generals have told me they're ready for it. Blood won't be shed here and there, but there'll be streams of blood! As in Fifty-six in Hungary! Grechko told me clearly!" Dubček realized the seriousness of Svoboda's words. The sacrifice of the lives of innocent people was the last thing he wanted.

"What you don't see is that they haven't understood at all what they've done. If we were united ..." he sighed.

"Sasha, please ..." Smrkovský laid a friendly hand on Dubček's shoulder, his closest ally, the one he trusted most. Finally, he nodded. Smrkovský looked at the others. "We have to talk to them!"

"If you don't believe, you must. Haven't I been right behind you all the time? Didn't I get the resolution of the Bratislava presidium reversed? Without your signature, you are putting the whole delegation at great risk! The main thing is to get back to our homes and then think about it as soon as possible. You have a wife in hospital, you don't even know how she is..." Husák calmly said.

"Brezhnev said that if you do not sign it, Kriegel won't return home," someone said.

"People won't forgive us."

"On the contrary. They won't forgive us if we don't return and the old Novotný cadre takes over the party and state leadership. That would be a betrayal. The Soviets will leave everyone left in their positions ... Don't you want to continue in the post-January politics? The draft document guarantees that they won't interfere in our affairs," Husák convinced him.

CHAPTER 43

A STRAP ROUND HIS NECK

They didn't even notice when President Svoboda had left. Biľak arrived. "The President asks you to return, our Soviet Comrades have said they're ready to sign. Let's go to the chamber! "He stood by the door and waited for Dubček and Husák.

„Šaňo, don't mess it up it!" Dubček was silent in a nervous shock. He opened the door to the next room, where the other members of the Czechoslovak delegation were waiting. They gazed at him, and he just stood staring in front of him without a single word. It was obvious in these last few days that he had suffered the most difficult mental trauma of his life. Someone placed a glass of cognac before him, which he picked unexpectedly. Dr. Bernath, the second doctor of the delegation, exclaimed, "You must not!" But Dubček had already drunk up. After a long while, he smiled strangely. "Their politicians have convinced me that I have threatened the entire socialist camp with my mistaken policies. They got a schooling in socialism from me that they never experienced before!" Husák grabbed his right arm and squeezed with his hand. He held it tightly, Dubček nodded and Husák smiled with satisfaction. "Thank you. I want to assure you that just as I was on your side in the difficult moments of your struggle to clear the injustices of the past, as I have been with you since January, as I am with you now, I will stand with you and under your leadership!" He turned to Biľak. "Vasil, tell the Soviets that we are ready to sign! Everybody!" Before signing it Kosygin laconically informed them that the protocol was drafted in the way that the Czechoslovak party would have suggested.

In addition, the protocol stated, "The defense of the achievements of socialism is a common, international duty of all socialist countries ... The presidium of the ÚV KSČ declared that the so-called XIV Congress The Communist Party of Czechoslovakia is invalid ... Those persons whose activities did not correspond to the need to consolidate the leading role of the working class and the Communist Party will be released from their posts... The Communist Party will control the means of communication to serve socialism ... The situation in the press, radio and television will be regulated by new laws ... The troops and other authorities of the Allied countries will not be involved in the internal affairs of the ČSSR ... The military command of the ČSSR has been given the order to maintain communication with the Allied Command troops ... The terms of residence and total removal of Allied troops will be the subject of a closed treaty between the Allied states and Czechoslovakia ... Representatives of the KSČ will not allow the removal from office or even repressive measures against comrades who have fought to consolidate positions of socialism and friendship with the Soviet Union ... The Government of the ČSSR has instructed its representative in New York categorically to protest against the handling of the situation in the ČSSR by the Security Council or by any organ of the United Nations ... The presidium of the ÚV KSČ will carry out urgent cadre changes in the party and state bodies in order to ensure rapid consolidation in the country ... The delegations have agreed that in the interests of friendship between the ČSSR and USSR contacts between the leading representatives of the Communist Party of the USSR and the KSČ in the period after August 20 and especially the contents of discussions will be considered strictly secret ... The leaders of the Communist Party of the USSR and the KSČ will make every effort to deepen the traditional historical friendship of the peoples of both countries, their everlasting brotherly friendship."

On Monday, 26th August, at 22 o'clock they entered the meeting chamber for the photographers to immortalize those signing the protocol. For the Soviet Union, Brezhnev, Podgorny. Kosygin, Voronov, Kirilenko, Poljanski, Suslov, Shelest, Sheljepin, Gromyko, Grechko, Ponomarjov, Katushev and Semjonov. For the Czechoslovak side there were Svoboda, Černík, Smrkovský, Špaček, Šimon, Biľak, Barbírek, Piller, Rigo, Plzeň, Jakeš, Lenárt, Mlynář, Husák, Dzúr, Kučera and Koucký, the ambassador. Dubček signed last.

The only one who did not sign was František Kriegel. There was a funereal atmosphere in the chamber. Many of them were in the mind of Munich in 1938, this time with their own participation. When the signing was over, the Soviet delegation stood up as if on command and each of its participants put on a wide smile and began to pump the right hand of the Czechoslovak counterparts opposite them. At that moment, the photographers and cameramen who immortalized these moments of "brotherly" co-operation were allowed in. At the end of the ceremony, Brezhnev asked sarcastically whether the Czechoslovak delegation did not need anything. "At least you could give me a clean one of these!" Dubček snapped pulling at his legs and dangling a trouser pocket before Brezhnev's eyes. "I stink from four days in the same underwear, socks and shirt!" When Dubček returned to his room, an attendant came to him, put a strap round his neck and took his measurements. Before he departed he received two shirts, socks, and clean underwear. He flew to Prague with the dirt of Moscow showered and cleaned off.

Part 3

CHAPTER 1

WE HAVE BEEN WITH YOU, WE WILL BE WITH YOU

On Tuesday, 27th August, at five in the morning sleepless, exhausted and humiliated, the members of the Czechoslovak delegation arrived at Vnukovo Airport. For the Soviet side, Suslov came to give fond farewells and heartily embraced everyone setting out on the journey. Kriegel was already sprawled out in a rear seat of the aircraft. When Dubček saw him, he calmed down. Nobody felt like talking during the flight. It was an inglorious return and questions and reflections ran through their minds how they would be welcomed home. They'd signed a document to prevent bloodshed. They'd signed because Brezhnev had given them hope that they would be able to continue what they'd started in January 1968. They'd signed a document for which they would be blamed by those who didn't live through those times and who'd never understand them. Only one who has walked in the steps of those whom he judges has a right to judge.

On his arrival, President Svoboda spoke briefly on the radio, declaring irresponsibly that the Soviets had agreed a gradual and definitive departure of their troops. This statement created a delusional hope and contradicted what was whispered by citizens. That is why the whole country expected with enormous tension the appearance of Alexander Dubček in a direct transmission at half-past six on the night of their arrival. People hung on Dubček's every word. There was no TV or radio in the country that wasn't switched on. Dubček's ideas on what he would say changed a number of times. He was under enormous pressure because on the one hand he wanted to remain faithful to his principles of honesty and openness, on the other hand, the Moscow protocol was secret. Finally, he came to his fellow citizens with a tremble in his voice, and began to read a speech that Bohumil Šimon and Zdeněk Mlynář for the most part had prepared. All the personal, human and emotional parts of the speech were put in by Dubček.

"... I find it hard to find words to express my gratitude for the tremendous expressions of trust in which you have included me and the other comrades for whom you have been waiting ... The life of our people will, after what has happened, continue in a situation whose reality is not dependent only on our will ... At any cost it is necessary to avoid suffering and other losses as this would not change the real situation and the abnormal situation in our country would be prolonged ... We are in a position to find a way out of today's situation ... Our ultimate goal is to complete the departure of troops as soon as possible ... We must not fall prey to passions and psychoses in this complicated period ... The normalization of affairs is a fundamental realistic assumption so that we can concentrate our efforts on how to go further without serious errors and substantial delays along the journey that you have believed so much with us and I think you still believe... Ignoring the real state of affairs could only lead to adventurism and anarchy ... The first thing we need is the most rapid consolidation ... even if we have to take some temporary measures restricting the degree of democracy and freedom of expression that we have achieved. .. Please understand deeply the times we live in ..." Dubček's voice failed sometimes, and he hesitated. "... please forgive me if there is a pause here and there in my speech and a lot which is improvised ... Today

257

we know that the next journey will not be easy, it will be complicated and also last longer than we until recently had imagined ... A nation in which everyone can be guided by their own reason and conscience will not perish ..." Dubček's voice rose again and he could barely hold back his tears. He knew that the borders were still open and he didn't want to indicate to people the real situation so that there would be no exodus. Millions of men, women, elders, children on radio, and televisions accepted that it was over. Though they would persuade themselves that it might continue because Dubček was with them, they all felt that something terrible had happened in Moscow, something that buried the hope of decency, which had buried socialism with a human face for good. They felt that Dubček hadn't told them everything he wished to express. As they knew him, it wasn't because he didn't want to, but because he couldn't. He wasn't allowed to. People had tears in their eyes, just as the man who had spoken to them was on the edge of weeping.

In Bratislava, Vasil Biľak was dismissed from the KSS congress on 26th August as the first secretary of the ÚV KSS, and they elected Gustáv Husák, who came to the congress on the day after his return from Moscow, as the new first secretary. By being elected First Secretary he automatically became a member of the presidium of the ÚV KSČ. On the initiative of Husák the Slovak congress voted a letter to Alexander Dubček, "Dear Comrade Dubček! We have been with you during the tough moments of your struggle against the regime of subjective power and during your struggle for new, healthy changes after January 1968. We have been on your side during the stressful moments of the last few days. We have been with you in our thoughts and will be with you in your actions. We know there are many tasks ahead of you that will not be easy. We want to solve these with you under your leadership!"

CHAPTER 2

YOU DEVIL, YOU TRICKED ME!

One of the basic conditions insisted on by the Soviet leadership in the protocol was the annulment of the results of XIV Congress of the KSČ. This meant particularly the liquidation of the new 80 member, pro-reform Central Committee. If this were to happen, it would mean almost the end of the reform-oriented party leadership. Following the agreement of the "Vysočanský" First Secretary of the ÚV KSČ, Věnko Šilhan and Alexander Dubček, the problem was solved with true Czech inventiveness. Although it adopted a resolution declaring the Vysočanský congress to be invalid but at the same time it was personally acknowledged that according to Moscow the illegally elected Central Committee was to be included in the legal one. Moreover, there was no place for conservatives such as Kolder, Švestka, Rigo and Kapek in the newly established ÚV KSČ. It was compensation for Kriegel, Císař, Pavel, Hajek, Pelikán and Hejzlar, whom they'd had to sacrifice. On the occasion of these transfers to the ÚV KSČ on 31st August, Brezhnev was informed by Svoboda's son-in-law, Klusák. Brezhnev flew into a rage and immediately telephoned Dubček.

"What's going on there?" Brezhnev asked impatiently. "Who are you trying to bring into the central committee?!"

"We want to expand the Central Committee with eighty-seven newcomers," said Dubček. "Seven of them are from the ranks of former candidates. Others proposed are regional secretaries among delegates at the party congress."

"This is not a democratic way to change the composition of the Central Committee!" The dictator worked himself into a rage over this non-adherence to democracy.

"It's a necessary compromise," Dubček said. "I told we'd do it."

"You did not say it would be so many," Brezhnev said.

"You did not even say how many they should be. So I thought eighty-seven was just."

"There are too many of them and I don't like it. We talked about eight or ten," said Brezhnev both his eyebrows bristling.

"I probably didn't understand. I felt I we were talking about eighty. It's that Russian ... Now it's too late to do anything about it. If we propose a change at this time, everyone would know that you'd ordered it. They know you call me ... "

Brezhnev gritted his teeth through the phone, "Cort odin, obmanul meňja! (You devil, you've tricked me!)"

Dubček was pleased. In his speech at the presidium, which was held at Prague Castle, he skipped the words of Moscow's criticism and didn't mention Brezhnev's terminology about counter-revolution and only explained that "It was an error that the party did not adequately take into account with weight and strength international factors, including the views of the states in our situation with whom we form the Warsaw Pact. The strategic and general interests of the Soviet Union and the other four Warsaw Pact countries have not always been seen as a real, objectively existent, limiting factor for the possible pace and forms of our own political development," Dubček said. And this was virtually his entire response to the Moscow hurricane. Information on the course of the Moscow "negotiations" was given by President Svoboda and Smrkovský informed the participants of the meeting about the contents of the protocol.

Dubček felt the wound that his soul caused the invasion hadn't healed. Not only did it not heal, but it hurt more and more. The feeling of humiliation was ever more insistent. For someone accustomed to acting and behaving honestly and openly, it was an insupportable idea that he would have to pretend. He felt deep depression when he saw the radiant faces of the people he met and looked at him with the hope he knew there was none. He persuaded himself that some of the great and noble goals of the action program would be met. That is why and only why he was willing to play-act, believing that not everything was lost.

CHAPTER 3

I'M OPENING A SALON

Undoubtedly the biggest disappointment after the Moscow diktat was felt by Vasil Biľak. Though it might seem that the cause of his group was victorious, Biľak, Indra, Kapek, Jakeš and the other conspirators returned at that moment from Moscow with their noses out of joint. Brezhnev did not personally stand up for him. In the Moscow protocol only at his insistence was a passage incorporated that nothing would happen to him and his pro-Moscow clique and that he would not be dismissed from his functions. Dubček, however, ignored the protocol and after their return the pro- Moscow wing was eliminated from the leadership of the party. The key step was replacing Biľak as the head of the Slovak Communists with Husák. The demoted Biľak remained an ordinary member of ÚV KSČ, which, of course, was not enough for him. Although Kosygin had indicated to him that Dubček would be left at the head of the party only temporarily, he hadn't said for how long. He wanted to know what fate was waiting for him in the coming days and months. The only one who could tell him was the man he hated with his whole being. Dubček. For him he was the betrayer of the Soviet Union and socialism. On the other hand, Biľak was for Dubček the one who'd betrayed socialism with a human face, and moreover, even sparrows cheeped that Biľak was at the head of those who invited the tanks into Czechoslovakia. Dubček postponed receiving Biľak in the building of the ÚV KSČ and sent messages to Vasil repeatedly that he had no time for him. Eventually Biľak decided to visit him in his apartment in Prague's Troja district. Dubček invited him only into the hall and made it clear that he was planning to sort the matter out there and then in the doorway.

"I did not come to beg, I just want to hear from you personally if it's true that you are saying that you won't let Biľak into politics any more ..." he began aggressively.

"I don't know who told you that but you have to see what the situation is. You've been accused of betrayal and until that is cleared up I can't do anything. You place yourself in Slovakia, Husák can make you the vice-chairman of the Slovak National Council. "

"Pardon, but you probably didn't understand me. I didn't come to ask for a job. I came to remind you how we fought against Novotný and what I did for you. I'm astonished that you declare me a traitor and those comrades who stand for the principles of alliance with the Soviet Union. Don't let yourself be glorified as if it's clear to everyone that your popularity is artificial. Give me two or three months with the media in my hands, especially radio and television, and we'll see whether you or me are more popular and who is declared a traitor!" Biľak barked in his peculiar language. Dubček just shook his head uncomprehendingly. "I'm not worried about myself, I've always been one of the best in my field. I will open a salon and hang out a sign RSDr. Vasil Biľak Master Tailor. In particular, I will have some assistants as it's now allowed and I will write my memoirs. You know very well that I belong among those who know best what is really causing the crisis in this country. Likewise you know that I belong among those who know the whole truth about you. I won't do it for sensation or for money, neither will I give it to the west, but it is up to me that the party and generations to come know what kind of hero the Communist Party and Czechoslovakia had and who actually betrayed them ... Pardon me for having stolen your precious time, needed for governing and accept my gratitude," he finished sarcastically in the entrance hall and turned to go.

"Wait, wait," Dubček caught his sleeve. "Come and sit down for a moment," he invited him into his sitting room. "You haven't understood me properly, it's a misunderstanding. I want to help you, but you probably don't see how public opinion is as people are angry with you. Especially here in Prague. I think deputy chairman of the Slovak National Council would be the most appropriate for you. "

"I'm sorry, but only a member of the Slovak National Council can be elected as Vice-Chairman of the SNR and I'm not a member of the SNR but of the National Assembly. And I didn't come to ask for a place. I just want to know if the party or you personally have decided to write me out of politics."

"That's nonsense, I'd like to help you, but many members of the Bureau are against you," said Dubček.

"I just want to remind you that at the next presidium meeting you will also have to report on how some of the non-public articles of the Moscow Protocol are being fulfilled, and as you know, one of them is the fact that Comrades who were pro-Moscow would remain in their places. Do you have the aim of filing a motion on my recall from the Central Committee? In addition, we are bound to create a commission to investigate suspicions of treachery by some members. Or we are guilty and it's necessary to draw conclusions or not and end up with dirty propaganda!" said Biľak working himself into a rage.

"What do you actually want? Tell me what you want." said Dubček. "Do you want to be an ambassador in Bulgaria? Will you take it?"

"Thank you, but you won't get me out of the republic even if I have to break stones for the roads. I want to see how you destroy what millions of people under the leadership of the party and with great enthusiasm, effort and sacrifice have created and what kind of socialism you are preparing for our children. If you think that Czechoslovak citizens, honest Communists and they are the majority, are going let themselves be fooled for long and that you and your crooks aren't revealed as renegades, you are a very naive politician and you should leave while there is time. Think, too, so that your children won't be ashamed of you!" Biľak spat out. Dubček's calm wasn't disturbed by this and he laconically made another suggestion to Biľak.

"So tell me. Do you want to be Minister of Foreign Affairs?"

It was an attractive offer, but Biľak felt that he had begun bidding and so he asked very seriously.

"And what about the secretary of the Central Committee?"

"That could be," Dubček said unexpectedly.

"I'm taking it," Biľak said without hesitation. Dubček paused for a moment, realizing he would have a Moscow agent right in a position of the highest authority, but he made the offer.

"Perhaps it would be best if you stayed at home for a while. You can re-evaluate your activities in August, time will pass as it does and smooth out how you've behaved so it will be easier for you after a while ..." Dubček thought. "You won't have to worry about material security, we'll give you the salary of the first secretary of the ÚV KSS. But if you decide for it, I won't vote against you. "

"Okay, I'm going to work on the UV, and by the time of the Central Committee meeting, I can be responsible as a member of the Bureau for a few sectors," Biľak struck while the iron was hot. He took his leave of Dubček quickly. He looked in his direction as he left for a long time, realizing that his offer wasn't a good solution. He knew that Moscow was biased towards Biľak, but also needed a reliable Trojan horse in Prague. He knew that Biľak would do everything behind his back so that Moscow could remove him as soon as possible and put their man in his place. Who would it be? And when?

CHAPTER 4

IT'S NECESSARY TO DESTROY HIM POLITICALLY

On 13th September freedom of the press came to an end and censorship was restored. The media that were the engine of reforms, an instrument that gave people determination and hope, were given a dog collar. The most fervent and courageous journalists were gradually dismissed in successive editions. Moscow delivered to Czechoslovakia half a million copies of Moscow's Pravda daily, the radio station, Vltava, spewed anti-reform opinions twenty-four hours a day, broadcasting from Dresden and at the same time the distributed newspaper, Správy, tried to create an atmosphere cutting the feet from under Dubček and his allies. But as long as he was in the post of First Secretary's people did not lose hope. Despite the evident increasing pressure from Moscow, his eternal optimism gave them strength and courage. It was clear to Brezhnev that Dubček alone was the key for the assimilation of Moscow's perception of socialism and for definitively eliminating its human face. He needed a decisive move to discredit the first man of Czechoslovakia in the eyes of its public. He knew that the Soviet troops in Czechoslovakia were the most serious problem. Moscow was determined to retain part of its forces in Czechoslovakia. They expected stormy expressions of disapproval if that happened. So Brezhnev devised a diabolic plan. It would take place with the help of Dubček! They would push him to accept an agreement to retain Soviet troops. This would definitely compromise him in the eyes of the Czechoslovak public. In order for his plan to look more credible, he decided to prepare him with his four lackeys; Ulbricht, Gomulka, Kádár and Zhivkov. He invited them to Moscow for 27th September.

"We need to develop a common position and act on it without repercussions," he said uncompromisingly. Kádár, Zhivkov, Gomulka and Ulbricht nodded earnestly. "In the month that has elapsed since the deployment of troops, it has been fully demonstrated that our joint action was necessary and carried out in time. We prevented a counter-revolution and stopped those who were its main engineers. It turns out, however, that not everything has been achieved and not forever! ... We've registered positive developments in the development of normalization. We highly appreciate the performance of Comrade Husák c after his return from Moscow. In contrast with what Svoboda, Smrkovský, Černík and especially Dubček have said, Husák's performance has been the most serious of them all. However, I openly say that the implementation of the measures agreed in the protocol is insufficient under the leadership of Comrade Dubček. I even feel as though our agreements have been deliberately sabotaged. The course of the meeting of the ÚV KSČ at the end of August and the way the XIV Congress was cancelled was contrary to the Moscow Protocol ... Dubček's and Smrkovský's propagation of the reform process as leaders is unacceptable. Can we expect that Dubček and the people around him, after the experiences we have with them, will work properly towards a real redress of the situation? Certainly not!" Brezhnev drank some mineral water and raised his right eyebrow slightly. For those present this movement of his eyebrow indicated that something important was coming. "Comrades, the current most pressing task is the conclusion of the agreement of the presence of Soviet troops in Czechoslovakia. We will link the agreement with the name of Dubček! We have no doubt that this connection will have a serious impact on the overall situation and mood in Czechoslovakia. We make it clear to Dubček that not a single soldier will be withdrawn until the agreement is signed. What is your opinion?"

"Everyone in Czechoslovakia must understand that the troops there will remain under the same conditions as in Poland and Hungary. Their stay will be a factor that will point people in the right direction," Gomulka said first. "It's clear to everybody that Dubček has to go. As far as I know, it's clear to Svoboda, Černík and Husák. As long as Dubček is head of the party, it isn't possible to talk about a fundamental turn in the political line!"

"Right, very right," Brezhnev congratulated him.

"Dubček will leave by himself with difficulty although, of course, his voluntary resignation would be the best. Therefore, it is right that today we should agree on setting a course for his prospective removal!" said Gomulka.

"I told Ludvík Svoboda that we would have a temporary presence for two years, but it all depends on them. We will say when the terms of the protocol have been fulfilled," Brezhnev encouraged his satraps. "I will also tell this to Dubček, Černík and Husák when they come to Moscow for the third and fourth of October. One thing is clear to all of us. It is not enough to stop Dubček, it is necessary to destroy him politically!"

CHAPTER 5
I'M LOSING MY TEMPER

The atmosphere of the Soviet leadership meeting with Czechoslovakia resembled a judicial process. Brezhnev, Kosygin, and Podgorny had bullied Dubček for eight hours, using the vulgar language of men in their cups, berating him as if he were a servant. Černík was careful and Husák silent for most of the time. "During the last ten months of the negotiations with you, you have not complied with anything we have agreed upon. Your implementation of the Moscow protocol has led to inaccuracies and even to restrictions. We haven't noticed even the slightest hint of self-criticism or an analysis of the mistakes you made after January. Mistakes, comrades, must be admitted. And it cannot be done by anyone else except Dubček. Alexander Stepanovich, it must be clear to you that without analyzing past developments and without condemning anti-socialist forces, it is impossible to go ahead!" Brezhnev cried.

"The Party expects a display of principle from leading comrades. You can't look for a centrist position between the right and the left. We want your display to be fundamental!" Kosygin turned to Dubček. "So far, we haven't seen a single display like that. On the contrary, we see your personal and constant effort to find compromises!" Kosygin looked at Černík and Husák, who were sitting either side of Dubček. They both had their eyes lowered and kept silent. There was a short break, with the room in an awkward silence.

"Our Presidium is dealing with the tasks ..." Dubček began with a heavy voice. "However, it is the deep conviction of the Czechoslovak peoples that the August intervention was unjustified and at the same time the activity of the intervening troops and their constant involvement in our affairs is also unjustified. I've requested you several times to stop the propaganda broadcast of your Vltava radio station and the issues your magazine, Správy ..." Dubček took a breath and then added laconically. "Which no-one listens to or reads anyway." Brezhnev gulped his saliva and controlled himself with difficulty.

"If you were carrying out the Moscow protocol, if you were the ones guiding your people, they wouldn't have either Vltava radio nor would our people need to do it ," he cried out angrily. "I have to say that none of the points in the Moscow Protocol are being fulfilled or are being fulfilled slowly!"

"You aren't correct when you say that our troops are involved in your internal affairs!" Kosygin objected.

"We didn't give such a directive to the army," Brezhnev added. "I doubt if you could give us the facts." Then suddenly he flared up at Dubček. "Excuse me, but I'm losing my temper. So even though you have fulfilled nothing you still have the arrogance to accuse us. I have yet to see a country in which there is such moral terror as in yours. I don't understand get your stone heart, Alexander Stepanovitch, that you do not have enough resolve to protect healthy forces, that you don't support them. It doesn't matter how many of our soldiers are in your country. If only one hair is out of place on a head, we'll regard it as counter-revolution!" Brezhnev had without temporizing smashed the message of who was master into Dubček's face.

In two weeks, on 16th October 1968, the Prime Minister of the ČSSR (the Czechoslovak Socialist republic), Oldřich Černík, and the Prime Minister of the USSR, Alexei Nikolajevich Kosygin signed a bilateral agreement, "The Temporary Sojourn of the Soviet Army in Czechoslovakia". The Soviet Marshals had achieved their strategic goal of having troops permanently in Czechoslovakia not only to secure strategic space for the Warsaw Pact, but also to gain a more favorable position in the negotiation of tensions with the West. A secret protocol to the treaty said that 75,000 Soviet soldiers would remain in Czechoslovakia, four airports, three hospitals, training centers of the Czechoslovak army would be available and the Czechoslovak side would allocate suitable housing, warehouses and barracks to the Soviet troops. On 18th October, ten days before the fiftieth anniversary of the establishment of the independent and free Czechoslovak Republic, the treaty was approved by the National Assembly, despite the mass resistance of the citizens. Hundreds of resolutions urged both representatives and the top leadership of the party headed by Dubček to prevent the approval of the treaty by the Czechoslovak Parliament. The vote was delayed by ten deputies and four heroes opposed it; B. Fuková, G. Sekaninová, F. Kriegel and F. Vodsloň. František Kriegel justified his disapproval with the words: "I declined to vote for a treaty on the temporary presence of troops in our territory, because it does not have the essential part of a contract, that is, a voluntary character. The treaty was not signed by a pen, but by gun barrel and machine gun. That's why I also refused to sign the Moscow Protocol, which was signed in the atmosphere of military occupation of the republic and contrary to the feelings of the peoples of this country." František Kriegel was relieved of all functions shortly afterwards and retired. He was one of the first signatories to Charter 77, but died in December 1979 of a heart attack.

On 30th October, 1968, President Ludvík Svoboda, President of the National Assembly, Josef Smrkovský and Prime Minister Oldřich Černík signed the Law on the Czechoslovak Federation on the Bratislava Castle. From January 1969, national Czech and Slovak authorities were established, but in fact the new state constitution of the republic didn't have a major influence on citizens' lives and the federation gradually became purely formal. The decisive force was the Communist Party and it ruled centrally from Prague.

At the beginning of November 1968, a meeting of the Polish United Labour party, the PZRS, took place in Warsaw, attended by a Soviet delegation headed by Leonid Brezhnev. The Czechoslovak delegation was led by Jozef Lenárt. Others prepared at home a key meeting of the ÚV KSČ, where there had to be a decisive meeting of reformist and conservative forces. The meeting was postponed several times and Brezhnev was heavily involved in the course of preparations of resolutions. Finally, a delegation led Dubček was headed to Warsaw. Černík and Husák were also members of this. Gustáv Husák had listened carefully to Brezhnev in Moscow during the previous month and understood that, in addition to legitimizing the presence of Soviet troops in Czechoslovakia, criticism of the developments in Czechoslovakia after January was still required. It was he who first came to Warsaw with the idea of condemning "right-wing opportunism." Brezhnev welcomed this suggestion and insisted that this term be included in the resolutions of the forthcoming meeting of the Central Committee of the KSČ. Černík hesitantly put forward this comment and it was finally accepted by Dubček. As Brezhnev had blessed the draft resolution on "right-wing opportunism", the members of the ÚV KSČ approved it. In the November plenary resolution, for the first time, a condemnation of "right wing-opportunist forces" appeared. Reform had practically stopped and the results of the plenary prompted a storm of protests. Prague students went on strike and marked this plenary as the betrayal of the Czecho-Slovak Spring.

CHAPTER 6

IN A YEAR AND A DAY

The "rightist opportunism" genie has been let out of the bottle. Dubček's days were numbered. The Pro-Moscow realists, whose core consisted of Husák, Svoboda, Černík and Štrougal, knew that Smrkovský was the last pillar on which Dubček still leant. So Husák attacked the Dubček' s closest ally at the earliest opportunity on Christmas 1968. On a television show, he asked that the future chairman of the federal parliament be a representative of the Slovak nation. It was clear that on the implementation of Husák's challenge Josef Smrkovský's political career was over. The broader population stepped into the struggle for the tribune of the masses to keep the popular speaker Smrkovský in office. Work delegations came to Prague and thousands of resolutions asked for him to remain. Warned by 900,000 members of the union of metalworkers, Gustáv Husák, however, was determined to cut the Gordian knot in the elimination of representation for reform. His first step was a strategic outflanking of Smrkovský. He knew that when he fell Dubček would have only a short time left. Smrkovský felt the enormous pressure. Moscow was demanding his head uncompromisingly, and his recent closest allies, President Svoboda and Prime Minister Černík were also obediently calling on him to step down. They judged that this would help confirm them in their own positions. Vasil Biľak busily eagerly published a lying brochure on Smrkovský called "The Politics of Two Faces." Eventually Smrkovský, "for the good of the Slovak nation", announced his resignation on 5th January, 1969. It was exactly a year and a day, as is said in folk tales, from when Alexander Dubček became the first secretary of the Communist Party.

CHAPTER 7

DEATH TO BREZHNEV!

On the 22nd January 1969 a special IL 18 landed at the Moscow Vnukovo 2 airport, which brought to the Soviet Union metropolis the heroes of the day, the cosmonauts of Soyuz 4 and Soyuz 5. A week before, they had managed a daring link-up of two piloted ships in space and a transfer from one to the other. The previous two attempts, in 1967 and 1968, hadn't succeeded. But those weren't talked about. Only successes were publicized with Brezhnev trembling with eagerness behind them. He loved glory, honours and titles. He was a marshal of the Soviet Union, holder of the Lenin Peace Prize and of the Lenin Prize for Literature, which by the way he got for a work he not only didn't write, but it was said he hadn't even read. The success of the cosmonauts in January 1969 was especially timely for Brezhnev. The previous year had not been very good. Quite the opposite. The tanks he'd sent to Czechoslovakia against the alleged counter-revolution damaged not only the foreign policy of the USSR, but the occupation also disturbed the relations of the KSSZ with some of its fraternal parties. In space the end of the year belonged to the Americans. They were about to land on the Moon. On Christmas 1968, the crew of Apollo 8 orbited it ten times.

In Moscow they prepared a celebration greater than ever before. Around 6,000 guests awaited the space heroes in the Kremlin's Congressional Palace. Leonid Ilyich would honour them on a live broadcast. To welcome them he even went with his entourage to the airport.

The cosmonauts from the successful Sojuz, Vladimir Shatalov, Boris Volynov, Yevgeniy Chrunov and Alexei Jeliseev were also accompanied by some of their colleagues, Valentina Tereskova, her husband, Andrian Nikolaev, Alexei Leonov and Yevgeny Beregov.

Millions of viewers watched the heroes being greeted. The convoy of luxury government limousines crossed the streets of Moscow, where, as always, workers and young people cheered them. The gleaming Chaika limousines approached the Borovitskaya Tower, one of the three entrance gates to the Kremlin, when from out of nowhere the live broadcast ended. No explanation. It continued after an hour. Also without explanation. To the astonishment of those gathered in the Congressional Palace, but also to that that of the television viewers, the General Secretary of the Communist Party of the Soviet Union, Leonid Brezhnev, as was expected, did not give the astronauts the Heroes' Golden Star, but the President of the Presidium of the Supreme Soviet of the USSR, Nikolai Podgorny. Some tension could be seen on the pale faces of some comrades. No one ever got to know what had happened. Only a selected few were informed that only some tens of minutes before there had been a shooting at the Borovitskaya gate. More precisely, someone shot at the ruling column. There were casualties ...

A dead driver, wounded cosmonauts. When a government space column with astronauts came into the Kremlin, a man in a militia uniform threw himself in front of the second car in turn, and with a shout "Death to Brezhnev" he started firing two pistols. Not once did he miss. He hit the windscreen of the Chaika sixteen times. He was convinced he had just killed Brezhnev. He had previously verified the "protocol". It was always so. In the second vehicle of the column was hired the Secretary General of the Central Committee of the CSSA. He could not guess that 22nd January was an exception. As soon as they left the airport, the cars were unexpectedly regrouped. The vehicles with the astronauts went first, Brezhnev's Chaika was third in the procession. The assassin killed the driver and injured the astronauts Nikolaev and Beregovoja. Nothing happened to Tereskova, who was also in the car. Nikolayev did not lose courage and, even when he was shot, he immediately seized the steering wheel and stopped the Chaika on the pavement. The shooter, who has discovered his mistake in the meantime, had a hysterical seizure. He didn't even try to escape. He was disarmed and arrested without any problems. It turned out that the assassin was a 20-year-old Soviet Army lieutenant, Viktor Ilyin. The militia uniform had been stolen from his uncle. He'd served in the military in Lomonos near Leningrad. There he seized two pistols and four magazine clips and went to Moscow to kill Brezhnev. It was said that among other things, it was because of the occupation of Czechoslovakia.

The attempted assassination of Brezhnev was a secret well guarded by the Kremlin until the collapse of the Soviet Union.

CHAPTER 8

HUMAN TORCHES

On 16th January, 1969, a Sunday afternoon at 4:30 pm, tram No. 7 was travelling around the National Museum in Prague. One of the passengers noticed a man standing by the fountain in front of the museum, pouring liquid over himself. When the tram set off and moved a few metres meters, he saw a blue flame on the man. The burning man stood for a few seconds, then leaped the railing, ran towards the statue of St. Wenceslas, turned to the House of Groceries store and thence towards the street, Vinohradská třída. A quick-witted transport supervisor from the transport company pushed the man to the pavement and extinguished the fire with his coat. An ambulance took the young student to hospital in Legerova Street. But the burns were so strong that he died after three days. At the place where he set fire to himself they found a letter in his discarded coat. "Given that our nations have found themselves at the brink of hopelessness, I have decided to express my protest and to encourage the people of this country in the following way. Our group consists of volunteers who are determined to burn for our cause. I was honoured to be the first drawn. Our demands are the immediate cancelling of the censorship and the prohibition of the distribution of Zpravy. If our requirements are not met within five days, i.e. by 21st January, and if the people do not rise with sufficient support, that is, an unlimited strike, more torches will flare. Torch # 1."

Torch number one was a twenty-year student Jan Palach. His death shocked the whole country. It had never happened in Czechoslovakia in the twentieth century, nor had it happened in Europe. The presidium of the Central Committee of the Communist Party issued a statement in which it condemned the suicide of Palach and called on citizens to calm down. Palach's funeral became a huge demonstration of defiance, but at the same time, of helplessness. Zprávy ceased publication on 10th May, 1969.

On 25th February, at the entrance to the 39 Václavské náměstí, near the statue of St. Wenceslas, Ján Zajíc, a student of the fourth year of the Secondary School of Industrial School in Šumperk, painted himself with the glue for parquets, poured petrol on himself and drank acid, so that he couldn't cry out with pain. Torch #2 flashed. On 4th April Good Friday, 1969, Evžen Plocek, a 40-year-old member of the KSČ District Committee, a delegate of the extraordinary congress of the KSČ in Vysočany, ignited on Peace Square in Jihlava.

Soon another young man in Plzeň burned, then two more in Brno and another in Prague. On April 11th, a soldier of the Strážske Military Unit, Michal Leučík, burned in Košice in protest against the occupation. These suicides were the best guarded secrets in Czechoslovakia for the next twenty years. Four months before Jan Palach burned in Prague, the Polish humanist Ryszard Siwiec was the first living torch in protest against the military occupation of Czechoslovakia. He burned on 8th September, 1968 at the 10th Anniversary Warsaw Stadium before the eyes of about a hundred thousand people, including the leadership of the Polish Communist Party. At the stadium he left leaflets. "I protest against unprovoked aggression against the Czechoslovak Brotherhood." The secret police totally suppressed this act by the 59-year-old accountant, the father of five children, for a long time. On 20th January, a 17-year old Hungarian student, Sándor Bauer, burned on the steps of the National Museum in Budapest to protest against the occupation of Czechoslovakia. No-one in Czechoslovakia knew anything about his heroic death.

Dubček was shocked by Palach's gesture. He was tired and thought more and more about the correctness of his decision in December to remain in office. He contracted an unpleasant virus with a high fever. He travelled to Bratislava, where he lay for two days at home, but the illness didn't clear up and he was hospitalized. He stayed in the hospital for two weeks.

CHAPTER 9

ON THE VERGE OF A FIGHT

Jan Palach's funeral took place on 25th January in Prague's Karolínum. It was a national demonstration against the Soviet occupation of Czechoslovakia. Prague on those days was shrouded in black. Around the statue of St. Wenceslas countless candles were lit with the words, "We will not forget!" The inscription on the statue, "Saint Wenceslas, the Duke of the Czech Lands, don't let us and the future perish!" aptly expressed the plea of a humbled nation. Dubček was in a state sanatorium. Only a few of the inhabitants of Bratislava knew that the entrance to the former Pistoris Palace, which had been converted into a Lenin museum, was also the entrance to the state sanatorium. Ravens croaked in the branches of the trees in the garden of the sanatorium. Their squawking created a stifling atmosphere. A muffled sound from the tramlines nearby on Obrancov Mieru Street reached the room. They'd hospitalized him for a severe virus infection on 19th January, the day Palach died. He didn't accept any visits, he wanted peace; from everything, from the whole world, from friends and enemies. After a long time he finally wanted to be alone. The only exception was his beloved wife, Anna. They let her through the entrance on Fraňa Kráľa Street, which was closer to their house.

They sat opposite each other in deep chairs in the "living room" of an apartment designed for the highest party and state officials. Anna held his hand lovingly. She had tears in her eyes. "Palach's suicide is terrible. The boy burned because of the ideas you put before the nation a year ago. If I'd guessed that it would come to this, I'd've tried to persuade you not to do it. I don't know if it's a good idea for people to die ... "Anna was in doubt. "My God, what can the boy's mother be going through?"

"It was a heroic act, but nothing can be done against the strength of tanks ... I'm tired ... I'm thinking that I'll finish with all of this. I'm exhausted. They've all left me. Husák blasted Pepík Smrkovský as well at Epiphany, I've remained totally alone among them ..." Somebody knocked timidly on the door of the hospital room.

"Come in!" The door opened and a grizzled head of a man appeared, someone whom the Dubčeks least expected in Bratislava, Josef Smrkovský. "What a visit! Pepík, what are you doing here?" Dubček stood up and embraced Smrkovský.

"Hi Anička," Smrkovský kissed Dubček's wife on both cheeks.

"I was just about to leave. So, you boys can at least talk," she smiled and left the room.

"So, Sasha?" Dubček smiled, Smrkovský seized his hand, and they both kept silent for a long time. They had so much what they wanted to say, but somehow the words didn't come.

"So what do you reckon, shall we fight again?"

"Does it make sense?"

"When I was taught by the baker, Master Vodrážka, he would say - lads never eat bread hot. It's unhealthy. Only fools eat fresh bread. We know that the true quality of bread is known only after some time. I think, Sasha, we have nothing to lose yet, so what ... we'll go on, shall we? After all, I'm still the vice-chairman of the parliament ..." The smile which had been absent for a long time returned to Dubček's face.

"What's going on? Jaroš called me that Brezhnev had requested me by letter to take measures so that Palach's action wouldn't be misused by anti-socialist forces ..."

"Horníček's, Škutin's and Seifert's statements on television were very wise. The older generation has calmed down somewhat, but students are protesting ..." Smrkovský sat in a comfortable chair as Dubček ordered coffee from the nurses on duty. He ordered black Russian tea for himself.

"I wouldn't drink that Russian tea in your place ... It bungs you up ..." Smrkovský grinned sarcastically. Dubček bitterly smiled as well.

"You will see, there will come a day in Moscow those like us will appear the Brezhnevs will be sent off somewhere ..." The nurse came in and for a moment they were silent. When she left them, Dubček breathed heavily and slowly apologized to Smrkovský. "I'm sorry I didn't stand up for you more resolutely. Perhaps you could have held on to the post of the Chairman of the Federal Assembly. Only, I'm sorry ... um ... it wasn't possible. We had a New year's statement from the presidium on the situation, but Moscow didn't want to approve it in that form. Katušev, who'd been fussing around for a week on behalf of the Moscow Politburo, told me verbatim, "The politburo thinks you are on the verge of fighting. The focal point is the Smrkovský question. A decision must be taken." I promised him we were going to deal with this question, the question of you. On the second day, we were allowed to release a statement in which we signed up for the post-January policy. I thought people would calm down. I was very grateful to you when you went on the radio on the fifth and asked for the recall of the planned general strike ..."

"I didn't do it with enthusiasm, but there was a serious threat of a conflict with Soviet soldiers. I was afraid that the worst could happen. Nine thousand metal workers were ready to strike. "

"Husák annoyed them by his tactless and non-tactical attack on your person," Dubček shook his head in incomprehension.

"I was grateful again that you ordered Biľak pamphlet about me to be destroyed."

"You mean that filth?" Politics with Two Faces?" Smrkovský nodded." They printed fifty thousand copies in Ostrava. That Biľak is a real louse. Husák counts on him, but he'll quickly find out what sort of person he is. The wretched man also tried to put Palach's death on our account! That's outrageous! "

"I still wonder if it was right that we signed in Moscow," Smrkovský said suddenly and unexpectedly. Dubček understood that Smrkovský also had suffered the same inner torments. For him, too, signing the Moscow Protocol was a nightmare that kept returning.

"Grechko told me that if we didn't sign it, there would be a war. And we wouldn't have had a chance, no one would have helped us. Nobody. The Americans had clearly told the Russians that they respected Yalta and we were in the Soviet sphere of interest. President Johnson heard out the Soviet ambassador and left peacefully for his ranch."

"There is an historical moment when there is a need to fight, even when it's lost in advance ..." Smrkovský nodded. "It's as it is! Let's try at least to save what is possible from January. All the more so as we both feel that we're both running out of time ... But I'm still the Vice-President of the Federal Assembly and the Chairman of the Popular Assembly ..."

"And I am still the first secretary ..." Dubček smiled bitterly. "Even though, as you rightly said, it is clear that the candles are burning low for us. I will show you something ..." Dubček pulled the letter out of his breast pocket and handed it to Smrkovský. "When I see how heroically you are fighting against time, I rein in my pen. It would want to write a lot and even more, but I will rein it in. I'll reduce a long letter to one word, thank you! Your Ján Smrek" Smrkovský gave him the letter. "But not any poet has written to me yet ..."

"Maestro Smrek is right. We have to play for time. The longer we hold, the more we save from January. Do we still have any chance at all?" Dubček considered. "If we come to even more concessions, will people understand that we can't do otherwise? Won't their anger be turned against us? Won't they reject us and disown us?"

"People have more understanding than we do. They know exactly what we can and what we cannot do. The only thing that they would not forgive if we didn't try anything. I think we have done more since August than we thought possible. We've achieved a federal reconstruction of the state, we are continuing economic reform, although in a limited form. In media reform there are still people dedicated to reform ... though ... even though I've learned that Moučková and Škutina are no longer allowed on screen ..." Smrkovský thought for a moment. "But you know, as Jirásek said - if I had to be the last, alone and abandoned, I'd endure!"

"What we have to do at any cost is rehabilitation. Pepík, if we don't get this done, those coming after will simply get rid of it. We can never go back to the time when non-communist citizens are unequal citizens," said Dubček, who'd cheered up a little. "But only if we still have time ... and the possibility ... um ..." he fell back into depression. He didn't know that in three months he'd be sitting in the post from which Smrkovský had been driven a few days before.

CHAPTER 10

CZECHOSLOVAKIA – OCCUPIERS 4:3

In a general atmosphere of gradual resignation, people had a little joy from two sporting events. A gold medal was won at the European Championships in the German Garmisch Partenkirchen by the young Ondrej Nepela and especially the two victories of Czechoslovak hockey players over the Soviet Union team at the Swedish World Cup. In particular, the second victory became fateful for Alexander Dubček.

The championship was originally held in Czechoslovakia, but the leadership of the International Hockey Federation, fearing possible violence that could have arisen during the matches with the Soviet Union, demanded a change of venue. At the beginning of the championships, a traditional party between the Soviet and Czechoslovak hockey players took place at the Soviet Embassy in Stockholm. On the evening of 14th March the "zborna komanda" (the whole squad) came to the Soviet embassy with their coach, Chernyshev, but only the trainers Kostka and Pitner, from the Czechoslovak side. In the game against the USSR, some players came on with a sealed red star over the head of lion in the Czechoslovak State Emblem. The great winger, Jaroslav Jiřík, commented: "Our grandmother says that the lion should have a crown instead of a star". After the first victory, 2-0 over the USSR in the group stage, before the semi-final match the Czechoslovak representatives stuck on their covers of their coats the emblem "World championship" with the date "21st August, 1968". From the start of the game, millions of Czechs and Slovaks were excited.

Czechoslovakia managed 2-0 after the first goals of Holík and Nedomanský. In the second period, the Soviets equalized, but a shot by the defender, Hořešovský, at the beginning of the third period was a signal for a heroic fight. Jaroslav Holík's successful raid buried the hopes of the Soviet Union for good. They could only pull back to 4-3. When our hockey players asked why they did not shake hands with the Soviets, one of them said: "In our country it's customary for the losers to congratulate the winners."

After the final whistle, the commentator Vladimír Vácha enthusiastically announced, "So celebrate this at home". These words were quickly regarded as a challenge and Vácha was thrown out of work. In seventy towns and cities on 28th March, more than half a million people waved Czechoslovakian flags calling out the glories of Golonka, Dzurilla, Jiřík, and the Holík brothers and mocking Soviet players such as Ragulina and Firsov. Gradually, they began to make fun of Brezhnev and Kosygin. Slogans like "Taras bububu, Brezhnev a smack on the gob for you!", "Czechoslovakia - Occupants 4: 3" or "For your tanks you have four goals" or "Dubček slivovica - Brezhnev a clip round the ear" followed the exasperated Soviet occupiers in Czechoslovakia. However, not only did fifteen million Czechs and Slovaks enjoy the victory over the USSR, but also a few people under Colonel Molnár in ŠtB, who, together with KGB officers, took advantage of the enthusiasm of the people and put together an unprecedented provocation. Demonstrations to celebrate the ice hockey victory gradually turned into anti-Soviet demonstrations. Demonstrators in Bratislava arrived in front of the Soviet consulate where they protested against occupation. The slogans from the hottest heads, "Brezhnev is a swine" or "Russians go home" were from young people whom the protesters did not know. Many civilians among the demonstrators who when approached by locals, surprised them by speaking with strong Russian accents.

Molnár's men arrived in several buses to Jindřišská Street near Václavské náměstí. They mingled inconspicuously with the enthusiastic crowd. In front of the Aeroflot airline office in Václavské náměstí, some inconspicuous piles of stone had been brought by somebody unknown the night before the event. When the crowd approached the display window of the company, an unknown "daredevil" took a rock and threw it at the window. After him another and another. The crowd threw and poured their anger and despair into the window. No one thought about who the unknown young men were throwing rocks and where the rocks were picked up. Secret agents under personal leadership of the Interior Minister of the Czech Republic and Soviet agent, Josef Grösser, had provoked the violence. Confrontations of demonstrators with policemen occurred in 21 Czech and Slovak towns. In Bratislava, students smashed the windows of the Soviet command on Miletičova Street. At around eleven o'clock, the Soviet Ambassador asked the Minister of Defence, Dzúr, to use the army against the demonstrators. Before midnight, Dzúr called Dubček as neither President Svoboda's phone nor Prime Minister Černík's had not responded and asked him for permission to use the army against demonstrators. Dubček refused. This was, from the point of view of the Soviets, another fatal error. They decided to act.

CHAPTER 11

OFF WITH THE HEAD OF COUNTER REVOLUTION!

Events after the hockey match played to Dubček's discredit. Brezhnev needed to get rid of Dubček at all costs. The international meeting of Communist and Workers' Parties was approaching, and it was unacceptable for Brezhnev that Dubček lead the Czech - Slovak delegation. As early as Sunday, 30th March, Moscow's political office of the Central Committee of the USSR met at an extraordinary session and decided to use the ice hockey crisis for a definitive power change in Czechoslovakia. Dubček was sent a "Statement by the Central Committee of the USSR and the USSR Government" in which they described the demonstrations in Czechoslovakia as counter-revolutionary. On 31st March, without informing the Czechoslovak authorities, the Soviet Defense Minister Grechko landed at Milovice Airport near Prague. On the second day, Grechko presented Dubček with two arrogant demands - to use Czechoslovak armed forces in the future to establish order and to introduce total censorship. Dubček replied that the Czechoslovak people had the right to express their joy and that sufficient public security forces were used to establish order. The

Deputy Secretary of State of Foreign Affairs of the USSR, Semjonov, who had come to greet him lost his nerve nerves and looking directly at Dubček's eyes, cried out: "Off with the head of counter revolution!"

"Did you mean me?" Dubček asked directly. Semjonov stopped and did not answer. For the first time, one of the Soviet leaders dubbed Dubček as the head of counter-revolution.

On the same day, tens of thousands of Prague citizens vainly waited on the way from the airport in Ruzyně to the city centre for the hockey players who had returned from the world championships. The coach route to the centre was not allowed for the hockey players. When Lieutenant Colonel Pitner came to work in his office, six coach officers from the Interior Ministry were waiting for him. They wanted to know how it the state emblem came to be sealed on the jerseys of the hockey players in Stockholm.

Although Smrkovský resigned from the position of the President of the Federal Assembly, he was still a member of the CPC Central Committee presidency, but lost power and energy under increasing Soviet attacks. Svoboda closed ever more in on himself and Černík adapted. On 2nd April, at the meeting of the CPC Central Committee, Husák did not leave a stone unturned over Dubček, criticizing the "exaggerated" concept of his reforms and ineffective interventions against mass media. He threatened that if the presidium of the Central Committee of the Communist Party under Dubček's leadership did not respond to the Statement of the ÚV KSSZ, the Central Committee of the Slovak Communist Party would do so under Husák's leadership. In Nitra, for the first time at a meeting of smallholder cooperatives Husák attacked Dubček for the first time in public and declared that the leadership of the parties could not be a weak person.

At the Prague Castle, Defense Minister Grechko, in the presence of President Svoboda, criticized Dubček for his ban on using the army against demonstrators. Svoboda was silent.

On 10th April President Svoboda secretly negotiated with Gustáv Husák in Bratislava on how to remove Dubček from the top party function. On 11th April Grechko announced that another eight thousand Soviet troops were arriving in Czechoslovakia. Dubček understood that the Soviets wanted to have the Czechoslovak reforms removed by the person who started them. They were threatening to set up a police regime. He did not want to be the cause of further reprisals. He invited two of his closest associates Jozef Gajdoš and Oldřich Jaroš and informed them of his decision to resign. He informed Svoboda, Černík and Smrkovský of his decision on the same day. "I understand you, there's probably no other way," laconically declared Svoboda.

"I understand you," Smrkovský said sadly when Dubček visited him in the evening. But he added, fervently, "Let's see what we can do after your resignation. They don't have our hides yet ..." On the second day, Dubček announced his intention to resign at the meeting of the Executive Committee of the Central Communist Party and proposed as his successor Oldřich Černík. He then visited President Svoboda and asked him to use his authority against the expected election of Gustáv Husák as the new first secretary of the Central Communist Party. Svoboda only hardly took in what Dubček had told him. He slipped unexpectedly from the low sofa on which he sat, as if to pray before Dubček. With a pale face he said, "For God's sake, Sasha, I have to tell you something. I promised to Grechko that your successor would be Husák ..."

Day D, which Husák had categorically rejected a short time ago, was here. "Sometimes reason comes to halt who is interested in inventing such moonshine that I should replace Comrade Dubček. You can ask Comrade Dubček by phone or me or any member of the government. Well, in a word, there is no truth in it, they are fabrications. We co-operate well with Comrade Dubček," he told reporters.

In order Moscow could make sure of everything, Brezhnev secretly invited Gustáv Husák to meet in Mukachevo on 13th April. What they said is not difficult to imagine.

On 17th April, 15:00 Oldřich Černík opened a meeting of the Central Committee of the KSČ in Prague Castle. The security of the meeting was ensured by the members of the ŠtB, who supervised a strict presentation of the participants and with the consent of President Svoboda blocked their telephone connection with the world. The participants were already aware of the proposed cadre changes, approved by the presidium of the ÚV KSČ, which met on that day before the afternoon. After a short introduction, Černík gave the floor to Dubček, who announced his resignation. Svoboda, Štrougal and Husák voiced their appreciation of his work in the past. Husák proposed he should become the Chairman of the Federal Assembly. Dubček timidly proposed that his successor be chosen between Černík and Husák. Černík called for a vote on Dubček's resignation. Out of 182 participants, this was acclaimed by 152. Gustáv Husák was chosen by 156 of the 182 present in a secret ballot. At the end of the session shortly before midnight, someone started singing the Internationale. Husák and Biľak sang it most prominently. As they left the hall, Dubček and Husák happened to stand opposite each other. "I'll take better care of you than Novotný did," the new most powerful man in the country ominously remarked.

When Ambassador Chervonenko telephoned Brezhnev after a few minutes, the Soviet leader said sternly, "It is the victory of the party over counter-revolutionary forces and right-wingers. Particular merit for success must go to Comrades Svoboda and Husák. They have demonstrated the determination and bravery that will be highly rated in history. In school textbooks they will write about them ..."

CHAPTER 12

SO WHAT! YOU DESERVE IT!

Husák's former friend, the poet, Ladislav Novomeský, after his election, declared: "God bless his steps." It was as shocking as the poem he wrote after the execution of Clementis. "You gambled yourself away in your triumphal victory and in doing us down dragged yourself down from on high. So what! You deserve it! "At that time, Novomeský did not even know that the words he once addressed to Clementis were perfectly applicable to Gustáv Husák two decades later. His lifetime desire for the highest level of power had been fulfilled. The most controversial Communist politician of Czechoslovakia had come to the forefront of the party. He refused to ride in Dubček's legendary Tatra 603 with the PI 97-34 number plate.

On 28th April Peter Colotka, who shortly became the Prime Minister of the Slovak Government, resigned from the post of Chairman of the Federal Assembly and was replaced by Dubček.

Although the function of the President of the Federal Assembly was formal, he was still in the public eye, which still gave people some kind of hope that some of the reforms would be implemented. However, they were reduced to a much weaker brew of economic measures and the introduction of a federal model. One of the leading figures of the Czech reform movement, Milan Hübl, shortly before the Soviet invasion stated exactly, "If we become a Soviet province, it does not matter whether we are in the form of a unitary, dualistic or tripartite ..."

The new party boss, Husák, was in isolation on his own, and most of the lower party officials did not go along with Dubček's exchange. They were open about it relying on the fact that there were hundreds of thousands of them. They didn't yet even know that Moscow was determined to make a similar experiment in Czechoslovakia after the model of a Stalinist purge. Simply if "the people" didn't like the new leadership of the party, then "the people" will be exchanged. On 23rd April Husák travelled to Moscow. Formally it was a meeting of the Council for Mutual Economic Assistance, in fact the first official brainwashing from Brezhnev.

In Czechoslovakia, after Dubček's recall, tensions increased, so the new party leadership for the first time in history cancelled the First of May parade. On 7th May, President Svoboda, First Secretary Husák, Prime Minister Černík, Defense Minister Dzúr, Chief of the Bureau for Party Work in Bohemia, Štrougal and the new First Secretary of the ÚV KSS, Sádovský, took their trip to Canossa. They visited the main command of the Soviet occupation troops in Milovice. President Svoboda delivered a shameful speech in which he described the occupiers as liberators, best friends and the occupation as international aid.

Husák decided to crush the right-wing opportunism bearers down to the last line of membership. The publication of Listy, Reportér, Studentské listy, My 69, Plamene, Svet v obrazoch, Reflex, Literárny život ceased. Mass purges were carried out in newspapers, television and radio. More than three hundred Czech and Slovak journalists carried out self-criticism and the statement "A word to one's own ranks" entered the Husák currency. Signatures under this declaration have gradually increased. The army has gradually changed after several mutual exercises with the

Soviet army to an obedient tool to defend the new powers against its own people. Pro-Dubček officers were replaced as the first anniversary of the August intervention approached to ensure there would be those willing to send soldiers against their own nation.

Dubček took part in the meetings of the CPC chairmanship as Chairman of the Federal Assembly, but his critical appearances and defence of the reform process became a voice in the wilderness, and only raised smiles on the faces of Husák and Biľak's supporters. When Piller presented a report on the completion of rehabilitation on 6th May, the biased Biľak said, "We must reject this. On the basis of this report, we would have to decide on the consequences for 52 comrades in the Central Committee and we would have to punish five members of the presidium and five secretaries. I can't imagine that." The party leadership never returned to rehabilitation. to the same presidium, Husák presented such a draft of his political conceptions, "To overcome the crisis and consolidate conditions in society" that he provoked horror in President Svoboda. In this conception, Husák virtually rehabilitated all of the Novotný supporters.

CHAPTER 13

WE'LL BREAK THEM

In mid-June 1969 leaflets were circulated in Czechoslovakia calling for non-violent forms of resistance against the intervention and the Husák regime. The first anniversary of the occupation was horribly close. Under the political oversight of Alois Indra, the army's top commander prepared measures to suppress eventual counter-revolution, which was also approved by the Military Council of the Middle Group of the Soviet Army, as the Soviet occupation army in Czechoslovakia had begun to be called officially. Gustáv Husák, as the new Supreme Commander of the People's Militia, said: "The opinion of the Party leadership is also that those who dare to put up active resistance somewhere in the street or something similar, we will break mercilessly, let that stand at any cost!" Nine thousand members of the militia who did not agree with Husák's opinion found themselves in disgrace.

On 2nd August, Husák, Svoboda and Indra left for a short "holiday" in the Crimea, where they "relaxed" with Brezhnev and Podgorny by 10th August. On 9th August Václav Havel wrote to the President of the Federal Assembly, Alexander Dubček, in which he requested him "as a symbol of all hopes for a better, dignified and free life with which he was associated in the first half of 1968 to publicly engage with the pressure of the current leadership, and defend the reform policies and the price that he himself and the people of Czechoslovakia will have to pay for it." Václav Havel, who was one of the most radical reform proponents, had welcomed the election of Husák as the first secretary of the Central Communist Party after the hockey crisis, because according to him Husák was the only person who has a firm concept and could bring the nation out of the crisis." He then called Dubček a "lyricist and dreamer." He now turned to "the lyricist and dreamer" who was already in total isolation without any influence. Havel showed himself to be a naive playwright unable to understand the hard reality.

Before the first anniversary of the invasion, Husák advised Smrkovský and Dubček not to stay in Prague. Smrkovský took a holiday in High Tatras and Dubček left for his cabin in Senec. Preparations for security measures were consulted with the Soviet Command in Milovice. At the Prague - Kbely airport they painted an exact size of the proportions of Václavské námestí with lime and militiamen and members of the public security service practiced against potential protesting demonstrators. On the eve of 21st August, 1969, 20,000 soldiers, 40,000 members of the popular militia, 30,000 members of public and state security, 310 tanks, 2309 vehicles, and 200 armoured carriers were in combat readiness. This was the fear the new leadership had of their own citizens.

In Prague and Brno the tanks really came out against the demonstrators. Deploying the army against defenseless citizens was the biggest deployment of the Czechoslovak army since the Second World War. Five demonstrators and one soldier were killed and dozens of people were seriously injured. In Bratislava, about 1,500 people gathered in Námestie SNP and in Šafárikovo Square. Advance units of the Public Security dispersed, but in the evening they reunited on

October Square and the Námestie SNP. At 10 p.m. the brutal intervention of the police imposed calm. One hundred and forty people were detained by public security. The events associated with the first anniversary of the occupation showed that Czechoslovak citizens, with the exception of a few larger cities had already been pacified by the pressure of normalization. Force celebrated victory. However, this "victory" was not enough for Husák. He needed to wash his hands of the taint of bloody reprisals. He was a lawyer, and he knew that the crackdown against the demonstrators had no support in law. Consequently he forced parliament to enact additional legalization for the August terror. On 21st August, the presidium of the ÚV KSČ without Dubček adopted bill 99 on "Some Transitional Measures Needed to Enhance and Protect Public Order." The proposal also included: "Whoever, after the this statutory measure comes into force, participates in an action of public disorder, whoever incites or encourages such action, whoever fails to obey a public official's protection of public order ... shall be punished, as long as it is not a criminal offense, with a custodial sentence of up to three months or a monetary penalty of CZK 5,000 or both." "Anyone who disrupts socialist social order ... may be dismissed from their position or may be immediately released from their employment ... a student may be excluded from the study under these circumstances..."

On the second day, the bill was approved by Černík's government, and on the same day, Dubček was quickly flown from Senec to Prague. Husák left a message for him to call the presidium of the Federal Assembly and approve the bill. Dubček insisted, however, that legal experts should first express an opinion on the proposal. He used procedural tactics, asking for a break to allow federal law experts to study the proposal. Husák understood Dubček's tactics and so came to the presidium of the Federal Assembly personally. It was in flat contradiction of parliamentary of procedure as Husák was not even a member of the Federal Assembly. As soon as he sat down, he began to shout at Dubček that if he did not approve the law, he would personally be responsible for further loss of life. He said there were crowds in the streets in Brno between cycle races and a football match and there were imminent bouts of civil disobedience. Tired and resigned Dubček gave in. He didn't vote for the law, but routinely signed it off as Chairman of the Federal Assembly. It was his most serious error of judgement, a failure due to the pressure of circumstances and his total isolation. The following day all the newspapers printed the so-called "Baton Act" with the signatures of Dubček, Svoboda and Černík. People understood the law as an obituary notice for the end of Prague Spring, with the signatures of those whose names were most closely connected with it. Many even refused to believe that Dubček, Svoboda and Černík had actually signed it. This signature weighed on Dubček to the end of his life.

CHAPTER 14

AGAIN RENEWED FOR ETERNITY

The normalized mass media attacked Dubček throughout August and September 1969. It was a clear preparation for his final removal. At the meeting of the UV KSČ on 26th September, a motion to dismiss Dubček as Chairman of the Federal Assembly and from the presidium of Communist Party was put. Despite the urging of Biľak and Svoboda to act reasonably, Dubček didn't engage in any self-criticism. On the contrary, he presented a fervent defence of the Prague Spring. He was formally recalled by the Federal Assembly as Chairman as was Smrkovský as Vice-President on 16th October. Instead of Dubček, Dalibor Hanes was chairman of the Slovak Federal Assembly. At the September session of the ÚV KSČ, Černík, hoping to save his skin, humiliatingly recanted his support for Prague Spring. He saved his position as Prime Minister for a quarter of a year. Černík's recantation of support of the Prague Spring launched an avalanche of dismissals. Immediately at the plenary session of the ÚV KSČ on 25th September, 1969 the declaration of the ÚV KSČ of 21st August 1968, which condemned the Soviet invasion, was revoked. Eighty reform members of the ÚV KSČ were excluded from this body. Husák officially reclassified the occupation to "international aid" and the reform process as "counter-revolution." This ÚV KSČ meeting witnessed the most tremendous treachery the politician could publicly commit. The first secretary of the Communist Party, Gustáv Husák, cancelled the letter sent on 18th July by the UV KSS from Bratislava to Prague, which clearly supported Dubček's reforms. He had been its co-author.

Subsequently, in the framework of "democratic centralization", thousands of lower party and state bodies and social organizations revoked their earlier protest resolutions against the Soviet occupation. But the worst was still to come. Mass Checks. The literary critic Alexander Matuška recalled that when he was asked by the chairman of the review committee how he accepted the entry of troops, he replied, "It wasn't all one to him." The chairman responded promptly with an order to his secretary order: "Comrade, write: he did not understand the entry of the troops." The checks were in many cases only a shadowy manoeuvre to settle personal accounts. After the initial screening, only two percent of party members were expelled, so Moscow increased its pressure. The presidium of the ÚV KSČ decided to repeat the reviews on 14th April 1970 on the basis of tighter criteria. 22 percent of party members were expelled, exactly 305,259 people, almost half of whom were members of the intelligensia. These people automatically lost their jobs and were forced into manual labour. Their children were banned from studying. Many people decided to leave Czechoslovakia. Emigration from the Czechoslovak Socialist Republic was more extensive than emigration after February 1948. It was estimated that one hundred to one hundred and ten thousand people left Czechoslovakia. On 1st April, 1970, the federal government restricted the travel of citizens to capitalist foreign countries and Yugoslavia. Owning a passport meant nothing; if a citizen did not get an exit visa from the security service, he could travel only to Hungary, Poland, Romania, Bulgaria and the German Democratic Republic.

By the Treaty of Friendship and Cooperation between the USSR and the Czechoslovak Socialist Republic signed on 7th May 1970 in Prague by Brezhnev and Kosygin, and by Husák and Štrougal for Czechoslovakia, fraternal friendship was again renewed for eternity. Eventually, it was for less than twenty years.

CHAPTER 15

ALEX, LET'S GET OUT OF HERE

After his recall First Secretary Dubček, forty-nine years old, was left without work, abandoned and betrayed. But he had to feed his family. His oldest son, Pavol, was studying medicine, the middle son, Peter was a first year student at the University of Economics in Bratislava, and the youngest, Milan, who had been called Mishko since childhood, was a first year at a secondary general school in Metodova Street. His wife had suffered a lot, after the year of her husband in the highest party position and the previous twenty years in the party apparatus her health had deteriorated. The media attacks on her husband and family had contributed most to her bad health.

After returning from Prague Dubček started to put things in order around the house, which he had not done since 1967. He cultivated the garden and with the help of two wine growers from the Rača district next to Bratislava, the Ivičič brothers, he put in roots of Iršay, Müller Thurgau and Rača Frankovka. He himself set up the supporting poles, strung the wire, and carefully fastened the shoots. At the back he built a rabbit hutch and a run for chickens. He repaired a neglected workshop in the cellar and went about the cultivation of his garden. The actor, Fero Dibarbora, who used to live in Urbánková, agreed with Anna Dubček that he let them have half of a cartload of manure which he had bought. And so the Dubčeks took several cubic metres of manure up the street by wheelbarrow.

The youngest, Mishko, sometimes played the piano, but he was more likely to play with Turo. Their favourite, Strelka, was no longer alive, so he and the new German Shepherd quickly made friends. Kynology was his hobby in Prague, where he went to train dogs in Stromovka, and he continued in Bratislava near Železná studnička. He trained Turo so well that the dog later became the main star of the film "Nero in Freedom". With the words "some crowns would help the Dubčeks," Katarína Lazarová spoke to director Spišek, to take Turo in the role of the wolf. It was well that the censor didn't know that Turo was the Dubčeks' dog.

The turbulent atmosphere in the family was marked by the death of Dubček's father, Štefan, on 31st May, 1969. On 4th June he had a funeral in the cemetery in Uhrovec. He rests there on the hillside with his son, Július.

In mid-October 1969, Dubček was summoned to Prague by Biľak. "You know what they say, each moment more, another tug at the saw," he smiled. "You offered me the foreign ministry last year, but I can't make the same offer as we have Marek already. I'm sorry that you didn't resign earlier as maybe it could have been managed. So I can only tell you the presidium's decision that you'll get a warm place. In Africa. Some of them wanted to send you to the equator, but I spoke up and we're only sending you to Ghana," Biľak grinned. "Do you have any objections?" He regarded the humiliated Dubček.

"I have the feeling you would like to send me to the North Pole, just so I'm as far away as possible." Bill"ak was silent. "No, thanks. I don't want to go to Africa or anywhere else! "

"I wouldn't be so choosy in your place."

"Don't worry, Vasil, I'll find work."

"You may wish for that," Biľak remarked, as the door closed behind him.

On his way home he thought about what was going to happen. He was out of work and outrageous newspaper attacks continued. When he came home, he found his wife, Anna, in tears.

"Ah, see what they wrote ..." She handed him one of the dailies lying on the table. Dubček took the newspaper and slowly began to read: "The right wing in the leadership of the party represented by Alexander Dubček totally paralyzed the work of the highest authorities of the party that ceased to perform its role as directing centre of Socialist construction. The anti-socialist forces and a number of their assistants from the ranks of revisionism and right-wing opportunism used Alexandre Dubček's non-conceptual and ideological hesitancy to promulgate a new political organization of society in which the Communist Party would not have a leading role. Alexander Dubček himself supported these forces by saying that the party should not lead society but serve it. This weakening of the leading role of the party has led to ..." Dubček threw down the newspaper in disgust.

"Biľak offered me the ambassador's job in Ghana."

"Where?"

"Ghana. In Africa, a bit above the equator. I refused it. "

"It would be good for me, even straight the equator than here. Alex, my nerves have gone ... It's getting worse. This nonsense and the lies they write about you ... and now about me ..."

"I'll write the letter to the presidium of the Central Committee. I'll protest against this mudslinging."

"It doesn't matter. They're aiming to disgust us. Maybe they're doing it just to get us out of here. So we'll be out of sight ... So people will forget about you ... Alex, I ... I'd go to the edge of the world ... Let's get out ... I want to have peace ... At least for some time while this dirty business lasts, out of this cruel world ... Alex ... "

"Anička, I understand you, but I'm afraid that the offer could be a trap. They'll just let us travel and stop us from coming back ... I can't imagine living in a foreign country ... And people would understand it as a cowardly escape ... "

"So many are leaving and no one thinks they're cowards," she said.

"No never! No one will ever make me leave the country where I was born ..." he looked at his wife. Tears ran down her face. "And then, you know ... I'm convinced that it will change ... that the decent people in this country have yet to speak. Lying and mischief-making can rule for a while, but not for a long time. It's against the laws of nature. Sooner or later it'll collapse. And I'm telling you that we'll be here! "

"I don't know if I will. I'm very tired. And my gallbladder hurts more and more. I don't know if it's just my gallbladder. "

"Don't be afraid, "we'll meet at Vlachovka again," he tried to calm her with his favourite sentence from a song. But she hardly heard him.

"Those who toasted me a few weeks ago now shun me. They're afraid to talk to me, afraid to be seen by the Secret police with me ... I have no one here ... And you? What are you going to do? What will we live on? The boys are studying, we have a couple of thousand crowns in both accounts ... If we didn't breed hens and rabbits, we wouldn't really survive..."

"Don't worry, if the worse comes to the worst, we can sell the cabin in Senec."

"No you mustn't sell it, it's our only refuge, the only place I still feel safe and ... free," she smiled bitterly. "Alex, let's get out. Please..."

CHAPTER 16

START OPERATION BUCCANEER

Dubček had the feeling that from that particular moment a listening device had been installed in his house. Husák must also have been informed about his conversation with his wife. Soon they called him back to Prague and offered him the ambassador's place in Turkey. When he announced this to his wife, she begged him to accept it. Ankara is relatively close, Turkey is a secular country with pleasant people. A small part is in Europe and at the same time it is far enough away so they could have a sacred peace at home from bad people. Without much enthusiasm, he accepted the offer.

The excommunication of Dubček from Czechoslovakia could begin. The chief of staff of the 1st department of Ministry of the Interior, Colonel Podzemný, drafted and submitted to the Minister of the Interior, Pelnář, a top secret instruction "Operation Buccaneer". It was stated in the order that in shortest possible time a cadre member of the 1st department of Ministry of Interior, Comrade Škácha, would be sent to Ankara in the official function of Counsellor to the Ambassador, technician Svoboda, who would conduct the installation of operative equipment in the building of the embassy and in the residence of the ambassador, Comrade Mašek officially as doorkeeper of the residence with a task to manage the operational equipment in the residence building and a cadre member of the 1st department of the Ministry of the Interior, a cipher clerk, Comrade Badalec. Our Soviet friends would be asked for cooperation and collaboration. The connection with the Soviet resident would be maintained by the resident Comrade Škácha. Chief officer of the 1st department of Ministry of Interior, Colonel Podzemný, would continuously inform Minister of the Interior Pelnář about the outcome of the operation and would then further inform the 1st secretary of the UV KSČ, Comrade Gustáv Husák. Pelnář signed the instruction, put it in the hands of his secretary and said laconically, "Start Operation Buccaneer."

Dubček completed formalities at the Federal Ministry of Foreign Affairs, which he joined on the 1st December. Pre-trip preparation began with an overview of some of the most important departments of the ministry. Of course the most thorough training was given on the Turkish department. He did an intensive course in English. The Turkish government had sent their "agrément" almost by return and so a deadline was set after the New year. Unlike First Secretary Husák, who did not follow custom and receive the new ambassador, President Ludvík Svoboda invited Dubček to dinner during which he handed him his credentials. It was a cold and sad evening. Dubček was glad to leave the castle palace.

On 26th January, 1970, he and his wife boarded a Czechoslovak Airlines' flight to Ankara. The boys had also received their passports with visas in January, but their parents didn't want to disrupt their studies so they stayed home. In the half-empty plane, passengers were seated, whose attendants had never seen the Ankara route before. When they spotted Dubček, they had tears of emotion. After the aircraft returned from Turkey, both of the airline attendants were dismissed. It was a Friday, which is a Muslim holy day. Nevertheless, crowds of people and 120 journalists were waiting at the airport for the Dubčeks. Police reinforcements were called up to keep order at the airport after the arrival of the popular Czechoslovak representative. They waited an hour in the reception lounge until the route to the city was free. In Ankara, the message was spread like a whirlwind that the hero of the Prague Spring had come.

Dubček rightly assumed that not only the five diplomats but also the technical staff were working for state security in Operation Buccaneer . Its main purpose was to push Dubček gradually into a decision to stay beyond the borders of Czechoslovakia and emigrate. Shortly after his arrival, a new diplomat arrived at the embassy, with only one task to watch Dubček at every turn. The new Ambassador at first did not understand why his subordinates watched him so clumsily and carelessly. After a while, however, it began to dawn on him. It was not about controlling Dubček at all, but about increasing his psychological disgust or even mental torture. His wife, Anna, realized with horror that her desire for room to breathe had not been fulfilled. On the contrary, a small embassy with frightened and hostile workers had a more depressing effect on her nervous system than if she were at home. The only one he trusted was his chauffeur, Majerský, whom he already knew from his former posting in Banská Bystrica. His occasional joy was fishing on the nearby Gölbasi Lake.

From the first reception of Dubček by President Cevdet Sunay, Turkish officials constantly tried to reach out to this popular figure and tried to make them as most comfortable as possible. Wherever they went, they met with spontaneous expressions of sympathy. Even a short break for petrol was always marked by handshakes from unknown citizens. In spite of all the efforts made by the host nation to make the Dubčeks more comfortable, their situation became worse. From the behaviour of some colleagues and especially headquarters in Prague, it was obvious that somebody had decided that they would try to drive them by all means possible into such a mental state that they would decide to emigrate. From the Ministry of Foreign Affairs, they even sent a special commission to Ankara to investigate an allegedly inappropriate situation at the embassy. The pressure on Dubček escalated. On 10th March, they announced the suspension of his membership in the Communist Party by a telegram from the international section in the ÚV KSČ. It was a blow for him and a disgrace he had not expected. He, who had entered the Communist Party at a time when they were persecuted and forbidden, was now harassed by people who then hadn't even heard of the party. Despite the deteriorating state of his health, he decided to resist the pressure. At the embassy, he publicly stated that no one would be forced to emigrate, although his ambassadorial colleagues told him that if it came to the worst, they promised to give him political asylum whether the US, Canadian, British, French, Australian or Swedish governments. It was clear to Dubček, what a huge disappointment it would be for Czechoslovak citizens if it could be said that he had made a cowardly escape. He was sorry for a wife who had suffered a lot of psychological distress. Everyday obstacles and administrative divisions of the Prague headquarters have gradually changed into bullying. He had learned from friends from Prague that Husák and his accomplices intended to prevent him from returning. The situation had intensified and reports of his planned excommunication had spread. He therefore decided to return home. He did not, of course, officially announce this and so told his headquarters that he needed to visit his sick mother for a few days in Bratislava.

So as not to arouse the slightest suspicion by taking his wife, he agreed with her that she would stay in Turkey and come to his home country after him. When Czechoslovak Airlines informed him three times that flights to Prague were fully booked, even though it had never happened before, it was clear that the plan to force him into exile was real. Dubček had to resort to a ruse. He continued to claim that he was waiting for a ticket to Prague, and at the same time he turned to a former colleague with whom he'd worked during the war at the Škoda works in Dubnica. He was the leader of an assembly line installing machinery in Ankara. He booked him a ticket on the Hungarian airline flight from Istanbul to Budapest. On 29th May, Dubček stole secretly from the embassy in the night, bought a train ticket to Istanbul, where he just arrived in time to catch the plane to Budapest. However, the Hungarian crew recognized him and reported a valuable passenger at Budapest airport. From there, information came to Kádár and from him to Husák. They briefly informed the new Czechoslovak ambassador in Hungary, František Dvorský, who arrived at Ferihegy airport at the last minute. Instructions resounded to drive Dubček at any price immediately to Prague. Dvorský, however, took Dubček to Bratislava, dropped him at the Mišíks and returned to Budapest. When Mrs. Brinzíkova looked at Dubček in the doorway, she clasped her hands in surprise and said "Šaňo, what are you doing here?"

"I'm going to Prague. On to the carpet."

"You look hungry, what can I do for you?"

"Bread and dripping with onion. I'm done with those oysters and salmon," he smiled bitterly.

"I'll make something hot."

"If you can, good bean soup. I'm going to Prague in the morning."

Dubček talked to his boys, with his loyal friend, Jožko Brinzík, who wouldn't be driving him to Ankara any longer. When they described the atmosphere in Czechoslovakia, his face became even more sombre. On the second day he continued his journey to Central Control and Review Commission of the Communist Party in Prague. There he was laconically informed that he had been expelled from the Communist Party. He was not allowed to return to Turkey and on 24th June he was dismissed as ambassador and was officially expelled from the Communist Party after two days.

The French writer Louis Aragon wrote to him, "Dear Comrade Dubček, they will be able to drive you out from everywhere, but they will never be able to expel you from my heart." Aragon.

CHAPTER 17

DUBČEK AGAINST DUBČEK

"Why was Alexander Dubček excluded from our ranks?" Husák justified his expulsion. "We all know that he was expelled because in a relatively short period of time at the head of the party, he brought it to a collapse that it hadn't known since 1945. He led our society, social organizations, trade unions and youth towards disintegration, our economy to such a wave of inflation, to such disorganization that we stood on the verge of an economic crash. And our international relations? He was breaking the bonds with the Soviet Union and the other allied states and Czechoslovakia remained isolated. If a driver has a collision on the road, he will lose his driving licence among other things. If the highest official brings misery to the party and millions of working people and the whole state - do we have to bow down to him? Should we honour him and not relieve him of responsibility and dismiss him from office? This is common sense! That's why Alexander Dubček was expelled from our party! "

However, redeeming his membership of the party was the last thing on Dubček's mind. His only concern was to get home a wife who was alone in a bad state of health in the unpropitious environment of an embassy whose officials had been persuaded that Dubček had escaped and they'd failed in their task of forcing him to emigrate. His wife was fortunate to be friends with a young Turkish woman who cared for her in the embassy residence and she must have provided information about the state of Dubček's family to the Turkish and world media. Husák played for a moment with the idea of holding Anna Dubček in Ankara as a hostage. Dubček, however, was determined to remain at home, so Anna eventually chose to go back on her own. The Ministry of Foreign Affairs did not respond to Dubček's request that one of his sons should go to his mother and help her pack her things. Before she left the residence for Ankara airport, The Turks poured water on the wheels of the car for Anna, which is traditionally a sign of wishing luck. The Dubčeks knew they would need it.

At home, they entered the most difficult and humiliating period of their lives. After his involuntary departure from the ministry Dubček started looking for a new job. At the beginning of October, Vačok, the secretary of the UV KSS invited him to discuss his job. He informed Dubček that the leadership of the party had decided to appoint him to the position of a senior counsel at the Research Institute for Pension Insurance. Dubček, however, feared that it was another trap - this work could be misused to accuse him of nationalism and subjectivism – and so he declined. Moreover, he was offended him that they had decided what he was going to do without his being aware of it. Finally, he decided to look for work himself. He looked at the listings in the classifieds and made a list of about twenty factories and workshops looking for lathe machinists, blacksmiths or welders. In view of the shortage of workers in these professions, he didn't expect any difficulties. But he was very much mistaken. He was not considered free to decide even to take on manual work as were nearly half a million people in a similar situation who'd been dismissed from the party during the purge.

At the end of October Dubček was called in by Lenárt, the first secretary of the UV KSS. His former classmate had finally fulfilled his dream; he'd become the most powerful man in Slovakia. He officially told Dubček that he had been expelled from the party and informed him that they were looking for a suitable job for him. He offered him a list of twelve jobs to choose from. Dubček did not choose a position with the highest salary, but the post of mechanical specialist in West Slovakia Forests. He assumed that in the course of securing spare parts he would be able to travel through the republic and meet people. For a long time nothing happened and their savings dwindled. Although at their height 75,000 crowns was remarkable in terms of the Czechoslovak situation, their savings didn't give them certainty, because they didn't know what would happen to him when he was working. His mother, Pavlína, who received a modest pension, also lived with them. After what happened to her son, she wrote a letter to her base organization, in which she returned her membership card and left the Communist Party.

Finally, Dubček was approached by the director of the West Slovak State Forests in Krasňany, Bratislava, where he joined as the head of the Technical Mechanical Department on 15th December, 1970. He was given a small office on the second floor. Although there were two tables between the two windows and a third on one side, no one was with him in the office. He was in charge of machine maintenance - from bulldozers and loaders to chainsaws and supply. His starting salary was set at 2,200 crowns, which was the average wage in industry at that time. By 1981, when he retired, his salary had risen to three thousand. The director of the company was Miroslav Hanák, with whom he was old friends. He accepted him very warmly. He was so warm that he was soon replaced by Ďuriš, a graduate of the Forestry University of Moscow. It was one of the many initiatives of repression that was meant to harass Dubček and his family as much as it could. Contrariwise, his colleagues were unusually friendly to him, although he initially shunned communication with them. He didn't want to get them into unpleasant situations as members of the ŠtB dogged his footsteps from the tram stop on Račianska Street to the end of Pekná road where the building of the company headquarters stood. People naturally had respect for until recently the first man in the state. Although alone he behaved in a kind and affable manner to everyone. The ice broke when two days after the celebration of the twenty-fifth anniversary of 25th February, 1948, they came to congratulate him on his name day. He brought his wine and his wife provided him with delicious cakes which from then on became very popular in the enterprise.

Occasionally, he went to a development and repair shop in Pezinok to make a part for his used Simca. He was afraid to put the car into service where a listening device might be installed. He was extremely skilled at manual work; after all he was trained machinist.

Dubček in overalls had been welding. He lifted his goggles, looked at the weld, blew on it and contentedly stated it was good. Beside him, a friend of his, Zdeno Pinkava, had a piece of iron in a vice on the workbench. He had been sitting on an old chair, smoking and reading the newspaper.

"How much do they pay you?" Dubček asked.

"For the ridiculous two thousand that they give us here, they should be glad I come to work at all. And those five saws can't be done in a day. Sometimes there are no chains or else no cogwheels, and then the contacts are missing. Why the hell do we buy Swedish saws when we don't have the spare parts?"

"If you read less, you could squeeze them in," Dubček chided him gently.

"Well, you should read these, too!"

"I read, but after work."

"Listen to what they write, "The US would like to see an accelerated stabilization in the ČSSR ..."

They, too, have shat on us," Pinkava commented the behaviour of the United States.

"The powerful will never hurt each other. Why are you reading the papers? "

"I have to know what I think! And I also have to be informed what wickedness you did against those bastards!! Uh oh, they're writing about you again." Dubček rubbed the cold weld with a file and listened with one ear to Pinkava who, after a moment put down the newspaper and slowly began to drill the holes into a lathe fixed in the vice.

"But being a worker has his advantages. They can't remove us from our shovels and vices. Yeah, you communists are right, there's no freer person than a worker"

"I'm no longer a Communist ... I'm not a member of the party."

"Did they throw you out?" Pinkava asked, surprised.

"It was in the newspapers and Lenárt told me personally."

"Oh, you have privileges! Comrade First Secretary in person! Congratulations! My son's expulsion from work was announced by Pišta Kubala. Pišta was the biggest waste of space in their faculty. Dead from the neck up, he worked as a dogsbody in the department. When the Russians arrived, he happened to be on vacation. When he returned, a re-evaluation began. He declared the occupation to be international aid and they made him party chairman. And now he's the tough guy in the cadre." Dubček concentrated on his welding. He wasn't in the mood for a debate about politics. He was a little afraid as he didn't know which of his colleagues he could trust and which not. His experience was that those who'd made the bravest speech were usually those who'd run to the director or a special body to give them information.

"Oh, everyone wants to live, people have children, they want to work and study what is left to them? Being a worker is certain. They will always need us. They can't even throw us out of work because there is nobody left below us. Who would do milling and welding for them?"

"Me, for example."

"You're different. We've always considered you normal. You were one of us. "

"And am I no longer?"

"I'll tell you something. When they told us you were going to come here, they trained the whole forestry works. Avoid conversation, restrict Dubček's contact only to necessary working contacts ... Our lords and masters have a fear of you. And before that, they glorified you," said Pinkava his head nodding. "Hell, in two days it's Christmas, and we have to return to a Trade Union meeting. In the enterprise the gossip is that they're going to screw you as you didn't vote in November. After the arrival of this new director it's no longer as it used to be. The old director was a great guy. He was your biggest fan in the works. This Ďuriš is new and ... what I know. Nobody knows him here. He was somewhere in the region as secretary for agriculture. After Husák's arrival he was fired. However, he was Šalgovič's friend, so they shoved him here. Before that he signed the instruction."

"And you signed it?"

"Um ... Everybody signed. We workers don't care one way or the other... You're just lucky that you're Dubček and they couldn't make you sign that you've always been against Dubček!" Pinkava snapped.

"But that's not bad. Dubček against Dubček would have suited them," he laughed bitterly.

"But everybody sympathizes with you. People like you and what's happening here is just a play we put on. You'll see, today at the meeting the workers will stand for you as one man. They can't take our shovels and saws," said Pinkava.

CHAPTER 18

HIS TERRIBLE GUILT

Ten days before Christmas in 1971, the enterprise headquarters tensely awaited the afternoon session of the Revolutionary Trade Union Movement. They knew what was going to happen. The only item on the programme was the exclusion of Alexander Dubček from social organizations. The face of Vladimir Ilyich Lenin on a poster on the left side of the stage was glum as were the faces of those present. For even the officials of the enterprise the afternoon session was an additional drudgery. However, a comrade from the organizational department of the city committee of the KSS had come. They'd sent him to supervise the correct course of the meeting.

A portrait of President Svoboda hung above the chair of the presiding board in the large conference room and the slogan: "With the Soviet Union for eternal time!"

The conference room was full, people fidgeted nervously on their chairs. In addition to the officials, there were many forestry technicians and maintenance workers. There was a table on the small stage, behind it five chairs. In the middle chair there was the director Ďuriš and to his left and right two senior officials. The director gestured for silence to those present.

"Comrades, the next point is to discuss some of the cadre measures against the Comrade Alexander Dubček, the head of the technical mechanical department of West Slovakia State forests," he began officially. It was felt that he wanted to have things over as soon as possible. "We will not go around this for long. After consultation with the higher party bodies, the leadership of our enterprise organizations of the Union of Czechoslovakia - Soviet Friendship, represented by its chairman, Comrade Lukáč," he turned to Lukáč, who acknowledged with a nod, "The Revolutionary Trade Union, represented by its chairman Comrade Kavčiak," he turned to Kavčiak, "The Union of Anti-Fascist Fighters, represented by its chairman Comrade Mikuláš," he turned to

Mikuláš, who also nodded, "and the Slovak Hunting Association, represented by its chairman Comrade Ignác," he turned to Ignác, "it is not possible for Alexander Dubček to continue to be a member of these organizations. Following Alexandre Dubček's previous expulsion from the Communist Party of Czechoslovakia, we have to take a position on his membership in these organizations as well. The behaviour of Comrade Dubček is not the responsible behaviour of a member of major social organizations." He looked through the crowd and found Dubček before turning abruptly towards him.

"Comrade Dubček is not only not involved in voluntary trade union activities, but has not fulfilled even his basic civil responsibility, such as participation in the election." Then the director threateningly raised his voice. "99.18 percent of the workers took part in the election of representatives of the Assembly, held on 26th and 27th November 1971, of which 99.9 percent cast their vote for the National Front candidate. It is the shame for our enterprise that the only one of our employees who did not participate in the election was Comrade Dubček. He even refused the electoral commission, who came in person with a ballot to his home. Comrade Dubček, can you tell us something about that?" There was a frozen silence in the room, which was broken by Dubček's calm voice.

"I don't know what rule I broke, but the Constitution of the Czechoslovak Socialist Republic does not force citizens to vote, but gives them the right to vote. And ... honestly, I do not have a great desire to vote for a party that constantly blames me for revisionism, opportunism, anti-Sovietism and hostility to working people. What kind of an enemy am I to you? "

"Indeed, Dubček is not an enemy, and he didn't vote because he'd just turned fifty and we were celebrating," Pinkava tried to relieve the tense atmosphere.

"Really, however, we were in a good mood at the elections and we were happy to vote!" some shouted. The chamber roared with laughter.

"We don't have the time to express our personal feelings. I have the written suggestions of the leadership of all four organizations recommending the exclusion of Comrade Dubček from these organizations. So as not to summon special meetings of each organization we've called all employees together at the same time. The individual chairmen will invite members of their organizations to vote. Are there any questions or suggestions? „There was a long silence, all eyes were fixed on the scuffed floor of the meeting. However, there was a daredevil. The Roma, Lakatoš.

"Why should Dubček leave the anti-fascist fighters? But he was actually in the uprising where he was wounded twice and his brother fell there. Mikuláš is the chairman of anti-fascist fighters and was never in the uprising!" Dubček stood leaning against the wall at the entrance and watched the cynical theatre. He'd become interested at Lakatoš's words which said exactly what he was seeing at that moment. There was noise in the hall. Mikuláš threw an angry look at Lakatoš, and then looked at Ďuriš, who hadn't expected that anyone would want to speak. The comrade from the city committee of the KSS volunteered a word.

"Sorry, comrade," he looked into the crowd for Lakatoš crowd. To make his situation easier, Lakatoš raised his hand. "What is your name?"

"Why are you asking me in this familiar way? I'm not a Communist," said Lakatoš.

The comrade from the city committee was bewildered. "Sorry."

"My name is Lakatoš. Alexander. Like Dubček," he said.

"It is not our task to investigate who was in the uprising and who was not. We must understand that the complex actions of Comrade Dubček and his activities since the January plenary have cancelled all his merits in the anti-fascist resistance. As Comrade Bil'ak said and let me quote him: "Many who cry today that they have been expelled and write letters begging that they have been misled and so on, can thank Dubček for that. His terrible guilt is that he has broken the lives of thousands of people. That is a sorrow for the people and we cannot forgive him." The comrade glanced at Lakatoš triumphantly.

"But what has the Anti-Fascist Resistance and the Hunting Association got to do with that?" the Roma, Lakatoš wasn't giving up. The situation was beginning to be unpleasant, the director noticed that the some people were gaining courage and nodding agreement with Lakatoš. He quickly gestured at Kavčiak to take the floor.

"Comrades, there was room for discussion at the public meetings of individual sections, we are now just engaged in the act of voting. So I give the floor to the chairman of the Revolutionary Trade Movement, Comrade Kavčiak." He nervously gulped his mineral water.

"Comrades, comrades," Kavčiak began in a trembling voice. "The presidium of the Consultative Committee of the Revolutionary Trade Union Movement in the enterprise directorate of West Slovakia State forests at its meeting on 16th December, 1971, proposed to exclude Alexander Dubček from its ranks. Since we are all members of the ROH, please vote. Those behind the motion for the resolution according to which Alexander Dubček is excluded from the ROH. Who is for?" The chairman's table lifted its hands and the remainder in the chamber followed slowly. He saw hands gradually rise. "Well thank you. Has anybody withheld their vote? „Kavčiak stared at the hall. "Pinkava. One, two, three ..." he counted the hands of the daredevil. "Seven have abstained. Is anyone against?" He looked into the chamber again with a severe look.

"Me. My name is Engineer Marendiak. "Ďuriš, Kavčiak and the other members of the tribunal looked at him with hatred. Similar condemnatory looks came at him from the chamber. A person most hates those who battle for what they would like to do but do not have the courage. Marendiak had found it. The only one. Dubček looked at him gratefully. So until today the thieves and murderers hadn't thrown out the last decent man from the ROH. Now they had thrown out a man whose father had founded unions in America.

"Is anyone else against? Nobody. Comrades, I note that Alexander Dubček has been excluded from the Revolutionary Trade Union Movement. Thank you ... I give the floor to the Comrade Director, "Kavčiak said with relief. This was perhaps the most shameful act of his life.

"I now give the floor to the Chairman of the Union of Anti-Fascist Fighters Comrade Mikuláš..." the chairman of the second organization called for Dubček's expulsion with an icy voice. Dubček was not in the mood for a four-fold execution, so he stood up and walked away with the walk of a ruined, totally humiliated man. No one had the courage to look him in the eye. People were silent and they were ashamed. He walked slowly through the hall. However, somebody applauded. Then a second, a third, until all gradually were standing and applauding. Many had tears in their eyes as did Alexander Dubček. The tears of fifteen million humiliated citizens of Czechoslovakia. The chairmen sat glum and embarrassed. Dubček left. His cashiering even went so far as to take away his hunting weapons and a hunting licence. From the rank of colonel-in-reserve, he was demoted to soldier.

CHAPTER 19

THE SILVER BIRCH OPERATION

Lessons from the development of the crisis in the party and in society after the XIII Congress of the KSČ inspired Moscow and Biľak to legalize the Soviet military occupation and condemn the democratic reforms. This pamphlet accepted by the supreme body of the Communist Party at the feast of Saint Nicholas (6th December) in 1970 became the definitive criterion for the existence of virtually every citizen of Czechoslovakia for the next twenty years. The "lesson" drawn perfectly falsified the modern history of Czechoslovakia. Dubček, Smrkovský, Kriegel, Špaček, Šimon and the other men of the Prague Spring were made right-wing opportunists by Biľak and, contrariwise, the representatives of the "healthy core" of the party were created from the pro-Moscow group of Biľak, Kolder, Švestka, Kapek and others.

The Prague Spring and socialism with a human face were definitely taken off the table, and those who led them became the biggest outcasts of society. Not only Dubček and his closest allies, but thousands of people had to leave their workplaces and they were gradually put on the lists of people who were under permanent control of the security authorities.

It became a period of permanent police control and psychological terror.

The ŠtB developed a "Silver Birch" campaign where Dubček was watched every step of the way as well as his wife, sons and mother. His mother, Pavlína, didn't survive the psychological pressure and died in 1971. In front of their house on Mišíkova Street, there was a permanent state security car and opposite in a wooden shack on disused land, the "eštébáci" (ŠtB men and women) placed an observer. He was in a hah-ha on the pavement opposite to young female members of the ŠtB playing at being Mummy in front of the Šimkos' house. When the Dubčeks watched them it looked as if they were walking their babies. Anna Dubček had the impulse to go downstairs and peer in the strollers, to whether there were real babies, a new generation of secret policemen, or just dummies. Two plainclothes ŠtB officers stood almost constantly in front of the entrance to the Dubčeks' house, but it happened that uniformed cops also patrolled.

The Dubčeks themselves discouraged those who just wanted to squeeze their right hand from contacting them so they wouldn't get into the clutches of state security. Only their oldest friends, mostly people who were in a similar situation to them and without Dubček's contribution at the margins of society, came to see them. The Television announcer, Dana Hermannová, the sculptor, Teodor Baník, the brothers Anton and Laco Ťažkí, his former chauffeur, Jožko Brinzík with his wife Vlasta, Hvězdoň Kočtúch and Viktor Pavlenda. Occasionally Jiří Hájek, Oldřich Jaroš or Václav Slavík stopped by from Prague. Pavol Breier, the actress, Mária Kráľovičová or the famous cardiologist, Professor Šiška also came, but all too rarely. That's why every ring at the door was somewhat unusual. Then, after the bell had rung, Anna would sneak to the curtain and twitch it aside to see the daredevil who had decided to see them. She noticed a family friend, the electrician Ondrej, in front of the gate being checked by the cops.

"It seems as if Ondrej has some problems ... He's never been checked for so long," she watched the scene on the street. Dubček stood next to her and they watched the scene together.

"They've also got a new car ... Up until now they have been alternating Škodas and Fiats ... Wait," he went to a drawer and pulled out a piece of paper on which was carefully inscribed all the licence numbers of the cars that alternated their supervision. "BAD 9381, BAD 9415, but this Saab 8425 hasn't been here so far ..." he nodded his head wondering. When Ivan had been checked, they let him go.

"Welcome ... Why so much detail today ...?" Dubček was interested.

"What ...? You did call that you have a problem with the television," said Ondrej taking off his shoes inside the front door.

"Well, you're an electrician."

"Quite so. Since when have you had the new television?"

"A month."

"Shortly before that, we pulled a bug out of your butane lighter ... Let's see the bugger," he said as he approached the TV and began to dismantle it. Dubček was looking through the curtain outside. "It seems a bit odd to me. For about two weeks, their car hasn't been standing right in front of the house and there's no sight of anyone, but every time someone rings, they're right at the gate!"

"Oh ... so here there she is, beautiful ... a lovely bug," Ondrej drew out of the television a part that did not belong.

"So they're also listening to us?" a shocked Anna asked.

"Where do you think you live?" Ondrej studied them. He walked over to the phone, picked it up and tapped it. He smiled, quickly taking off the bakelite cover and examining the coloured wires.

"Clear," he said to Peter, who was watching the whole scene gloomily. "Go and ring the bell ..."

"Ring the bell?"

"Sure, as if by mistake. Take out the rubbish just in case and bang the door shut. Then ring and see how they come!" Peter took the rubbish and went out. All three watched him from behind the curtains. As soon as he rang, there were two civilians at the entrance. When they saw that it was Dubček's son, they returned pissed off to a car that wasn't visible from behind the house. Peter came back.

"It's clear. The bell is connected to the phone and it immediately signals that someone has come ..." Ondrej said laconically. "Mrs Anka, when the next thing goes wrong, don't call the repairman. I'd be happy to come," Ondrej smiled.

One day, Anka Dubček banged herself under her right ribcage. She began to swell up and made it difficult for her to swallow. Her husband came quickly and considerately laid her out on the sofa. Her gallbladder attacks were happening more and more often. Dubček handed his wife Cholagol. When, after a while, it hadn't done any good and his wife abruptly threw up, Dubček said briskly, "Peter, get Mummy's coat, we're going to emergency ..."

As soon as Dubček's white Simca was on the streets of Bratislava, an ŠtB vehicle attached itself to them.

"Dirty bastards, they're harassing us even now," said Peter, sitting behind the wheel.

Dubček knew the faces of his persecutors by heart. He estimated that about forty men and women had been assigned to watch his family. The worst was at night. The starting up of patrol cars changing went on the whole time. Not only the Dubčeks, but the neighbors slept badly. When tossing and turning in bed didn't bring on a longed for sleep Dubček would take his German Shepherd, Turo, who'd been given to him by guards on the East German border, and go for a walk beneath the hill, Slavín. Once in December when the north wind was whistling in the street as he walked past a car with the familiar sign of the ŠtB, he knocked on the window.

"Isn't it too cold for you to turn on the engine so rarely?" A young man was sitting in the car. Dubček was surprised as there were always two. The other probably wasn't enjoying it anymore and had gone to see a girl.

"It is."

"If you want, I'll bring you tea with some rum in a thermos."

"Thank you, we can stand it and we've got tea with rum," he thanked him and couldn't come out of the shock that the persecuted wanted to make things more pleasant for the persecutors.

"Mr. Dubček, I wanted to tell you that you have a bug in your phone," he said rapidly, seeing that his colleague who'd taken a few steps to relieve himself was returning.

The ŠtBs were everywhere he went. There were two secret policemen on the tram going to and from work. There was a third in a car behind the tram. People, of course, recognized Dubček in the tramcar and at the stop showed their sympathy. So as not to get them into an unpleasant situation, he'd indicate that he was being watched, but people heed what he'd said. Several of those who spoke to him were identified and called for interrogation after leaving the tram. Dubček didn't want the people to be uncomfortable because of him, and so he closed himself off even more. And it was just what the security intended: to isolate his family from the public and create a wall of fear and stress around them. The situation became embarrassing even for the ŠtBs themselves. Once Dubček approached one of them and asked, "As there are two of you always watching in the tram and another in a car, wouldn't it be more economical if you just took me to work?"

"It would be against regulations." They were with him everywhere. Even at the maternity hospital when Dubček's grandchildren were born. They were interfered with and intimidated at every step. Paľo's highly pregnant wife was walking on the pavement sidewalk and beside her an ŠtB car followed her step by step. She looked back, made a misstep and fell. There were guffaws in the car of the pursuers. When Paľo was returning from the weekly shop at Gunduličova street with Peter, they noticed a young man and woman sitting in the car with the familiar number plate in front of their house. "What are you just sitting there for? At least have a kiss, the time'll go quicker for you!" He exclaimed. The man sitting behind the steering wheel angrily pulled up the window.

Dubček cultivated apples, peaches and grapes. Once he saw his neighbour Šimkova as she was cutting a tree and came up to her fence and grumbled, "Mrs Šimkova, you're cutting it badly, you'll destroy the whole crop."

"Then show me," she invited him into the garden. Dubček cut it all instead of a demonstration. And indeed, her harvest was great.

Occasionally, one of the hens went to the neighboring garden of the Ilčíks who lived above them. There was no fence between their gardens, so the hens were happy to gobble up the Ilčíks' caterpillars. The reward for Peter Ilčík was an occasional egg with a beautiful yolk, personally donated by Mrs Dubček.

They watched him at the chalet in Senec where he spent a lot of time. There were some colleagues and friends who came to see him. Most often Václav Slavík and Zdeněk Mlynář came from Prague. Once he and Mlynář took a boat on the lake to have peace from the ever-present ŠtB. Those didn't waste time bringing a boat into their immediate vicinity. Dubček and Mlynář had much on their minds and so the cops were nervous. One of them couldn't contain himself shouted, "How long do you want to stay?"

"Definitely longer than you," Dubček called back.

CHAPTER 20

A GAME OF LOVE AND DEATH

Mrs Švendová in the grocery shop in Vlčkova Street below Slavín had an impeccable white scarf. The small shop was as much a place of exchange of information as a shopping centre. Behind the counter were shelves with basic groceries. For bigger purchases people from the area went to Palisády or to Gunduličova. The house was known to have been where the family of the writer Katarína Lazarová lived with her sons Boris and Roman and the actress Viera Bálintová. When little Miško Dubček, after moving to the house in Mišíkova street for the first time, began to hear the familiar voice of Auntie Viera, who almost every day read a fairy tale for children on Slovak radio, he thought he was in a fairytale itself. Auntie Viera, however, stood in a queue and debated jointly with Mrs. Šimková, the mother of a later politician, Ivan, who lived a short way off. Later, when Miško grew up, he and Lazar boys went to the dog-training ground with Turo.

The shop was patronized by people who made up a special sample mixed with long-standing residents, actors, writers, politicians, and senior state and party officials. The Quarter under Bratislava Slavín was, on the one hand, the seat of long-standing residents and art studios, as well as the successful, wealthy, powerful and citizens who were the protégés of power. Even during times when Slavín itself, the place of last rest for Soviet soldiers, did not exist. The inhabitants of the blocks of flats from Štrkovec to Petržalka looked with envy at the proud family houses between Palisády and Slavín.

311

The busiest days in Mrs. Švendova's shop were Thursdays. It was a day of ordering. The shop served the needs of people living in his neighborhood, the foreigner only lost his way if he got tangled in the criss-crossing streets below Slavín. As Alexander Dubček was in disgrace the ŠtB members, who guarded him in his nearby house in Mišíkova street occasionally visited it. Even ŠtBs get hungry. On Thursday householders ordered bread, whipped cream and milk for Saturday and Sunday. The shop was small and it did not have storage facilities. Thursday, 1st October, 1973 wasn't a random ordering day. The store was unusually busy. Alexander Dubček came at about eleven to buy and order bread. He rarely came there as usually his wife or sons came. Mrs. Švendová was pleased, on the one hand, to see Dubček in the queue and she had not seen him for a long time, but on the other hand she was nervous as it was clear that after Dubček a few strangers would appear in the shop about whom everyone knew. Dubček had just returned from a hearing at the ŠtB, where he'd been summoned in connection with the premiere of Cikker's opera "The Game of Love and Death". After the World Premiere in early September in Munich, the Slovak premiere took place at the end of the month in the opera house of the Slovak National Theatre with the participation of top party and government officials. Ján Cikker wrote the opera on the subject of Romain Rolland and Branislav Križka directed it with the musical coordination of Zdeněk Košler. Cikker's drama described the suffocating atmosphere of the Jacobin dictatorship, talking about Robespierre's crimes, the cowardice of politicians, the absence of morality in politics, and the revolution that devoured its children. The libretto so much resembled the fate of Alexander Dubček that it was difficult for the maestro Cikker to explain to ŠtB's staff that he was not inspired by Dubček's fate. Their suspicion was compounded by the fact that during the premiere an unprecedented event occurred. Shortly before the start of the show, the audience found that Alexander Dubček sitting in the tenth row. There was unusual consternation among the high party and state officials present. Dubček, of course, could not be shown out of the chamber.

The strictly secret theme of Dubček's visit to the premiere was the most discussed topic in Mrs. Švendova's store. The actors Karol Machata and Maria Kráľovičová spoke intimately about the visit to the theatre of investigators, as did the football coach, Jim Šťastný, the writer, Vlado Mináč, the poet, Štefan Žáry and the young actors, Milan Kňažko and Fero Kovář, but also the older Karol Machata, all of whom were constant customers of the small shop. Ján Husák, son of the most powerful man of the country, Gustáv Husák, also used to shop there. Whenever he went there people were silent. Although Ján Husák gave the impression of being a decent man, he often smelt of alcohol and as with any drunk one never knew what he would blurt out. The shopkeepers knew that Alexander Dubček had been taken to the theatre by a distant relative, Emil Orlík, who worked at the College of Performing Arts.

When, a few days later, a group of Slovak theatricals went to visit Moscow, a writer in Moscow's writer's club Slava Dangulov, asked Križka, what he had been directing recently.

"Cikker's Game of Love and Death."

"Is that the opera that Mr. Dubček was in, too?" Dangulov secretively smiled.

CHAPTER 21

HOW MUCH DO I OWE?

In time Dubček gained a new colleague in his office, Jožko Križanovič, twenty-five years younger. It turned out he knew Adela, the sister of the Carpathian wolf, Karol Ivičic and his brothers Vojto, Albert, Rudo and Ivan, to whom Dubček sometimes went in Rača with his friend, Robert Harenčár. He was a member of a wine-making family and so they had a common interest. On Jozef's name day Dubček congratulated him with his excellent Irsay after working hours. He brought several litre bottles. Their colleague liked the wine so much that they even sang. It turned out that the former first man in the country was a normal person, one of them. He liked wine, but wasn't averse to a good beer or home-made slivovica (plum brandy). With his colleagues, he occasionally patronized his favorite inn in the old town on the corner of Hejdukova and Mariánska streets or went to the private beer cellar of Vojto Ivičic in Rača between two churches.

He was always willing to help, with everyone he'd had a friendly word with, and with those that he knew had sneaked on him. With a bunch of co-workers, he went to help on a building for a colleague, Greppelova, on Koliba. His building skills were renowned. When the first snow fell, the secret police, who wouldn't let him out of their sight even on the scaffolding, were stamping their feet in the street to get warm. Dubček called out them with a trowel in his hand to come and help. "It'll make you warmer, we'll finish soon and we'll go into the warm!" The men on the scaffolding laughed, the secret police peevishly smoked.

The employees of the enterprise directorate went to lunch at a nearby printing plant. Dubček would bring food from his home. Occasionally, for elevenses he had bread and dripping with onion that smelt all down the corridor. "I hope you do not mind, I spread the smell to Gunár a little bit," he smiled at Jožko, looking significantly at the portrait of the president. However, the onion smell was drowned by the heady scent of the flowers that filled all the free shelves in the small office. Dubček loved flowers.

The building of Duchonka, a forestry plant in Topoľčany, was surrounded by a farm courtyard covered in snow. It was before Christmas in 1973. Men in forestry uniforms were coming downstairs. Training had just ended. One of them was Dubček.

"Let's say cheers to Bratislava, but I guess before the journey might sample our Frankovka here ..." the field leader invited the group into the wine cellar. Dubček was the last one when suddenly the sound of a blacksmith's hammer began to clang in the courtyard. While the others went into the cellar, he went towards the sound. He came to a blacksmith's workshop, where a powerfully-built blacksmith bent over the fire. Dubček stood behind him, watching the man silently.

"Hello," he said after a moment. The blacksmith didn't hear him, Dubček went closer. "How's it going?"

"Oh, good ... Just as the newspapers say ..." the blacksmith's mouth stayed open. "You're Dubček! Goddamn it, it's a visit! We knew you were here, but they told us not to show up outside for no reason ..." he took Dubček's hand.

"You don't have anything in the fire. I'd like to give you a hand and try to see if I've still got it ..."

"And could you?"

"I don't know, but when I was in the Škoda works I knew how to. I was originally a machinist, but I did some years in the blacksmith's, too. If you have nothing against it, I'd like to make a horseshoe. For luck, for my cabin."

"Why would you do it? There in the pile there are plenty of old ones. If you want a new one, then take it, they're there according to numbers," said the delighted blacksmith.

"I don't want those, they're ready-made, they must have put these together with screws and I'd like to have traditional horseshoe made out of one piece." The blacksmith nodded his head in agreement, chose a suitable piece of old iron from the pile, weighed it, assessed whether it would be suitable. Then he switched on the motor, threw on some coal and put the piece into the white-hot fire.

"How are we going to do this?"

"You're the master blacksmith and I'm the apprentice, a smith's-assistant," joked Dubček.

"Then put on the apron and take this heavy hammer!" the blacksmith ordered. Dubček stripped off his jacket, pulled on smith's apron, took the hammer and started beating the iron that the blacksmith held for him and who picked up the iron after a moment with a nod of appreciation." I noticed at once that you know what you're doing from the way you stood at the anvil and the way you held the hammer." Dubček beat some more with drops of sweat on his brow. After a while the horseshoe was ready. The blacksmith put it in the water, hardened it and gazed at it. Then he handed it to Dubček.

"What do I owe you?" Dubček asked. The blacksmith was puzzled.

"Hmph ... We owe you ... All of us who keep our mouths shut and are afraid ... Excuse me ... Could you do one for me too?" Dubček looked at him with affection. He nodded. "I'll have Dubček's horseshoe for luck ..."

"On the contrary, I have a horseshoe for luck from you!" he thought and added, "Don't worry, it'll surely bring us luck. I believe it. Our luck will return!"

CHAPTER 22

PRESIDENTIAL SILENCE

On 14th January, 1974, Dubček's closest associate and friend died, his great supporter, Josef Smrkovský. Husák's normalization regime did everything to prevent the public from learning this sad event. A telegram about the death and burial site that his family sent to Dubček was kept back and he only got it a day after the funeral on 18th January. The place and time of burial was to be kept secret. The funeral ceremony in the main crematorium in Prague's Strašnice was forbidden and the family received a directive for 18th January, five in the afternoon at the crematorium in Motol. The Prague Spring tribune's death report, however, had spread through Prague and, despite the strictest police checks and obstructions, one thousand five hundred people arrived with Josef Smrkovský. To say their farewells everyone had to go through a squad of police who humiliated and photographed them in front of the crematorium. Dubček had only sent a short telegram to Smrkovský's widow and on the following day he wrote a comprehensive letter published by the Italian weekly Giorni - Vie nuove. Le Monde and the New York Herald Tribune also took extracts from the letter. Husák was furious. So that the grave did not become a place of unwelcome political demonstration state security banned the widow, Katrin Smrkovská from carving her husband's name on a parental burial plot, where she had placed the urn with the ashes of her husband after three days. In March, she was given a shocking message - the urn with her husband's ashes had been dug up and stolen. The grieving widow was satisfied with the information that the urn had been found at the railway station in České Velenice, but the culprit was not caught. The funeral director, on the basis of a security service order, refused to give back the urn reasoning that it was evidence in a crime. At the same time, he informed her that there was a ban on the burial of the Smrkovský urn anywhere in Prague and can only be given to her if she kept it at home or placed it in a cemetery at his birthplace in Velenka. Crushed Katrina Smrkovská decided to turn to the President of the Republic Ludvík Svoboda for help. "It is clear from the current legislation that it is not possible to deny me and my family the right to bury the urn according to our wishes. It is unheard of to forbid burying the urn in Prague and determining where it should be placed. I hope that my family will be guaranteed this right, and this whole shameful affair will soon be over." Katrin Smrkovská never received an answer from the ailing president.

CHAPTER 23

A GARDIST IN THE ŠtB

In August 1974 the celebrations of the 30th anniversary of the Slovak National Uprising took place in Banská Bystrica. The highest party and state officials gathered on the podium. Most of them had nothing to do with the uprising. Those who'd actually fought in the uprising stood below the tribune or were not in Banská Bystrica at all. Among those who missed the celebration was Alexander Dubček. He and his wife were at their chalet in Senec. The sun was already dipping under the horizon and the marauding mosquitoes, which had tormented him as he sheeted the stairs, were also departing. It was Thursday and on Sunday his sons and friends would lay the concrete footings for a small pier to launch a discarded dinghy, which his friends from the Slovan yacht club in Bratislava had promised him. Dubček had been sheeting the stairs with planks and sweat was pouring from him. He drank beer and was looking forward to the grilled sausages that his wife had turned over. In the frenzy of work he hadn't noticed a group of men and women who were approaching the hut.

"It must be here ..."

"But it's not him."

"No, it's Dubček," cried the man and with his arms raised wide, he ran to Dubček's chalet. "Hello, Šaňo ... Hello ... Don't you need help?" Dubček paused and stared at the twenty guys and the three women standing nearby by, holding cases for musical instruments in their hands. At the same time he glanced at the lake, where two ŠtBs squatted in a vessel and watched the situation with binoculars as if they were demonstrating to all that Dubček was under their control. Another pair watched the scene with surprise from behind a window of a Škoda car close by. When Dubček realised that this was a surprise even for his guards he approached the unknown arrivals.

"Indeed I'd need some."

"We'll help you with that," said one of the Czechs with a strong Ostrava accent.

"Šaňo, don't you recognize me?" the man who'd brought the whole group approached Dubček.

"For God's sake, you're Ernest Stanovský ..." Dubček's voice trembled slightly. The two grown men fell into each other's arms. The secret policemen behind the fences watched him dully.

"You're still alive!"

"I'm still alive..."

"We haven't seen you for a whole age! You didn't tell me, I thought you'd ... fallen ... sorry ..." Dubček was crestfallen.

"Me? Only on my head ... But I'll tell you all," he said, staring at his old wartime friend.

"Come on ... there's plenty of space ..." Dubček called out to the arrivals who gradually filled the small lawn. "What are you doing here?"

"We came to play for you. We're returning from Banská Bystrica. Today is the thirtieth anniversary of the uprising," said Stanovský.

"You see, I almost forgot, you know, work up to here ..."

"Why aren't you celebrating?"

"No one invited me. I wanted to go home to Jankov Vŕšok, but over there," he jerked his head towards the cars of the secret police," they advised me to be at home today."

"You see, I told you they'd banned him," said Stanovský to his friends. "They banned me too."

"Hanka, come and see who's come. Some socialist work squad," Dubček laughed. "Look this one, you remember him ..." he enthusiastically drew Stanovský to his wife, who was turning sausages behind the cabin.

"Ernest ... Is that you?" She looked disbelievingly at the arrival until she recognized him. Then they embraced. The last time they had seen him was in his native Selce at a dance also during the time of the wartime Slovak state. His hair was thinner and what he had left was silvery. His eyes, however, flashed with his unmistakable humour.

"I have a speciality from Myjava," he pulled out two bottles of slivovica and poured it into a variety of tassies. Although they were accustomed to numerous visits, they didn't have enough glasses for a dram, so they had to borrow some more. "You must be hungry. Anka, put these sausages on the grill," he said, not taking his eyes off Stanovský who introduced his friends one by one. They were obviously moved and surprised. Some apologized for the intrusion, but they felt they were honoured to be in the company of a home that was not even expecting them, but all at once had ten bottles of Moravian slivovica on the table. He stared at the bottles. "Ours from Haná," Stanovský explained.

"This is a surprise," Dubček didn't know what to make of the unexpected visit. "But it's clear to you that they already have you all under supervision ..." He glanced toward the plainclothesmen from the ŠtB looking into Dubček's garden along with curious neighbours and holidaymakers.

"Šaňo, for us everything's in the shit. We're miners and we can't take our shovels and hack away," said Stanovský.

"Where are you working?"

"The cooperative in Hošťany near Ostrava. I got married there ... It's a long story ... Oh, Šaňo, if wasn't for you, then they'd've taken me in the Škoda works. God, I wouldn't be still around ... From your taking office in January, Sixty-Eight, I worked like a madman ... We did everything for you and the new politics," said Stanovský with a faint Ostrava accent.

"Why didn't you get in touch with me?"

"I didn't want to intrude, but I followed your every step. I thought that you had a lot to do and that after the fourteenth congress I would come and see you. I didn't want you to think then that I was coming to beg for a position. I bet there were many like that. Well then there was no congress but the invasion ... Well, as I insisted that it was an invasion and not fraternal assistance, I was thrown out of the Brno Academy of Music and came to the cooperative in Hošťany ... But it's fine there ... I'm content ..." Stanovský said slowly.

"But you are a top trumpeter," Dubček remembered. "I'll never forget how you played in Selce at that time."

"Oh my God, it's not true anymore ..." he remembered. "But I've put together a top band. Our miners' top band," he called out to his lads. "Boys, let's play something here for our Šaňo ... So let's move it, move it ..." he began to organize the musicians. He stood up alone and took out his trumpet from its case. The twenty-man band was lined up and before the wondering gaze of the ŠtBs and the neighbours they were ready to play. "And I already know which ... So, lads ..." Stanovský nodded to the band. "Dear God, how it hurts." The singer of the band sang and Dubček listened at first, but then he started to sing quietly. His voice gradually strengthened, the musicians muffled a little and Dubček sang alone in a vibrant, high voice as if he were not present. People watched him and the secret police gazed not knowing what to do. Gradually they joined and the song became a chorale, a beautiful, sad song floating above the lake. There was a sense of sadness, yet defiance. Everyone felt the unique atmosphere of that moment. "Lord God, how it hurts when youth is squandered, over the world's wide field, for bread he's wandered. All have gone from his side, a drifting life without haven, flocks of hawks changed to solitary ravens..." When they had finished singing, there was a moment of dignified silence, the lads took more plum brandy and continued with a nimbler song: "Trenčín Dolinečka, Camaradas don't leave me, To the black hills of Balog or gendarmes from Detva". Dubček once again sang, but this time he went over to his wife and took her to dance as though they were young.

"As it was in Selce," exclaimed Stanovský and blew on his trumpet. In the garden they were cautious at the beginning, but some of the curious holidaymakers saw the master of the house, beckoning and the gradually joined in. They created a circle around the dancing Dubčeks and applauded them.

The ŠtB men were nervous. They saw that people were starting to assemble and looked at each helplessly. One of them called their commander. He had to shout, for the band and singing people drowned him out. He shouted loudest into the radio just as the group paused, "Emil here, Emil here. Citizens are assembling at Dubček's, there is a music band and they seem to be organizing something ... Yes, Comrade Colonel, we'll wait for you. We won't intervene." He then turned to his colleagues. "The boss will be here in a moment." People started laughing aloud. The ŠtB's officer hadn't realized that they'd all heard him. Angrily he shifted off and nervously lit a cigarette.

After a moment brakes squealed and a pale blue Zhiguli stood on the road above the cabin. Colonel Kulifaj was sitting in the rear on the right. He wound down the window, but didn't get out of the car. There were two more Zighulis behind it, from which eight uniformed VB (Verejná bezpečnosť) members jumped. Kulifaj saw what was happening, summoned one of the secret men, and said something to him. This one nodded, hurried up to his side, instructed one of the uniforms and they arrogantly forced their way into Dubček's garden. They began to insist that people disperse. It was evident that the police felt that the whole situation was awkward for them. People left out of fear, but the musicians, Dubček and his wife sat down calmly and ate sausage.

"You don't have permission to enter private ground," he shouted sharply at them, as they silently pushed people out of the garden. "These are my guests, leave my land immediately!" Dubček stood and protected one of the neighbours against a policeman making him leave. But people were afraid and left. The musicians stopped playing and watched the situation until Stanovský gave a wicked wink and they stood up and began to play the Czechoslovak national anthem.

"That's provocation ... That's not good behaviour, Mr. Dubček!" squawked their commanding officer.

"We're celebrating the 30th anniversary of the Slovak National Uprising. And you're interrupting the national anthem!" said Dubček standing to attention with the others. The surrounding people lost themselves in their cabins. For a while the members of the police force hesitated over the national anthem, but their commanding officer told them to break up the musicians.

"You're disturbing public order!" the police justified their intervention.

"I want to talk to your commander!" demanded Dubček.

"I am the commander!"

"With your superior!" Dubček glanced at the nearby Zhiguli. At that moment, their eyes met. Kulifaj was taken aback for a moment, but he wound up the window and his car abruptly left. Stanovský was standing next to him and also recognized Kulifaj.

"He was quite familiar to me," he said trying to guess where he'd seen that man.

"Kulifaj, the gardista," Dubček said shortly.

"The Gardista from the Uprising is in the ŠtB?" Stanovsky shook his head disbelievingly. Dubček nodded, looking for a long time at the departing car. The music was over. The musicians were collecting their instruments and putting them back in their cases. The police went. The last of them out of nowhere considerately handed Dubček his yachting cap that had fallen to the ground in the commotion.

"Excuse me ..." he said shamefacedly. The mood was no longer there. Ernest Stanovský said "So we'll go. We're glad we saw you alive and healthy. That's what we wanted to know and we'll talk about it at home". The musicians stood with their packed instruments and smiled apologetically. Mrs. Dubček noticed that they had virtually demolished the flowerbed with chrysanthemums. "Excuse me," exclaimed one of the musicians. "But we wanted to have something to remember you by. But we promise to bring you some cuttings in the future. We've cultivated a new variety of rose. We've called it Dubček."

CHAPTER 24

HUSÁK HANGS OVER ME

The harassment of Dubček and his family continued. He decided to write a protest letter to the presidium of the Federal Assembly and the Slovak National Council. The long, twenty-four page letter, which he sent on the anniversary of the Republic's establishment on 28th October, 1974, was a break in Dubček's approach to the leadership of the Communist Party. This letter stood in clear opposition to the regime. He described not only the specific cases of his monitoring and restriction by members of the secret security services, but also made an extensive analysis of the situation in society. He was one of the first to warn of human rights violations in Czechoslovakia before the Helsinki Conference on Security and Cooperation in Europe in August 1975. "In the totalitarian system, there is a free scope of activity for the abuse of power and position in the organisations of the armed forces and, in particular, of the Ministry of the Interior, powerfully supreme in all matters. Their "web" spreads over the courts and the judiciary, which have long since lost their true face and mission. The courts are in the hands of the authorities of the Ministry of the Interior and are totally dependent on them ... Certain components of State Security are abused for illegal activities and in state security itself there are forces and tendencies seeking power and control of political and public life ... They organize informers not only at my workplace in the state forests but in the whole of society ... Indifference has taken root between people, an atmosphere of underhand tale-telling, suspicion and fear, hypocrisy ... The entry of troops of the Warsaw Pact into Czechoslovakia was an insult and a disgrace, a moral and ideological humiliation of our nations ..... I express my disapproval of the "Briefing" and I accuse the current leadership of moral violence ... It doesn't even need a comment that perhaps the President of the Republic, too, has the habit of putting a transistor radio in the window during various discussions ... "

Milan wasn't accepted at university after matriculation, so he began to study the superstructure at the Secondary School of Economics, where they had a typewriting course. He liked to write and wrote well, but his father wrote much and to many people. Protest letters went to the Central Committee in Prague, the Slovak National Council or abroad. Milan sometimes grumbled and so some letters with over six and seven copies were transcribed by Alenka Orlíková. Dubček carefully signed each side so that the letters could not be misused. The father did not ask his son to recheck the letters, so they were sent with grammatical errors and typos. The letters were taken to Prague by Milan. He would come home early from work, go unobtrusively over the back fence so the secret police wouldn't notice him, travelled by the afternoon train to Prague, handed over the letter, returned on the night express and in the morning he would act at work as though he had slept well.

Husák, who was one of the most intelligent and acute but also the most ambitious politicians, obviously knew that Dubček was right. Surrounded by the pro-Moscow tell-tales, the last elements of the courage to implement at least some of the brave plans of January 1968, which he and Dubček had prepared, gradually trickled out of him. In his mind, thoughts to be President of the Republic after Ludvík Svoboda's long-term illness, took over and took root. In order to persuade Moscow and the ultra-conservatives at the highest party and government level, who would be deciding on the future president, he set upon on Dubček. At the joint meeting of the Central Councils of the National Front of the Czechoslovak Socialist Republic, Czechoslovakia and the Czechoslovak Socialist Republic in Prague on 16th April, 1975, a good month before his election as the President of the Republic, he belched fire and brimstone on Dubček for a letter published in the meantime by all the leading European newspapers. The Swedish Prime Minister, Olof Palme, had praised Dubček's letter of protest against his harassment. Husák almost insanely bellowed at the television cameras, "The bourgeois states have made a lot of noise around Czechoslovakia over the past few days, and their mass media have unleashed hysteria about the so-called Dubček letter. Smrkovský died, and they're looking for a new leader who can be used to abuse the Czechoslovak people, our institutions and Dubček has taken on this shameful function, probably not by accident. Now, in recent days, there is a great sensation over Dubček's letter, which is formally addressed to the Federal Assembly. In fact its content is determined by international reaction and the bourgeois propaganda against Czechoslovakia.

Such things are bestowed upon a person who for some time carried the identity card of our party and even, apparently an unfortunate accident for this state, was at the head of the party. One wonders how it is possible for people responsible for such a crash, for such disruption, to find courage or, I would say, the nerve to tell anyone how politics is to be done in our country ... They have arrived at the position of open traitors, open enemies of the people ... A few days ago, the Swedish Prime Minister, the Social Democrat, Palme, spoke fiercely about Dubček that he was guarded by six state security officers day and night, and how he is a great representative of democratic socialism. As far as I know, Mr Palme is also considered to be a representative of democratic socialism. We can offer him Dubček tomorrow ... If he wants, he can go!"

Most astonishingly, the content of Dubček's letter was not published in Czechoslovakia, but all newspapers contained violent reactionary reactions from the top representatives of the Communist Party. At workshops, schools, offices, workers' assemblies were organized and resolutions were passed, expressing a profound condemnation of Dubček's anti-socialist activities. At the Krasňany enterprise headquarters there was also an anti-Dubček meeting of workers. They called the meeting before the end of working hours so people would not discuss the needlessly. The leadership was afraid of it becoming a scandal and thus party and trade union officials prepared the people for the smooth running of the meeting. Director Ďuriš read the draft resolution he'd received from the senior party organization. "Comrades, comrades, I'm putting this to a vote, who agrees with such a proposal?" he asked, lifting his hand and looking into the hall. Every hand was raised. Ďuriš smiled with satisfaction. "Does anybody abstain?" He looked into the hall. "Nobody. Is anyone against?" He didn't even glance at the chamber, but was beginning to complete the resolution formula and thanking the employees for their attendance when a voice was spoke up, "One."

"Which one?" He couldn't believe his eyes.

"One is against. Me! Even I would be against Dubček, but I wouldn't know how to explain it to my wife," Dubček added sarcastically. His presence was noticed only by those sitting at the end of the hall. He'd come at the last moment and sat down under an oil painting of a landscape. The director looked at Zeleník, the head of the special unit, who was the representative of the ŠtB in the works. Zeleník turned green. He didn't understand. He'd given his people a clear instruction to prevent Dubček attending the meeting at any cost.

"I want to ask if you, comrade director or anyone present if you know the content of my letter. It's long, so I'd like to read just a few parts so that you know what you're voting for!" Dubček began to look at a copy of his letter. Ďuriš looked in dismay at the delegate from the party's city committee. He shook his head inconspicuously.

"Comrade Dubček, I'm sorry, but there is no discussion at today's meeting. At today's meeting, we only accept the resolution ... Um ..." He stared in the hall. People looked shamefacedly in front of themselves. "So thank you for your attendance and I'll end today's meeting."

The chamber emptied. There was silence as in a tomb, the same silence as in all chambers like it throughout Czechoslovakia.

When he arrived at work in mid-June 1975, he was surprised. Besides Jožko Križanovič, there was a third in the office, one he desired least to cast his eyes on. A portrait of Gustáv Husák hung above his work desk, who on the next to last day of May had been chosen, with the consent of the Soviets, as the new Czechoslovak president. When the long ailing Svoboda refused to give up his presidential office, the federal assembly adopted a special law so that Gunár, as Dubček dubbed his rival, took over the presidency. He didn't hesitate and laughed out loud. He called his wife. "You're not going to believe this, but here Husák now hangs over me."

CHAPTER 25

THE LOUSIEST OF THE LOUSY

Frequent and constantly repeated verbal assaults not only from Gustáv Husák, but also from lower party officials on Dubček, had their effect in the worsening of his wife's state of health. The surgeon urgently recommended a spa rest for her. The most suitable place was the Dudince Spa, which also treated patients with gallbladder problems. However, to receive an official voucher for treatment was impossible in the case of the wife of the most disgraced man in the country. Fortunately, the forest administration had gamekeeper's lodge not far from Dudince where the employees of the State Forests could stay and relax.

At the end of spring 1977, he took his wife to the bus station near Avion, where a colleague of his was waiting. He said a pleasant farewell to both ladies and went home. On the way he bought ham, cheese and bread, then stopped off at the market for some home-grown eggs. In the afternoon, Jiří Hájek was to come from Prague. The last time he had visited him was in mid-March when Hájek had come to talk him into signing Charter 77 statement. Whenever he was expecting a visit from Prague, whose dates were signalled in an agreed manner by innocent looking postcards, he was not sure if the person would come. A number of times it had happened that when Hübla, Hájek, Jaroš or Slavík had arrived the policemen in front of the house took them back to the station and put them on the first train to Prague. This time, however, the former foreign minister did arrive. They embraced and at first began to talk about general matters. Dubček prepared a favourite fry up in a pan with onion and Orava bacon. Hájek joked that it was only because of this that he had a reason to come to Bratislava. When they ate, Dubček took a bottle of Račianska Frankovka and they went into the "illegality," a small boiler room next to the cellar so called because it was the only place that was not under surveillance.

"How do you know there's no listening device here?" Hájek asked.

"I know it from ŠtB. There are still people who sympathize with me. But just a few. Otherwise, they go after me and my family like wild dogs. Recently I went to Senec to the cabin and beyond Veľký Biel by a long field of maize two Saabs appeared and started driving me into the field. So I stepped on the accelerator, but so did they. We drove like lunatics. Cars coming the other way flashed past us. It was literally life-threatening. But where I could have got away from them in my old Simca ... A big haulage truck appeared and there was no room. They had boxed me in completely, so I rushed at full speed into the maize ..."

"That's unbelievable villainy. They're trying to eliminate you physically? That's strong stuff."

"I have the feeling that even the Škoda car that squeezed me up against the wall a little before you last visited was not a coincidence."

"What did they say you about your complaint?"

"That they had no such licence registered and that it had to be a foreigner. How foreign can BAC 2245 be? It's an ordinary number ... Anička went to Dudince today, I'm afraid for her ..."

"How did you manage that?"

"The forestry enterprise plant has a lodge. When they refused to take her to the spa house, a dear lady from our training section took her to the lodge. Employees are used to staying there. At least she will have peace from the wild beasts. I am glad that after so many years, this at least is successful. Booking treatments in the main spa should no longer be a problem."

"I'm concerned that these attacks don't connect you with the Charter," said Hájek.

"Yet I'm not in touch with you at all. I'm completely blocked from the outside world."

"It's just that. Perhaps they're worried that you'll sign it. You know, Sasha, your signature would make the Charter much more significant."

"I read it. It is an excellent material, I practically agree with everything, but ... there's nothing at all about Slovakia or about our mutual relationship. I feel that this is not even Czech, but exclusively Prague. Of course, we also want democracy here, but as an equal state with the Czechs. Miro Kusý came to see me, too. With all due respect to you, Slavík, Mlynář, Jarošs and all my former colleagues, I was one of the leaders in the process of reformation. You know, I could have been one of the founders of the Charter and not one of the signatories ... "."

"We only want the government to observe what it has signed in Helsinki. I understand you, maybe it was a mistake that we didn't ask you, but you were, somehow, sorry, at the side of things. But you say you agree with everything."

"At the side. Every day I'm guarded by six public and secret security agents. There are perhaps fifty others as well. I know you don't have it easy, but for me communication with the outside world is almost impossible. "

"I understand."

"And then, I feel that you've given up the idea that the party can be reformed. But there's no other option. If you don't want to reform the party, you can only go against it. And that's unrealistic. It's a very difficult situation for me ... understand me correctly ... I agree with everything that the Charter says and I will support you, but there is a different situation in Slovakia. I believe that even in the party there will be currents of revival, as in our time. And then, I'm afraid I could expose you to even more repression with my signature." Dubček tried to tune in Voice of America, but the radio emitted just a screaming sound. "I suspect that the jammers have got stronger ... They might have feared that they have revealed an ŠtB communication among us."

"I can understand you, but Tatarka and Mlynárik have signed it."

"They live in Prague and yet they weren't among the leaders of the Charter ... I think the protest letters that they send to the Husák gang perform a similar function."

At that moment the bell rang. The men looked at each other. "Eleven in the evening. A visit now?" Dubček quickly took the bottle and went up to the kitchen. Hájek was closed in the boiler room but there were keys chinking in the door. Afraid Dubček walked to the front door. There in the doorway, he almost collided with his wife, who walked in with a suitcase and a large bag.

"Anička? You were supposed to be at the spa ..." he looked at her blankly. Anna sat down in a chair and after a moment of silence, her face twisted into a weeping grimace. The day-long mental pressure was released.

"What happened?"

"Everything was fine, your colleague Plačková was very kind. Until the moment I wanted to sign up for a course of treatment in the main building ..." she swallowed a tablet nervously. "They told me it was not possible because ... because Mrs. Lenártová had just had procedures and there is no way for a Dubček to have to the same treatments as the wife of the first secretary ... So I packed ..."

Dubček embraced his wife. "Come on, Jirko from Prague is here. He'll stay the night with us."

CHAPTER 26

YOU'RE A LABOURER, SO RULE

In the spring of 1982, Dubček was sitting in the studio of his friend, the sculptor Teodor Baník, on Pionierska Street. The sculptor was sketching him with an attentive eye. They agreed that he would make a bust. Dubček was not excited at first, but Teo spoke to him because he had only a few models. Although he lectured at the University of Fine Arts, not many dared come to his studio.

They knew that Dubček was coming there. The radio was interrupted by the occasional whistle of a locomotive from the nearby railroad. Baník put down his sketchpad, brushing the charcoal from his hands. He was visibly nervous. "Let's go for a glass," he asked Dubček to go to the cellar under the studio made up of various tubes and pipes. It had shelves with carefully arranged bottles of wine on them. "Rizling?" Dubček nodded and signalled they should return to the studio. "Wait. I was going to tell you something important ... a disturbed Baník began. "That's why I asked you here ... Um ... I was at the ŠtB yesterday." Dubček listened without batting an eyelid. "They called me there and asked why I was friends with you. And why was I doing your bust. Imagine, they knew it. How could they know? Only the two of us know. I felt as though they were with me in my studio ... Um ..."

"What else did they want?"

"To inform them about who is visiting you, what you say and so ..."

"And you?"

"I said I wouldn't do that to my friend. If I get thrown out of the school, I can do six crafts and I'll survive."

"And they?"

"I should consider, I'm an artist, a lecturer, a college teacher, I can travel, and that needn't be the case ..." Dubček thought.

"Thank you. I really appreciate your telling me. It makes no sense for you to spoil your career and endanger your family. You should meet them, tell them what they want to know anyway. For they, too, have to report "upstairs" about me and refer to reliable resources. It's a game, don't let them down. It's even good for us. We can lead them by the nose and tell them only what we want them to know or what they already know." Dubček trusted his friend absolutely because he knew him well and knew he could count on him for everything. He never doubted this. He trusted him with many things, consulted him, left documents, letters and gifts he had received from people, and Baník never abused the trust. Often in Baník's cellar, where they couldn't be overheard, they formulated sentences that Baník repeated to the ŠtB. Finally, it became a good channel for Husák to learn Dubček's views. They knew that the most powerful man of the country was personally interested in his predecessor.

After reaching retirement age, Dubček decided to leave the office and asked to be transferred to the repair and development workshops in Pezinok. He could no longer tolerated hanging ceaselessly over papers and giving senseless reports of plans to deliver spare parts. The company's management discussed his application with the relevant staff of the ŠtB. Dubček's transfer was not recommended. Ten years on, they had a sophisticated system of tracking him and moving to a new workplace would require them to build up a whole new network. The workshops were on the outskirts of Pezinok near the Regen plant, which would complicate the daily monitoring and also increase costs. Dubček, however, insisted on it. He didn't ease up on the management and he announced that if they didn't agree, he would retire. The ŠtB was scared that Dubček would have a lot of spare time and checking on him would be more complicated.

"You're welding seems to be going well, Doctor," Lukáč the lathe operator said with a smile. "When did you last do it?"

"At home all the time, and finally, I'm a trained turner, and I did a welding course," Dubček crawled out in grimy overalls from under the oil-clad heavy steel chassis of the truck. Every day about a ton of iron material passed through his hands. The work came to his hands and even though he was retired he had a solid, sportsman's figure.

"So now we'll have our Brazil." He walked over to his bench and turned on the boiler. The water in the tin mug boiled after a moment of heating. He poured three cups of ersatz that he had prepared to be almost indistinguishable from the real thing. Lukáč and his colleague Arpád from the other side came over. Dubček's "Brazil" had a beautiful smell in the workshop.

"It seems that after a lifetime as a white collar worker you do know how to do things properly," teased Lukáč.

"You ought to get a little bit of order on this bench," Dubček retorted and he himself put tools on Lukáč's work bench where there was hopeless disorder. It was known that tidiness was a virtue with Dubček.

"How do you feel as the leading force in the state?"

"Am I the leading force? I'm no longer in office or in the party. "

"Well, you're one of us. You're a labourer, so rule," said Lukáč. Dubček and Arpad laughed with him.

"Well, if you hadn't told me I was the leading force, I wouldn't even know," he laughed. "I was a labourer and I think I don't have a problem with that even now."

"A labourer is always just a labourer, but that coffee is just like Brazil," Lukáč smiled. After three years of work in the workshop, Dubček retired for good.

CHAPTER 27

THE SHORT GRAVE OF BREZHNEV

Gustáv Husák was elected as the first Slovak as Czechoslovak president following Ludvík Svoboda on 29th May, 1975. He'd reached the summit of power combining in his person both the highest party and state functions. But what, in fact, was his power was illustrated by the fact that when he wanted to lay a wreath on the tomb of the first Czechoslovak president Tomáš Garrigue Masaryk after his election he was forbidden to do so. While 37,000 people were rehabilitated in the less than fourteen months of the Dubček era, rehabilitation was stopped by Husák.

The leadership of the Communist Party condemned Charter 77 as an anti-socialist pamphlet and organized a counter-statement "The Declaration - New Creative Acts in the Name of Socialism and Peace", which received the popular name "The Anticharta". It was signed by 7,500 writers, actors, academics, journalists, artists and other members of the intelligentsia.

The Soviet leadership was in a difficult situation, and so decided, as always, in similar cases, on an action that concealed internal problems. Before the Christmas of 1979, Brezhnev sent fifty thousand Soviet troops to Afghanistan. At the time of the Afghan invasion, Brezhnev was in physical and psychological trouble. He was suffering from that most typical of Soviet diseases, alcoholism. His doctors sought to counter his excessive smoking with a special tobacco case, which released a cigarette only every forty minutes. The General Secretary begged for cigarettes from his personal guards. The highest representative of a world power had turned into the demented old man, who during a visit to Germany in 1978 as a guest of the West German Chancellor, Helmut Schmidt, kept addressing him as Willy Brandt. The first secretaries of the Communist republics Party sent whole trainloads of gifts to Brezhnev in Moscow so as to keep their master's favour. In Buchar they even cast Brezhnev busts in gold.

10th November 1982 the main architect of the military invasion of Czechoslovakia, Leonid Ilyich Brezhnev died. They buried him as he lived. When the soldiers wanted to put the chest into the tomb at the Kremlin, it turned out that the grave was too short. Somehow they jammed it at an angle in a direct television broadcast before the eyes of the world. His successor, the relatively modern-minded KGB chief Yuri Andropov, after the start of an uncompromising anti-corruption campaign, during which many party officials, including Brezhnev's son, went to jail, however surprisingly quickly became sick and a year and a half after taking office unexpectedly died. Andropov's successor was the seventy-three-year-old Konstantin Chernenko, who spent most of the year during which he was the first man of the Soviet Union in hospital. 10th March, 1985 Chernenko also died. In the drawers of his work desk in the Kremlin, they did not find a single working document, but a countless number of envelopes containing huge sums of dollars.

Two hours after his death, nine members of the politburo, present in Moscow, met to discuss the Chernenko's successor. Four were behind Gorbachev, four against. And so the vote of the foreign minister, Andre Gromyko was decisive. He threw his hand in with Gorbachev. So perestroika began - a reconstruction of the country of which Gorbachev said in his first statement, "Our rockets fly into the universe, but our refrigerators are not working."

CHAPTER 28

HUSÁK GET OUT!

On 11th April, 1987 Mikhail Gorbachev arrived in Bratislava. The security measures were extremely strict and the city did not operate public transport throughout the day. At the tram stop near the Kriváň hotel below the station, somebody had written on the timetable, "Gorbachev yes, Husák no!" The graffiti captured the mood of citizens, and the security authorities and party leadership knew it.

Dubček and his wife watched a direct broadcast of the visitors from their living room. The screen alternated shots of enthusiastic people waving Soviet and Czechoslovak flags. The commentator without emotion commented on the screen shots. "The Secretary General of the Central Committee of the Communist Party of the Soviet Union, Mikhail Sergeyevich Gorbachev and his wife, Raisa, visited Czechoslovakia including Bratislava. He was accompanied by the General Secretary of the UV KSČ and President of the Republic, Gustáv Husák. He was welcomed in Slovakia by the first secretary of the UV KSS, Jozef Lenárt. Mikhail Sergeyevich received an unusually warm welcome."

"For the first time in my life I see a Soviet representative welcomed by crowds with real enthusiasm," said Anna. "Didn't they invite you?"

"Not. I wanted to go down to the city, but they didn't let me."

"I'm afraid I wouldn't have really enjoyed it. The traffic went up Malinovská to the Central Committee ... As if they were afraid they might meet the people. "

From the screen was a chant, "Gorby, Gorby"

"Did you hear? Somebody there has started shouting, "Husák get out," Anna turned up the sound.

"He's getting from the people, just what he deserves."

"I've been watching carefully what Gorbachev wants. His perestroika and glasnost can't be compared with our Action Plan of April Sixty-eight," Dubček said laconically.

"I thank God for at least that. I'm just afraid of it getting out of hand," said his wife.

"He's out of hand already. Banning alcohol in the Soviet Union is political suicide."

"It looks as if he came to support Husák," Anna said accusingly. Then she turned to her husband. "And didn't anyone from the Soviet consulate call to say he wanted to meet you?" Dubček shook his head sadly. "I don't understand this."

"There doesn't seem to be any time yet for Gorbachev to rehabilitate Sixty-Eight."

"So far, everyone has shouted that the Soviet Union is our example and all at once everyone talks about different conditions," she frowned." They can't keep things down anymore. Look at Husák. In fact, next to Gorbachev he behaves as though he were homeless waif... Ah, he stands there so lonely, no one takes any notice of him ... Šanko, don't worry, you'll soon shake hands with Gorbachev. There's only twenty years between him and you. Your moment is coming," his wife pressed his hand firmly. Suddenly "Gorby, Gorby" was mixed with "Dubček, Dubček."

"And I didn't speak!"

"If Husák suspected this, he'd wouldn't even have invited Gorbachev," said Dubček. There was laughter in the room, but it was bitterer than it appeared. Mikhail Gorbachev didn't bring much joy to the Dubčeks or to the Czech-Slovak citizens. Expectations that people had for the visits were disappointed. He not only didn't say anything clearly about the necessity of rebuilding in Czechoslovakia, but on the contrary, it was as if through his discreet approach to the Czechoslovak leadership that he supported its reluctance to reform. Gorbachev bathed in the crowd, glad-handing the people and that was all. Or perhaps he only said something. He commended Husák for keeping order in the country after 1968 and praised Czechoslovak conservatives for having learned from mistakes of 1968. "You've come far. Czechoslovakia is today a modern state in the world. If it isn't among the top five, it is definitely one of the ten most developed countries in the world," Mikhail Sergeyevich said such nonsense during his visit to Prague's ČKD plant. The Soviet leader was probably afraid that criticism of Husák's leadership, and indirectly of the justification for the invasion in 1968, could result in destabilization in the Eastern bloc, where nothing had yet been decided.

In December 1987, the highest party leadership underwent a cosmetic change. Gustáv Husák was replaced by Miloš Jakeš as General Secretary of the UV KSČ. Husák retained the post of President. Jakeš, a politician with the intelligence of Bacílek, commented on the Soviet reconstruction with the words: "It's not a simple process, that rebuilding or perestroika, it isn't! It's a process, I would say, about which not everyone knows enough! And a process into which enemies can enter and appear to be friends!"

CHAPTER 29

GORBACHEV, THE DEVIL SICKED HIM ON TO US

In February 1988, Miloš Jakeš could have torn himself apart with wrath when he read the reports from the district committees of the Communist Party. They looked alike as two peas in a pod. From Cheb to Snina, district party officials reported that party functionaries in their talks strongly condemned the interview given by Alexander Dubček in January to the left-wing Italian journalist from L'Unitá, Lucian Antonetti, who through the merchant Vittorio Caffe, who owned Rifle, a firm in Brno, delivered Dubček's questions on the occasion of the twentieth anniversary of the beginning of Prague Spring. At a time when the Czechoslovak leadership had stubbornly rejected Gorbachev's perestroika, Dubček's opinions and, in particular, the fact that they had reached wide range of citizens, called forth the fury of Prague,

"Perestroika is essential, it answers the mature problems of the entire socialist community," Dubček said in the interview. "I welcome and support it. I see a deep inner connection with the questions that arose in our country twenty years ago ... Between Gorbachev perestroika and what we wanted is a unity of form in basic inspirational sources ... I find it hard to think what could have happened in these years from the "new course" and how our country, socialism and the whole movement might have benefited... It is necessary to stimulate initiatives in fulfillment of the pluralist interests of social, cultural and other organizations of the social system ... For it is especially necessary to create political space... Wounds can be healed, but with good medicine, not cosmetics ... The cause of our problems is primarily the limitation of democratic life in our country."

"Goddamn how does he know what the vast majority of our people think," Jakeš tossed the translation of Dubček's interview on the table. "And how is it possible for all district organizations to report that our people condemn the interview and here the ŠtB's informers tell us something quite different?" Jakeš looked out of the window and then turned abruptly to Jan Fojtík, a member of the UV KSC responsible for propaganda.

"What do they say?" asked Fojtík.

"They're talking about Dubček's interview in pubs, workplaces and even hospitals. How did it get to these people? We've already given a clear directive for a strict ban on the dissemination of material from foreign countries except to the party!"

"So that's how it got to the people. It came through the party. It is clear proof of how many rightists in the party we still have, how many opportunists live here among us. And that's after almost twenty years of international aid!"

"Yes, yes," said Jakeš, "We still have a lot of work to do. We'll have to summon a core district secretaries. Can you tell me everywhere the Dubček interview was published?"

"In almost all the Italian newspapers, Le Monde, the British Guardian, the Danish Information, Swedish Dagens Nyheter and in many letters in Germany, Denmark, Sweden ... The Pelican Letters took it all, and then it came to us ..."

But we only gave it to regional and district secretaries! "

"I'm telling you that it got out through some of them," said Fojtík exasperated. "And is the interview truly authentic? What if the Italians invented it? "

"It is indeed," Jakeš replied. "Read this ..."

"What is it?"

"Dubček wrote to me."

"Dubček wrote to you?" Jakes nodded. Fojtík read aloud some of the passages of Dubček's letter to Jakeš in mock Slovak. "In Trenčín, Comrade Janák made a statement to challenge the authenticity of the authorship of my interview for L'Unita magazine. Obviously this is originated in the Presidium. It's nothing new!" Fojtík looked angrily at Jakeš. "In Trenčín, there was a core of original Slovak regional and district secretaries ... You see how reliable they are. As soon as it was done, Dubček already knew everything," he waved his hands.

"At the party's eighteenth congress in May of next year, we'll have to deal with some of our comrades," Jakeš nodded.

"Let's hope we can survive until the congress ..."

"Ján, don't panic like everyone else. The party has already ridden out a storm and will ride this one out, too, Jakeš said to the gloomy Fojtík. "Come on read it!"

"What led me to this letter chiefly is the publication of Biľak's diaries in the newspapers. Biľak deliberately spreads half-truths and falsities with such a clear intent, aggression and cynicism that not everyone understands from where the anger, the superficiality, the shallowness and purposefulness actually come. It would have been desirable if he had got close to the culture which is expected from such a high-ranking official ... he, he, he ..." Fojtík laughed. "Sometimes Dubček is right; there are very few people as stupid as Biľak."

"We should do something about publishing Biľak's memoirs. It's really nonsense. Jano do me a favour. You're in charge of the press. Let our comrades know that they should stop this!" said Jakeš decisively.

"You want to forbid Biľak?"

"Yes!"

"That's good, so people will take notice of you. I will appreciate that, too. But what do I tell Vasíl? He is after all a member of the presidium responsible for ideology and foreign affairs. It won't be that simple ..." objected Fojtík

"If he doesn't like it, send him to me!"

"When should I stop it?

"Now!"

"Very well," said Fojtík. When he came to his office, he instructed his secretary to summon all the chief editors of the party press, radio and television in the morning. Then he called Vasíl Biľak. Briefly, he announced the decision of the General Secretary of the ÚV KSČ. With sadness in his voice, he added, "I did what I could, but I did not convince Milouš. I'm sorry. "

Two weeks later, an enraged Biľak invaded the secretariat of Secretary Fojtík and waved a fresh edition of Pravda newspaper, which on the first page reported the events of a candlelit demonstration of the faithful in Bratislava on 25th March, 1988.

"That's because you conceded!"

"Calm down Vasíl, I'm not conceding to anyone and we won't concede. And I think our comrades in Bratislava controlled things well this time. "

"So they controlled things well, how well. Nothing should have happened; nothing should be permitted to this Mikloško."

"He wasn't allowed to do anything. The District National Committee in Bratislava did not agree to Mikloško's request. It was an unauthorized demonstration," Fojtík explained. "Our law enforcement forces responded adequately."

"How did they formulate that request?"

"Just for half an hour to commemorate religious freedom and respect for human rights."

Biľak considered for a moment, and then shouted. "This is all due to Gorbachev, the devil sicked him on to us." Then he turned to Fojtík. "Who were the organizers?"

"Known groups. Non-legal structures Čarnogurský, Mikloško, Jukl, Korec. The stupid thing is that Tomášek also supported them. "

"God knows that sort of clips that hostile television broadcast did us no favours," said Biľak. "How is it possible that we didn't have the technical means to prevent Mikloško from connecting with the Voice of America and Vatican Radio? They were actually encouraging people to the demonstration."

"At least the Slovak secretariat ensured that the Roman Catholic and Greek Catholic Churches distanced themselves from this," Fojtík said heatedly. "Are there reactions from abroad?"

"The Austrian government has protested that the security forces' intervention was contradictory to a Czechoslovak interstate commitment with respect to human rights. I suggested postponing the visit of that Chancellor of theirs, Vranitzky ... No Austrians are going to bugger about ... But in your place I would put a little pressure on the mass media," Biľak insisted to Fojtík. "If we don't there'll be a repeat of Sixty-eight. You know how right-wingers are trying to call for "The Briefing". That's never going to happen. The workers stand on our side. They've understood the real form of the enemies of socialism. Dubček and his revisionists are definitely a thing of the past for us!"

In nine months, in December 1988, Vasil Biľak was removed from all functions. Jan Fojtík, too, finished that year.

CHAPTER 30

TWENTY YEARS OF TEARS

At the time of the beginning of Soviet reconstruction, a group of reformers from the Dubček circle came alive. He abandoned his conspiracy precaution that he would always meet with only one person. If the contents of their conversation had accidentally reached impermissible ears, it would be clear who had betrayed it. Security pressure had diminished so they could meet away from his home, in private wine cellars or at Baník's studio. When searching for a suitable meeting place, Dubček with Ivan Laluha and Hvezdoň Kočtúch sought out a bench in the western corner of Horský Park. It became their constant and silent friend. At the beginning of May 1988, Laluha and Kočtúch were waiting on the bench when they heard dogs barking. "They've got us now," Kočtúch said with a worried look at where the barking was coming from. Fortunately, it was evident that it was where the inhabitants of the surrounding area would walk their dogs. In a moment a smiling Dubček appeared. He walked as if he were floating on air.

"And what's made you so happy?" Laluha asked. Dubček drew out a letter with an Italian stamp and the seal of the city of Bologna. The university had announced to him he'd been awarded

Doctor Honoris causa from this oldest university in the world. At the same time, they'd invited him in November of the same year to receive the title. The Dubčeks were still recovering from the shock of having this delivered to them in the first place. It was clear evidence that the situation was changing. Another surprise came when Dubček's request for a passport and the granting of an exit visa to Italy was permitted by the state authorities. The granting of an Italian entry visa was only a formality. Before leaving for Italy Dubček wanted to make certain he would be allowed to return. He asked the Interior Minister, Vajnar, for a written assurance that there would be no obstacles to his return. Vajnar gave him a promise and so Dubček, after nearly twenty years of total isolation and police supervision, travelled to Bologna. On 13th November, when he entered the baroque church of Santa Lucia, transformed into the Aula Magna of Bologna, the chamber, packed to the last place, stood up and welcomed Alexander with rapturous applause. In his introductory words the Rector of the university, Fabio Roversi Monaco, said: "We are honouring Alexander Dubček today in the same spirit that we have had faith in people like Nelson Mandela, who has fought racism for decades, to people like Andreas Papandreou, like Juan Carlos Bourbon, who are returning their people on the road to democracy ... We pay honest homage to a statesman and pioneer. We accept him among our doctors, and we know that we do so on behalf of all righteous people ..." Then Dubček took out his words. He was obviously moved, his voice trembling a little. "... Your important medieval philosopher and poet, Francis of Assisi said, God, give me enough humility to bear things I cannot change, give me enough courage to change the things that I can change and give me enough reason to know how to distinguish between these things... In the life of a person, a collective, in the lives of nations and in the history of the states, there were and are periods of humility and courage, times in which, despite everything, a person must remain himself."

The hall, deeply moved, listened to the man who had hoped twenty years before that a social system based on the ideals of humanism, democracy, solidarity and decency could be built. A voice silenced for twenty years suddenly sounded in a country that had ruled over the world two thousand years before and who crucified the one whose thoughts and ideas Dubček consciously or unconsciously adopted. To help, he quoted the Bengali poet, Rabindranath Thakur Tagore, who'd commented on the situation in the Soviet Union in the thirties. "I ask you - do you demonstrate good service to your ideal when you sow anger, class hatred and vengeance against anyone who does not agree with your ideal and whom do you consider your enemy? If you have a task that touches all mankind, you must recognize the existence of different opinions in the interest of this living humanity. Attitudes develop only through the free movement of spiritual forces and moral conviction. Violence generates violence and blind stupidity. Freedom of thought is necessary in the interests of acceptance and understanding of the truth, terror kills it," Dubček quoted a great poet, speaking calmly. At the end of his performance, he confessed: "Only evil, only evil is measured just by pain. And leaving it as it happened, as it happened to us, where we started, I would start again gladly. Like a scientist, looking for the bacilli, which killed him."

When he ended his speech, Rector Fabio Roversi Monaco approached him, handing him the parchment scroll of an Honorary Doctorate of Political Science, and placed an inception ring on his finger. The eight hundred guests headed by the city, university, the province of Emilia-Romagna, political, cultural and social life figures, four hundred and fifty representatives of Italian and foreign media, stood with a prolonged applause for the most famous Slovak. In the direct transmission by Italian television, a miracle had just happened. It was disarmingly human, when the rector, wiped the tears from Dubček's face, who was not ashamed of showing emotions, with his own handkerchief.. Tears of relief, twenty years of tears...

During the two weeks of Dubček's celebratory Italian visit, ordinary people in the streets, greeted him as an old friend, and students invited him to trattorias. When he was about to throw a coin into the famous Roman Trevi Fountain, a Russian painter threw herself on him and apologized for the Soviet occupation on behalf of all the Russians. She and then Dubček wept. It had finally come. Not the calculated excuses of the powerful, but one of the millions who had been violated twenty years before and forced to an act which was not actually their fault. The highlight of Dubček's visit was a reception by the Holy Father, Pope John Paul II.

After his return, the Rude právo reported his triumphant Italian visit with words that more than anything else, demonstrated that the then Czechoslovak leadership had stagnated in their thinking in the times which being thrown into the dustbin of history. "The granting of a doctorate and the very fact of Dubček's travel abroad, as is currently confirmed, was one of the focal points of the West's ideodiversionary influence against the Czechoslovak Socialist Republic."

CHAPTER 31

FALL OF THE IRON CURTAIN

The Polish trade union movement Solidarity had been persecuted by the Communist authorities for seven years until finally, at the end of 1988, the first secretary of the Polish Communists, General Jaruzelski, chose instead of repression to start a dialogue with Solidarity. He recognized Solidarity as an equal partner, and in June 1989, for the first time since the end of the Second World War, the elections were partly free. In Eastern Europe, this happened for the first time after forty years. Moscow did not intervene and it stimulated hope among the citizens of other countries that Soviet domination would end.

The second litmus paper was Hungary. From the departure of Janos Kadar from office in May 1988, reforms began in Hungary more rapidly than in Moscow itself. However, Moscow did not block Hungary's efforts. Reform-minded members of the Communist leadership actively began to dismantle the party from within. In May 1989, representatives of Hungary and Austria cut the barbed wire on their common border. The iron curtain began to fall apart. On 10th October Hungary raised the Iron Curtain completely as the first country of the Eastern Bloc and through the Hungarian-Austrian border Socialist bloc citizens from the German Democratic Republic began to leave and to the exasperation of East German officials no-one tried to stop them. In Prague thousands of East German refugees climbed across the wall of the premises of the West German Embassy in front of the eyes of the members of public security forces who didn't intervene. By the end of September there were eleven thousand people living there in temporary

conditions. The Czechoslovak authorities were forced to act and allowed them to travel through

the GDR to the Bavarian Hof from the 4th of October in special trains and buses.

In October 1989, celebrations for the fortieth anniversary of the GDR were held in East Berlin. The

Soviet leader Gorbachev travelled with great trepidation to these celebrations. When Honecker

highlighted the unity of the party and the people in his celebratory speech, the chanting of "Erich

Get Out!" of a million people could be heard from outside. Gorbachev travelled from the GDR with

the words: "This is the beginning of the end." Ten days after his departure, mass protests rejected

Honecker. In early November the East German politburo fell. Its representative, Schabowski,

announced that citizens could travel abroad with immediate effect. The Berlin Wall began to

crumble.

CHAPTER 32

LET THEM CLEAN UP THE STREAM

The first days of 1989 were marked especially in Bohemia by unusual activities of opposition groups. Several hundred cultural and scientific workers in Prague, Brno and Bratislava protested in a letter to the Prime Minister of the ČSSR Ladislav Adamec, who had replaced Lubomír Štrougal in October 1988, about the police action against demonstrators on the occasion of the twentieth anniversary of the burning of Jan Palach. They imprisoned Václav Havel when he tried to lay flowers in the place where Jan Palach had burned twenty years ago. Dubček sent a sharp protest to Jakeš and Husák. "If you still want to do something, I advise you to start by releasing Havel." It was obvious that two determined opposition streams had formed in Czechoslovakia. One was headed by Václav Havel, consisting mainly of signatories to Charter 77 and a movement of followers of the reforms of 1968 called Obroda (Renewal), headed by Alexander Dubček. In times of a common enemy, understandably the contours of a future conflict between a right-wing and a left-wing movement are still not recognizable. After taking power after November 1989, however, the contradictions between the right and the left sharpened.

The Obroda Political Club, in connection with the serious illness of President Husák, issued a memorandum on 25th March, 1989, in which it proposed Alexander Dubček as the new president. In justification it stated, "As a person he is generally known by his character and civic integrity. As a Slovak he enjoys respect not only in Slovakia, but also in the Czech lands, out of all proportion in comparison with others."

A sensation occurred on 17th April. Twenty years after Dubček was expelled from office Hungarian television broadcast an interview with him. His performance caused great enthusiasm just because the banned Prague Spring leader had the opportunity to talk on the state television of a socialist country. The interview, in which he categorically condemned the Soviet invasion in 1968 and unambiguously supported Gorbachev's reforms, was broadcast by Hungarian television at a time when Miloš Jakeš was visiting Moscow. He rejected the similarity between the Slovak and Czech Spring in 1968 and the Soviet reconstruction, as well as the rehabilitation of the Dubčeks. The Czechoslovak state authorities sent a protest note to the Hungarian government, in which Dubček's interview was regarded as a breach of mutual agreements. The result of the protest was that the Hungarian television broadcast the second part of the interview within the week. It was clear that Budapest and Warsaw had finished with communism. People started to raise their heads. Jakeš commented on the people's dissatisfaction with the words, "We need them to move, let's say for instance to go and clean the creek and not hold demonstrations."

On 17th May they released Václav Havel from prison. When Váslav Slavík, Dubček's friend took him to Havel's house on the banks of Vltava, they were accompanied by a squad of the ŠtB. The meeting of the two politicians was more than friendly, symbolizing a necessary alliance between the two opposition currents. On 23rd June Dubček wrote an open letter to the presidium of ÚV KSČ, asking for immediate accession to the reforms, inviting leaders to make a corrective confession of the truth directly to all the people, however difficult it might be for them. As in all cases before, he received no answer to his letter. It was the last letter that Dubček sent to the leadership of the Communist Party before it was brushed aside by the events of 17th November 1989.

CHAPTER 33

THE END

On 16th November secondary school and university students gathered in Mierovo namestie in Bratislava on the occasion of international student day. The security authorities were on the alert. The students' procession adjourned to the building of Ministry of Education, where they asked for a dialogue on their ideas for social reforms. The determination of Bratislava students to name the problems in society became a prologue of the events that took place a day later in Prague.

On 17th November, a gathering of students was organized by the City Council of the Socialist Youth Union of University Students in Prague on the occasion of the 50th Anniversary of the Anti-Nazi rising of Czech Students. Permits to organize the assembly had been given by the city authorities 14 days before. November 17th was International Student Day, but only the more perceptive noticed that in two weeks' time a meeting of the top US and USSR representatives, Bush and Gorbachev, was to be held in Malta. The relationship between these two events could not be ruled out.

On Friday, 17th November students of Prague colleges gathered in the courtyard of the Charles University Medical School in Albertov, where they commemorated the fiftieth anniversary of the closing of Czech universities in 1939. From Albertov they were supposed to march through Karlovo náměstí, Štepánska to Opletalova Street where they would lay flowers in the park in front of the Main Railway Station to end the march. Under pressure from the security forces, however, the organizers took the march from the city centre to Vyšehrad to the grave of the poet, Karel Hynek Mácha.

Part of the student body unexpectedly moved along the river Vltava by the National Theatre after this pious act of commemoration. Residents of homes in the Národní třída , Perštýn and the surrounding area were surprised when approximately two hours before the arrival of the procession in Národní třída, tram services was halted in both directions and the residents were given orders to close all their front doors. The emergency sections of the Department of National Security were on alert in Mikulandská and Konviktská for three hours before the student procession arrived. A platoon of URNA (Útvary rýchleho nasadenia - the rapid deployment units,) known as the red berets, were concentrated in Bartolomejská from eleven-thirty.

The Minister of the Interior, František Kincl, with a cock and bull story had fled to his family in Ostrava. The leadership of the ministry had been taken over by his deputy, the commander in chief of the ŠtB, General Alojz Lorenc. At the time when students marching from Vyšehrad turned into Národní třída , Lorenc was dining in the Břevnov villa of the Ministry of the Interior with a delegation from the Soviet secret service, the KGB, headed by a deputy commander, General Viktor Grushko. A visit by the Soviet delegation had been planned long before. They were supposed to discuss issues of cooperation between the Soviet and Czechoslovak counter-intelligence.

As for when a visit by another Soviet general, Gennady Teslenko, had been scheduled, no-one knew. A Soviet General of the Ministry of the Interior, he was at the time of the Národní třída demonstration in the command staffroom of Colonel Danišovič, who directed the attack on the demonstrators.

On 17th November, the two delegations signed a final protocol. Before General Lorenc left for an evening with the Soviet delegation, he called the First Secretary of the ÚV KSČ, Jakeš, and gave him a brief report on the course of the demonstration. He told the KSČ's top official that it was an anti-state demonstration with a clear political focus. Jakeš noted of information.

"What are you going to do?" he asked.

"I've ordered violence not to be used, it wouldn't help."

Jakeš thought for a moment and then said, "All right. I'm leaving for the cabin at Slapy. If there's anything, call me," he added and put down the phone on Lorenc.

On that day, Václav Havel picked up his girlfriend, Jitka Vodňanská, and left with her from Prague for his cabin in Hrádek. The entire leadership of Charter 77 had left Prague, including their families. Only Uhl, Benda and Němcová remained.

The evening of for Soviet and Czechoslovak delegations was constantly interrupted, so Lorenc took his leave of Grushko at half past eight. He went to the Národní třída to apprise himself of the situation. The police had blocked about five thousand demonstrators in the road in Národní třída. Students in the immediate vicinity of the police cordon sat down and chanted "We have bare hands, we have bare hands." They gave the police carnations. After less than an hour police officers started to push forward. Batons came to their aid. The Independent Student Investigative Commission reported 66 people hurt a month after the events. In March 1990, when the loss of the former regime was definitive and courage came to them more easily, they declared another five-hundred injured.

General Lorenc returned to his office and a number of times attempted to contact the Minister of the Interior. But Kincl did not pick up the phone.

Czechoslovak television reported on the dispersal of the demonstration in Národní třída, during which fifteen students were slightly injured by the orderly use of force. The next morning, however, the whole republic got out of bed to the information from Voice of America, BBC, Deutsche Welle, Radio Free Europe, and especially from Austrian and West German television. In Narodní třída armoured transporters had allegedly been deployed and during the clashes with the police a student, Martin Šmíd, had perished. Although no transporters had been seen in Národní třída, no-one was dead and the student, Šmíd, spoke the next day to Czechoslovak television. The nation was starting to move. It was not worried that Lieutenant Žifčák of the ŠtB played student Šmíd. This time a lie helped the right thing. Nothing can arouse emotion in people like the death of an innocent man. Rumours spilled into the world and the days of the communist regime were numbered.

Václav Havel and several Charter 77 members returned quickly from their cabins and cottages to Prague on Saturday. In the afternoon on 18th November, representatives of independent initiatives were welcomed by Václav Havel in his flat and called for their unification under the title Občanské fórum (Civic Forum.) In the evening, Civic' Forum was officially announced at the Drama Club, and the first, cautious demands were formulated. They demanded the resignation of the most corrupt politicians, the release of political prisoners, a commission appointed to investigate the intervention in Národní třída and support for a general strike. That was not enough for the revolution. Power was lying on the ground and the Chartists, instead of picking it up energetically, wanted to negotiate with it. So the public took power. On Monday, 20th November 1989, the first mass demonstration, about one hundred thousand citizens, took place in Václavské náměstí (Wenceslas Square.) It had no leaders. The new leaders were found next day. Václav Havel appeared for the first time in public before two hundred thousand people. On Friday, 24th November the entire presidium of the ÚV KSČ headed by Miloš Jakeš resigned. He was replaced by Karel Urbánek. It was said that he became the first man in the Communist Party because he just happened to be passing by ...

The actor, Milan Kňažko, was coincidentally in Prague on Sunday, 19th November some of his Czech colleagues took him to the Drama klub. Kňažko was also signed under the Civic Forum declaration. He took his copy and got on the next express to Bratislava. On Sunday evening, about 500 members of arts associations met in the arts club at the Art Gallery at the Dostojevského rad in Bratislava. Milan Kňažko read a protest statement on the events in Prague. On 20th November there was a student demonstration in Hviezdoslavovo námestie, where Kňažko read the declaration again. On the same day the newly formed Verejnosť proti násiliu (Public Against Violence - VPN) presented itself for the first time in the vestibule of the Small Stage of the National Slovak Theatre. The police did not intervene. In the evening, VPN representatives read their first

open document in the aula of Comenius University. Together with Bratislava environmentalists
headed by Jan Budaj, the VPN movement was established.

On 26th November, Václav Havel and Alexander Dubček appeared for the first time together on
the balcony of publishing house Melantrich on Václavské náměstí. When they clasped hands
people wept with emotion. After three days the Federal Assembly abolished Article 4 of the
Constitution and the Communist Party ceased to be the leading force in the country.

CHAPTER 34

YOU CAN'T STOP THIS ANY MORE

On 17th November, 1989 Alexander Dubček arrived in Prague. A car with a driver and telephone
had been hired for him by the regional director of Czechoslovak Television in Slovakia, Jaroslav
Hlinický to travel to the capital. He had a meeting with the leadership of the Communist Party of
Italy and a member of the European Parliament, Luigi Collaiani, who'd come to announce joyful
news; the European Parliament had nominated him for the Andrei Sakharov Prize for his
extraordinary commitment to human rights protection. He was staying with Jaroš's family, who
were telephoned by Ján Urban, a signatory to Charter 77, calling on Dubček to attend the youth
demonstration in Albertov. Dubček knew that his personal presence at the demonstration could
result unexpected reactions and perhaps this is why he decided to go to the students. With his
friends, Jaroš, Slavík and Collajani, they headed in the direction of Albertov. It was enough to
register the excited atmosphere, chanting passwords: "Cancel the KSČ", "Cancel the ŠtB", "We
don't want Miloš", "Vivat Havel", "Vivat Dubček". People recognized him and showed their
sympathy demonstratively. They didn't know that all the time they were being watched by agents
deployed by the ŠtB, who were listening on the phones of his former secretary, Jaroš. A crowd of
people around Dubček suddenly solidified, uniformed public security officers surrounded them
calling for them to board a police car. People whistled, shouted and threatened. Dubček, however,
smiled, waved at people and, with Slavík, Jaroš and Collaiani, they boarded a green Anton vehicle.
It paused for a moment at the Palace of Culture in front of a door with an official address plate,

the District Department of the National Security Corps. Collaiani was shortly released. The security officials behaved well, some of whose youngsters made it clear that Dubček's arrest was distasteful. "It will only be for a few hours. We have an order to hold you only for the time of the demonstration. All the Charter has left Prague, Havel is in Hrádeček and you're the only one who is here. They're afraid you might speak ... When it's over, you'll go home," ŠtB officer informed him in almost friendly way.

"It isn't over, you can't stop this any more," Dubček looked at his embarrassed face.

At the mass meeting in Bratislava on Thursday, 23rd November 1989, a representative of the Civic Forum, Jiří Dienstbier, was present in SNP Square. After Dienstbier, following two days of talks with representatives of VPN, Alexander Dubček, appeared for the first time in public in twenty years. The negotiations for this were complex and their participants had to overcome mutual mistrust resulting from different life experiences and generational viewpoints. When the presenters of the rally, Milan Kňažko and Ján Budaj, announced his appearance, there was enthusiasm in the square.

"I speak to you for the first time after many long years. I turn to everybody with an urgent challenge to regenerate our society. I support civic initiatives that seek to uplift our society, our country to a higher level in its material, spiritual, cultural, humane and democratic development. As you know after more than twenty years, I lift my voice as part of the popular movement for a new revival of socialism ..." Dubček read, the people listened to him at first, but afterwards the applause swelled into a chant of "Vivat Dubček" until finally Dubček's sentences disappeared under the enthusiastic chanting of his name. He folded the paper, smiled broadly, and stretched out his hands in a typical gesture, as if he wanted to embrace the entire square.

After the demonstration Milan and Peter stopped at home and Paľo came from Malacky. They felt a moment of wonderful strength and energy having survived. Although their father had had a difficult day, he didn't miss out his customary walk to Slavín. His boys went with him. They stood by the marble wall of the monument and looked at the Bratislava evening. The last time they'd stood with their father like this was when they were still children. "You see, boys, so many years, and yet it's happened." They stood there for a long time, watching the city where the first snowflakes were falling silently.

CHAPTER 35

TAKING POWER

The Czechoslovak democratic revolution, led to people who did not consider politics as their business. For the Czech dissidents gathered in Civic Forum, politics was a matter which should later be defied rather than fully embraced. However, power lay on the ground and the Communist Party of Czechoslovakia remained in a desolate state after the resignation of its General Secretary, Miloš Jakeš. The only state institution that was able to negotiate with representatives of Civic Forum, headed by Havel, and the VPN, headed by Budaj, was the federal government led by the moderate and pro-Gorbachev Communist, Ladislav Adamec, who, in dramatic circumstances, broke with the leadership of the Communist Party on 25th November. Adamec had the state structures, including the army and security services, behind him and Václav Havel had millions of dissatisfied citizens behind him.

Political developments focused on two key issues, the creation of a government of national understanding and the election of a new president. It was clear that Gustáv Husák's days were numbered. However, he had to fulfill a last state role as the current president, to appoint a new government. Since the newly born political power, composed of representatives of Civic Forum and the VPN, did not have the tools of power in its hands, it couldn't consider using them against state leadership and eventually didn't intend to. It wanted the transference of power to take place through negotiations and not violence. One of the leading representatives of Civic Forum, Zdeněk Jičínský, explained why the representatives of Civic Forum and the VPN didn't dare to create a completely new government without Communists. "It isn't possible to consider a situation when they depart completely and tell us - form your government! We are incompetent, inappropriate and it would end in a real catastrophe. We do not have it in us. There are professionals who have been in the administration for twenty years. For twenty years we've been washing window cases."

Civic Forum and VPN didn't want to propose a Prime Minister, because then they would have to construct an entire government. They came to the view that Adamec should remain the Prime Minister, with whom they would discuss its composition. However, the idea that Adamec should remain Prime Minister was not abandoned by those who were cautious, but increasingly decided on making Václav Havel the new president. They knew that the Slovaks wouldn't allow Czechs to be in the top two state positions. Adamec, who relied on the support of citizens, among whom he was still more famous than Havel, was also interested in position of president. Adamec made a move forward and announced to Civic Forum officials that he was resigning from the post of prime minister. He proposed as his successor a young, insignificant member of the government, Marián Čalfa. Václav Havel and his closest allies formally condemned Adamec's decision, but actually they did not mind it. On the contrary, it appealed to them. Čalfa was a Slovak. And a Communist.

CHAPTER 36

DUBČEK TO THE CASTLE!

There was a busy afternoon on 10th December in a room on the ground floor of the Dubček house. Ivan Laluha, Teodor Baník, Róbert Harenčár, Ján Uher, the brothers Laco and Tono Ťažkí analyzed the situation before the key events at the end of 1989. Vlado Krajči came from Trenčín in the evening.

"Jičínský has suggested you as President. A Czech, head of the Conceptual Commission of Civic Forum. Despite the complete resistance of Civic Forum. He justified it by saying that at Letná everyone was calling "Dubček to the castle!" And all of the Slovak VPNs, except for Jan Budaj, is against you, but fourteen university professors in Bologna and Perugia have nominated you for the Nobel Prize ... that's how we are, us Slovaks," Ťažký worried at the issues.

"Jičínský and Dienstbier said it clearly - if there is one Czechoslovak citizen who the whole world knows, it's Dubček!" added Laluha.

"I talked to Havel. He told me he would be a candidate only if I said clearly that I wouldn't be. He doesn't want to stand against me. But how can I say that I won't be a candidate if the whole of Slovakia backs me and what I experienced in Václavské náměstí,, when half a million people called "Dubček to the castle" can't be ignored ..." Dubček sighed. He thought then and smiled unexpectedly. His friends looked at him in surprise. "I remembered how Havel told me a recent joke that he hoped that at least he would be the Minister of Culture in the new government ..."

"Civic Forum will never allow you to become president. Not because you are a Slovak, but because you symbolize them for something that has been overcome, to which they give no prospects ... Do you understand? We are all former Communists for them. Although we're renewers, but still Communists. Pithart made that clear. Havel is the man of 1989, Dubček is the man of 1968," said Laluha.

"Fero Mikloško said to his people that Dubček and his people can't be trusted. They are former communists and their behaviour clearly states that they are on the left. I'm afraid they're not joining us, but we're joining them. They won't follow the reforms of sixty-eight. It's not about repairing the old system but replacing it. Not one worker went on the streets to defend socialism," said Harenčár.

"And aren't former Communists in the Charter and in Civic Forum?" Dubček asked.

"Yeah, but all of them stood up against the party throughout those years.. You stood on the side of those who didn't want to remove the Communist Party but give it a new mission and continue the reforms. But this isn't a return to sixty-eight but a gradual replacement of the old and the renewal of civil society. Isn't that enough for them?" asked Laluha.

"I'm afraid that they're worried that socialism with a human face has far deeper roots in our people than they think," added Uher.

"You have just said why the entire West will press stubbornly against Dubček. They will formally clap him on the shoulders, but in fact they will support Havel whom they will be able to manipulate more easily," said Harenčár.

"Lads we don't have to be downhearted, modesty in such situations won't do. It's necessary that Šaňo and we with him clearly indicate his interest in the post of president. We should be a bit like in America. You can't be bashful, but say clearly what we want! And that's what Slovakia wants!" Laco Ťažký said heatedly.

"But the Czechs told you that we had and still have a Slovak president. Fifteen years," Laluha said. "It will be crucial whether Husák appoints Čalfa as Prime Minister."

"It is said that the hottest candidates for Premier are Komárek or Adamec," Anton Ťažký added.

"Čalfa is nearly Havel's right hand man," Harenčár nodded his head.

"I also think that Husák will appoint Čalfa with pleasure. It'll be his last revenge on Šaňo. He knows that if there is a Slovak prime minister, the president must be Czech," said Laluha.

"Husák couldn't bear my replacing him," Dubček smiled bitterly.

"In the opinion polls, Havel is almost invisible. Look ... On the question - "Who would you like for President?" the greatest number respond Dubček. He even leads in Bohemia. Some of them mention Komárek, Čalfa, Císař, Havel is only fifth ..." Harenčár argued.

"Havel suggested that I be the Chairman of the Federal Assembly and he would be president only until the elections next June. Then he would give up the presidential function in my benefit ..." Dubček thought aloud.

"What did you tell him?" Laluha asked.

"That we could do that, but the opposite way round. Let him be the President of the Federal Parliament and I would be the President, and I would give up in his favour after the elections. I've been arguing over the moods between citizens and opinion polls."

"The federal assembly in this design would never elect Havel," Harenčár objected.

A news jingle came from the radio. Harenčár turned up the sound. "Today, in the afternoon, President Gustáv Husák appointed a government of national understanding, headed by the Prime Minister Marián Čalfa. After swearing in the Prime Minister, Gustáv Husák informed the presidium of the Federal Assembly by letter that he was resigning from the position of the President of the

Czechoslovak Socialist Republic." There was a gloomy mood in the room, Dubček stood up disappointed and walked out to the front of his house. The others stayed inside. They felt he wanted to be alone at this moment.

CHAPTER 37

IF THERE WAS THE MISFORTUNE THAT I SHOULD BECOME PRESIDENT

Before the arrival of the VPN at the unofficial centre of the Civic Forum during a dramatic night from 5th to 6th of December 1989 there was a vigorous debate at the studio of sculptor, Joska Skalník in Prague's Špalíček. "I think that what Zdeněk Jičínský said yesterday is very reasonable," Jiri Dienstbier began cautiously. "From a political point of view, Dubček's candidacy would be ideal, even if the candidate is not the ideal person at all. There is no other person who could be used politically in this way for a peaceful transition to democracy." Václav Havel listened to him and frowned slightly. When Dienstbier had finished speaking, he said in a low voice to Radim Palouš, chairing the discussion, that Kocáb wanted the floor. Those present had noticed Havel's warning. Palouš gave Kocáb the floor.

"You know, for me, as a representative of the younger generation, there is a definite idea of who should be president," he said in a slightly trembling voice. "Mr. Dubček is, for my generation, a representative of Communism, even though a reformist. Communism would become a real danger if the position were taken by the Communists Dubček, Adamec or Císař. For us, the presidential question is clear. The embodiment of a guarantee of democracy and a barrier against communist reformism is Vašek Havel. If Civic Forum immediately launches a campaign, in a few days every Czech and Slovak will know who Havel is and what his merits are for his country."

There was a hum in the studio. The audience stared at each other and an increasing number of heads nodded at Kocáb's proposal. The floor was again taken by Jiří Dienstbier. But it wasn't to defend his original proposal but to abandon it and to look for a new one. "Of course, that's completely another idea. Yes, Havel for President!" It's simply basic and decisive. We'll bring millions of people to the square. It's simply an absolute requirement." Then he turned to Havel. "Vašku, what is your opinion?"

Havel was somewhat bashful, mumbled in his characteristic way and then said the sentences, which he often repeated in the days which followed. "Of course I don't want to be a president. But if the situation becomes so tense that it's in the interest of the country to have this for a short while, then I'm capable of being president. Because I've always had the interests of my homeland over my personal interests, otherwise I wouldn't have gone to prison and so on. I'm prepared to make this terrible sacrifice if it's unavoidable and is the only salvation of our nations. If this misfortune happens, it would be worth considering for the time up to free elections."

The delegation of the VPN Coordination Centre of Budaj, Kňažko, Čarnogurský, Kusý and Ondruš arrived at 1.30. It was just Jičínský, who, after the introductory formalities, asked their Slovak friends their opinion on who should take the posts of the President of the Republic and the Chairman of the federal government. He asked directly to avoid possible deals on the side. The Slovaks took their time to consider. The floor was then taken by Ján Budaj.

"It is complicated for a Slovak President besides Alexander Dubček, whom I don't consider to be the ideal representative of Slovakia's interests ..." at that moment, some of Havel's supporters began to clap, but Budaj continued, "Perhaps it's ideal to install one from there at the moment. But the question is, how would he represent us and you ... So we dared to offer three variants. The first is Miro Kusý ... In the second case, if it were politically urgent, Dubček could be considered. We present this variant here, I repeat, only with great unease ... The third alternative is Milan Kňažko, who is considered the tribune of revolution in Slovakia. End of story." Michal Kocáb used the embarrassing moment of silence and again with his own fiery conviction that Václav Havel would be the best head of the state. They all looked at the dramatist. He looked ahead and slowly chose his. "Um ... I, as a private person, of course don't want to be president. I want to go back to the theatre, which I have said publicly many times. I can only accept if the situation is so limiting that there is no other way out for this country. If it's the only solution, I'll take it with the great hope it won't be for long."

In a moment Rychetský broke the silence, turning to the Slovak representatives. "I think your opinion is important. If Slovakia does not accept Dubček, it doesn't make sense to talk about it."

"Slovakia will accept it. People, the people would accept it," said Budaj.

"But the people are perhaps quite important," Jičínský said, with heavy sarcasm.

"I'm just saying it as the experienced man of the theatre says ..." Budaj turned to Havel.

"No, sorry, we're not directing a play!" protested Jičínský.

"Zdeněk, you're expressing yourself theoretically about Dubček," Pithart objected.

"Wait Peter," said Jičínský, "Here you have the results of a poll. From a sample of 30,000 people. Dubček has eleven per cent, Walter Komárek almost 8 per cent, and Čestmír Císař, Ladislav Adamec and Václav Havel are third with one percentage point ... "

"That's just Prague," Pithart said angrily.

"And what do you think will happen in the countryside? In Moravia? "

"Dubček will get the most," said somebody.

"Of course Dubček," added another voice.

There was a silence interrupted by Václav Havel.

"So I can't be president, that's clear."

"Do not forget that 80 percent of the people said they didn't know. The mass of the undecided will be inclined to the side of whoever we start to promote," Oslzlý said sharply. "And it will be Vašek!"

"The Student Information Centre in Bratislava carried out a survey where five thousand respondents gave Dubček five times more votes than Komárek and twenty times more votes than Havel," some objected. The audience looked at the Slovak delegation which was silent.

"I would like to say that the artistic and intellectual environment that dominates our Coordination Centre is far from representing public opinion in its complexity," Jičínský noted. "I think Dubček is a solid, calculable assurance as a political symbol," he said, and looked at representatives of Slovak VPN in anticipation of their support. But they remained silent.

Jičínský, together with several representatives of the Club for Democratic Socialism, Obroda explained to the VPN on the second day it should be President Dubček. The Slovaks generally agreed, but they feared that Dubček's coming to the castle would result in a reversion to socialism and that Czechoslovakia would not move away from Soviet influence. The VPN did not exclude Dubček's candidacy, but continued to support Havel. One possible reason was that VPN did not trust Dubček and their mutual communication was weak. Dubček relied on popular support as though he didn't know that the President was elected by the Federal Assembly. Finally, the VPN leadership confirmed Havel's candidacy, provided he was only president only to the free-elections, from which a newly elected Federal Assembly would elect a new president. Havel accepted this solution. The worry that Václav Klaus voiced at this time no one listened to. "Would Havel be an integrating personality for fifteen million Czechs and Slovaks as with the narrowly-based community of Civic Forum?"

CHAPTER 38

ŠALFA, ŠTOLFA, ŠALFA OR ČALFA

Havel had decided to be a president and he wanted, naturally, to surround himself with his own people. He couldn't imagine as he'd said several times that the chairman of the federal government was an unknown functionary - "Šalfa, Štolf, or whatever his name is ..." When representatives of the VPN supported his intention to run for president, he declared that his presidential nomination was conditional on the nomination of Ján Čarnogurský as Prime Minister. In the complex combinations of the rising power groups by the very early morning of 6th December, there appeared to be only one clear point; Havel would stand for the president. The only Dubček supporter Jičínsky in Civic Forum suggested that the selection of the candidate be postponed until the results of an improvised opinion poll were announced. From the Slovaks the most vehement supporter of Havel was Ján Čarnogurský who was in favour of Čalfa, his fellow student from the

Faculty of Law, as Chairman of the Federal Government. His goal was not Prague, but Slovakia. Adamec would not give up the struggle for power. He relied on the support of Mikhail Gorbachev as indeed did the majority of Communist MPs in both Chambers of the Federal Assembly, which chose the President. But he was unlucky; he was Czech. Havel's people thus plumped for Čalfa who was optimal for their intentions. He was not only a Slovak but also a communist. It was clear that the president must be Czech and non-communist.

A key round table negotiation took place on 8th December in the Prague Palace of Culture. Václav Havel commented on the negotiations with the words, "Everyone actually agreed with each other, including the Communist Party, which was almost shocking to me ... the Communist Party agrees that the President will be Czech and non-party ... we took Čalfa as the Prime Minister, as he would probably soon be replaced ... it turned out that we have far more influence on things than we thought ..."

Two days after that, when President Gustáv Husák appointed the new federal government, led by Marián Čalfa, the presidium of the Slovak National Council engaged with the issue of the candidate for the presidency. Civic Forum and the VPN officially announced Václav Havel's candidacy. Representatives of the Communist Party, the Party of Slovak Revival Party and the Freedom Party agreed unanimously on the candidacy of Alexander Dubček. This proposal put VPN representatives in a difficult situation. Its leader, Jan Budaj, later commented, "We were in a difficult situation. Alexander Dubček is an undoubted political power in Slovakia. Apart from the VPN, it represents the only real political party, but has no members, except for few of his friends. In our opinion, it was a mistake to issue a decree from the roundtable on 8th December that the president could only be Czech and a non-communist. From the Slovak point of view, it was a delegitimization of Alexander Dubček. There was a feeling in Slovakia that it was a defeat in which the VPN assisted."

The fact that the supporters of Václav Havel were not sure of the success of their candidate also demonstrates their categorical rejection of the proposal by the Communist Party on the direct election of the president by the citizens. Civic Forum reached a paradoxical situation. Instead of using the most democratic means, direct elections, they insisted that the president be elected by the Federal Assembly, which was composed almost exclusively of old Communist deputies.

Two weeks after Husák's resignation, the new president had to be elected. The democratic movement didn't want to put pressure on the deputies through the public because of concerns over parliamentary vacancies because if its membership had fallen below three-fifths, the house would lose legal validity. It was a difficult situation - to convince deputies who were as yet unable to speak Havel's name to elect him as President. A man whose name Havel could not remember a few days before decided to engage with this difficult situation. Marián Čalfa.

A pragmatic and crafty lawyer, he quickly realized that the communist regime was over. When the outgoing President Husák appointed him as Prime Minister he realized he'd become the most powerful man in the country. Representing the President and, in particular, the chief commander of the armed forces. He later commented on his entry into the political affair, "Civic Forum didn't know how to make Havel president." He invited Danish specialists, who cleared a room in the government offices of eavesdropping devices. On the 15th December in the afternoon he invited Václav Havel for a secret meeting to this room. He smiled at Havel's objection that the current communist parliament would never elect him as president. "On the contrary, they will choose you. Deputies are not dimwits and they calculate well what they threaten when they dare to. And vice versa, what are they expecting when they meet our expectations? The Federal Assembly cannot obstruct; they've never had the chance to try. They're used to voting for everything that is presented to them as authoritative. I will arrange for a deputy from Slovakia to resign and Alexander Dubček will be co-opted in his place. Everything has to happen before 19th December, when I give a government statement to the Federal Assembly. At the same time, I'll urge deputies to elect Dubček the chairman of the Federal Assembly and he will direct your election as president."

"How do you want the deputies to be compelled to respect your plan?"

"Leave it to me," Čalfa smiled. Then he added, "Can you, Mr. President, imagine that you'll enter the New Year before the nation with a New Year's speech?" Havel was fascinated by Čalfa's plan and his determination. After the hour-long meeting with Čalfa, the actress, Bartoška took him by car to Joska Skalnik's studio in Vinohrady. Havel told his friends that he, a dissident, had just concluded a secret deal with the communist bureaucrat. "It's terribly good news from Čalfa. But we have to conceal everything. Not from the ŠtB, but from that part of the public which suspects us of hole-in-the-corner politics. For now, I ask you to keep silent as the grave about everything that I tell you in this room."

Shortly before the vote for president, Havel gave Dubček and the VPN representatives a promise, after his election as president, that in his New Year's speech he'd promise to support Dubček's candidacy for the president after the free elections in June 1990.

"Communists will scare you about unemployment, it's not true, do not worry. For twenty years, official propaganda has been saying that I am the enemy of socialism, that I want to restore capitalism in our country, it was all lies ... I promise you that I will take the position of president for one election period, but then I would like to devote myself to my work as a playwright. I also promise you on my honour that if I do not improve the standard of living in the ČSFR during my term, I will resign myself ... I imagine that the security of society should be far greater than under what many have called socialism. You may be wondering what republic I seek. I say to you: the human republic that serves people and therefore has the hope that people will serve it ... We all want a republic that will take care of the disappearance of all the humiliating barriers between the various social strata, a republic in which we will not be divided into slaves and masters. I long for such a republic more than anyone else ... There are people who muddy the waters and panic that there will be price rises. Watch out for them! No gigantic price increases or even unemployment, as the panic-mongers systematically put about, we aren't preparing such a thing ... We will never enter any pact anymore ... Moreover, our many declared intentions to reform so as not to create great shocks, huge inflation or even loss of basic social security, our economists must accept simply as a task assigned to them. There is no space for such a thing as "It's not possible" here." The people that gathered at Letná at the end of November, enhusiastically applauded these words from Havel and trusted them.

CHAPTER 39

I GIVE MY VOTE TO HAVEL

On 18th December representatives of Civic Forum and the VPN agreed that their joint candidate for president of the republic would be Václav Havel and Alexander Dubček as chairman of the Federal Assembly. It was the second highest constitutional function in the country, but it was essentially formal. It was explained to the current chairman of the Federal Assembly, Stanislav Kukrál, who'd been in office for only six days, that it was necessary to install Dubček instead. On 28th December at the 20th meeting of the Federal Assembly, the Vice-President, Jozef Šimúth, took the floor and announced that Alexander Dubček was the only candidate for the chairman of the Federal Assembly, based on the agreement of all the political forces of the Czechoslovak Socialist Republic. His information was received with a storm of applause. After his election, Dubček came to the microphone and with a trembling voice thanked them for the vote. "I can't prevent personal memory. Just twenty years ago, I had to leave the position I'm taking on now. The profound social changes in our country that took place after 17th November have resulted in me returning to responsible work in the highest legislative body ... Honourable Assembly, tomorrow 29th December there will be according to the Constitutional Act of the Czechoslovak federation the election of the President of the Czechoslovak Socialist Republic. In accordance with the recommendations of all the parties of the National Front, Citizens' Forum, Public against Violence and other initiatives that have so significantly influenced the political face of our country, I will call for a vote on the proposal of Václav Havel as the President of the Republic, to whom I will give my vote ..."

On the second day, after the election of the two chambers of Parliament, the new President of the Republic, Václav Havel, took the presidential oath, "I promise on my honour fidelity to the Czechoslovak Socialist Republic ..."

Dubček didn't listen to him. He looked over Vladislav Hall and observed faces of which many were very familiar. "What is it with these people? Yesterday they chose me as their chairman without hesitation. Me of whom they weren't able to say my name for twenty years ... For twenty years I wrote letters to them ... They didn't even answer me ... Yet again they've applauded me. They truly didn't have to ... representatives of the people ... If they the most principled of the Communists, then the party collapses like a house of cards ... self-seekers and place fillers... Not a single one of these joined the party in Thirty-Nine either. Why would they? What would they have got out of it? When it turns out that the membership in the Communist Party doesn't confer any benefits, they'll run like rats ... And now they've elected Havel, a man whom just a few months ago they sent to prison ... My God ... Such a Communist Party has no future. .."

After the election of the President, a solemn celebratory Mass of the Te Deum was held in St. Vitus' Cathedral. The television cameras showed long detailed footage of the three highest constitutional actors. The federal prime minister grinned slightly, satisfied. The President radiating balance issued a declaration that testified to his inner peace. The Chairman of the Federal Assembly had an absent gaze in which there was deep sadness.

In his New Year's speech Havel kept his promise only partially. He spoke only commonplace phrases, "... I feel different after the various bitter experiences Slovaks had in the past, a special duty with regard to this in respected of all the interests of the Slovak nation and that he should not in the future be denied access to any state office, including the highest."

CHAPTER 40

WE'RE SORRY, I APOLOGISE FOR US

At the end of February 1990 negotiations began on the departure of Soviet troops from the territory of Czechoslovakia. The departure of the 126 artillery regiment from Rožňava on 22nd December, 1990 ended the twenty-two year occupation of the country.

On 19th February a Czechoslovak delegation, headed by President Václav Havel, visited the United States of America. Slovak political representation in a nearly fifty-member delegation was represented by Prime Minister of the Federal Government, Čalfa, Foreign Trade Minister, Barčák. Both of them were Communists, of which Barčák proudly declared that he would never deny the party book. The VPN was represented by Ján Budaj, Milan Kňažko, František Mikloško and Martin Bútora. Alexander Dubček's invitation to the delegation was refused by Havel. He may have feared that in the US, the more popular Dubček would increasingly diminish his performance with the American political elite. Ján Budaj was so upset by the fact that Dubček wasn't in the delegation that during the stopover in Reykjavik he seriously considered leaving the delegation and returning home. "Alexander Dubček is the most famous Slovak for us and, despite the fact that we have objections to him, he could have done much for Slovakia and for Czechoslovakia in the USA!" he said.

On 22nd April Pope John Paul II arrived for a visit. He came to a country with a new name, the Czech and Slovak Federal Republic. In Bratislava, Dubček and the pope recalled his meeting less than two years before in the Vatican, when Dubček was still in political disgrace. In early June, the first free elections took place since 1946. Dubček was re-elected chairman of the newly-elected Federal Assembly. President Havel appointed Marián Čalfa as Prime Minister of the government. The Chairman of the Federal Assembly engaged in an unprecedented foreign policy activities. An historic event was a visit by a 50-member Slovak delegation in May 1990 to the USA and Canada, where they attended the celebration of the twentieth anniversary of the founding of the World Congress of Slovaks in Toronto. The Cathedral of Transfiguration, built by Stefan Roman, greeted Alexander Dubček, Milan Čič, Rudolf Schuster and other Slovak officials by ringing the bells. Before the conferring an honorary degree of Doctor of Science by the American University in Washington, hundreds of enthusiastic students welcomed the legendary Dubček on the huge lawn in front of the University.

World statesmen sought to meet the Prague Spring leader. Dubček experienced a period of amazing gratification. Only one thing did not, the justification by the Soviet's highest representative, Mikhail Gorbachev, for the occupation of Czechoslovakia. At the end of April, however, he received an invitation from the highest Soviet politician, Gorbachev, to visit the Soviet Union. When his aeroplane landed at Vnukovo airport on 18th May, his throat constricted. The last time he landed in Moscow twenty-two years before was as a captive of the Kremlin overlords. Now their successors had invited them with all the glory of an official visit. After settling in a government villa in Mitschurin pereulk, he didn't stay in and went on to the streets of Moscow. Memory on memory crowded into his mind; to the year 1956, when Khrushchev historically condemned Stalin and to the 23rd August 1968, when he arrived and dirty from a mountain cabin in Transcarpathian Ukraine.

On the third day of his visit, he was received by Mikhail Gorbachev, President of the Soviet Union, who had been engaged that day in a demanding meeting with the US Secretary of State, Baker. Dubček had said he would like to talk to him face to face. However, Dubček also took on his own responsibility, the Czechoslovak ambassador, Rudolf Slánsky and the advisor, Hubert Max. At two p.m. the door opened in the Soviet-era Kremlin office. Gorbachev and Dubček had a long and friendly handshake. Because of the hum of the cameras and the number of clicks from their lenses what was said by the two of them could not be heard. Dubček's face radiated contentment. The journalists left the room and Mikhail Sergeyevich cordially invited guests to the table. Ostroumov his adviser took his place beside him. With his characteristic vigorous speech accompanied by dynamic gestures and a wide smile, he brought to the audience a warm and loving atmosphere. Dubček listened attentively, but sometimes his thoughts went away. In front of him, Brezhnev's thick eyebrows seemed frowning. When thinking of the "negotiation" in August 1968 in the same premises, he felt a chill run down his back.

The interview with Gorbachev was thirty minutes in place of the scheduled hour. At the end he moved to the subject they were waiting for. 1968. "It was a strategic fault of Brezhnev's leadership.

It undermined the reform process not only in Czechoslovakia but also in the Soviet Union. We're sorry, I apologise for us ..."

Gorbachev continued his interpretation, and Dubček listened carefully. From his concentrated expression, it was clear how much satisfaction Gorbachev's words meant to him. His life-long wish, which had been a dream for years, had been fulfilled. The highest Soviet representative personally apologized for the invasion. He accepted Gorbachev's words as a rehabilitation of Prague Spring, famous and unknown people, who had made their commitment to the Prague Spring a milestone in Czech-Slovak and European history. The past was closed, before the two statesmen were the huge tasks of a present and a future that had begun in January 1968.

CHAPTER 41

LORD GRANT

Dubček's apartment in a villa near Hradná brána was full of flowers. He loved them. He was sitting in his room alone. It was night and heavy rain clouds were forming all over Prague. On a table lay some of his favourite books that he'd brought from Bratislava, Fuser's biography of Gandhi or JFK's Profiles of Courage. Milan, who worked in Prague and lived with him, was somewhere out with his friends. He noticed that some of the geraniums had dried out and had to be cut. Usually his wife did this when she came to Prague. She hadn't been there for a long time. She was lying in a hospital at the Brothers of Mercy in Bratislava under the supervision of their son Pavol, a doctor. The situation had deteriorated, yet she tried not to show her suffering. She gritted her teeth and smiled. On the last Sunday of August, they had bathed in Senec lake and Anka had swum to the island almost in the middle of the lake. On Saturday, the 1st September she was picking beans in the garden with Jožko Brinzík in the early afternoon. Several times she went to lie down in order to relax. Brinzík noticed her yellowness and as he already knew that she was ill he realized that it was bad. He called Paľo, who took her to hospital. It turned out that the worsening of the condition wasn't due to her gall bladder. When they operated, they detected pancreatic cancer at an advanced stage. Experts at home, as well as in the US and Germany, said that cancer at this stage was no longer operable.

September 1990 was coming to an end. Thoughts whirled in Dubček's head and he couldn't sleep. A few days before the British Prime Minister, Margaret Thatcher, had visited Prague. She made a tribute to Dubček as a courageous leader of "an experiment, the remarkable expression of which is inscribed in our memory." On 19th September on the second day after his release, Sláma, a former political prisoner, criticized Dubček severely. While for the British Prime Minister 1968 was the time when "the sun showed its face to us", for Sláma it was only "the settling of accounts between red and pink." The next round of anti-Dubček attacks was initiated by a typical representative of late-arriving heroes, those who had never been tested, but knew what to do if they were tested, Deputy Bratinka. He has called for a judgement on Czechoslovak leaders of the previous forty years.

Dubček thought of Milan, who was to leave at this time for a study visit in the USA and Canada. He wished this for him very much, but he didn't have a good feeling. Some unknown intuition told him that something was going to happen to his wife during his absence. He looked out of the window at night in Prague where countless pubs and locals made a cheerful row. The clock tower of the nearby cathedral struck midnight. Suddenly longing and loneliness crushed him. A candle burned on the table. Below it was a tiny picture of his wife. "Lord Grant that she won't leave yet ... She's suffered enough in life and now at last she can lead a better one ... I've had some tough and beautiful moments with her. She's the mother of my sons ... Please make these medicines they've given her work, to relieve her from fever, from pain ... Lord, I beg ... if you exist, don't let her die ..." Suddenly he realized he was addressing a Lord he thought he wouldn't need much in his life. His soul was alarmed that even if the Almighty had heard his plea, he might be too late.

Milan Dubček returned from his American stay earlier to get to his mother's funeral. It was held on 5th October in Bratislava. Dubček was left with three sons and four grandchildren who made him very happy. The family was companionable and supportive of their father, but no one could replace a life partner. After Anna's death, he closed himself off for a while, but life continued, and his tenacious nature wouldn't allow him to be distracted by emotion. His friends admired how quickly he recovered from his beloved wife's departure. But only he knew what he was actually going through. Whenever he could, he went to her grave at the cemetery in Bratislava's Slávičie valley. Even during the pre-election campaign two years later he his chauffeur automatically drove him to the cemetery whenever he returned to Bratislava.

CHAPTER 42

PUTSCH IN MOSCOW

Spring 1990 brought in great changes in the Soviet Union. The power monopoly of the Communist Party ended and new political parties began to emerge, the most powerful of which became the Democratic Russia bloc. The chief representative of the bloc was a former Communist, Boris Yeltsin, who in May was elected as the President of the Supreme Soviet of the Russian Soviet Federal Republic. Understandably, he supported the national republics' aspirations for sovereignty, in particular, demanding sovereignty for Russia. While his Soviet counterpart, Gorbachev, was to be elected Soviet President by the Congress of the Supreme Soviet, the prescient Yeltsin had himself elected in June 1991 in direct elections by citizens as President of Russia. The pressure of the federal republics to break away from the Soviet Union increased, and when the Supreme Soviet of the USSR under Gorbachev's leadership voted for the right of the republics to break away, party conservatives began to be desperate. A group of high-level Soviet officials began to prepare a coup. During his holiday in the Crimea on 17th August, Gorbachev was asked to hand over his presidential powers to the State Committee due to a state of exceptional circumstances. Gorbachev refused and thus the chief of the plotters, Vice-President Janayev, in a state of total drunkenness declared a state of emergency. Most top army and secret service officers have refused to back up the rebellious officials. Janayev's group managed to occupy the White House building of parliament, with conspirators. Yeltsin described it as a coup and stood at the forefront of resistance urging citizens to defend democracy. On the night of 20th to 21st August demonstrators met an army and the coup leaders were defeated. That night, during which twenty-three years before the Soviet army had invaded the Czech-Slovak Republic Mstislav Rostropovich played his cello on the ninth floor of the White House in support of Yeltsin. An exhausted and anxious Gorbachev came in haste to Moscow from his cabin in Foros in the Crimea. For many Russians, the August events were the real anti-communist revolution. Gorbachev resigned in three days as General Secretary of ÚV KSSZ, but it was too late. The confused and uncertain times were used by most of the federal republics, followed by the Baltic republics to declare their state's independence. For the first celebrations of Christmas 1991 the Russian flag replaced the Soviet insignia on the highest point of the Kremlin. Mikhail Gorbachev resigned his post, emptied his office in the Kremlin and Yeltsin moved in. At midnight on 31st December, 1991, the Soviet Union ceased to exist.

CHAPTER 43

I'M GRIEF-STRICKEN

Events in Moscow were used by the Czech right for new attacks on Dubček. His deadly sin was not 1968 itself, but Dubček's current orientation to Western-style social-democratic models that combine transformation with a social, ecological and ethical content. They dragged out again his signature under the Moscow Protocol and the so-called baton law. The Czech right, which didn't like the recent visit of Boris Yeltsin to Prague at Dubček's invitation, also used ambitious, unknown Slovak right-wing politicians to attack it. One of them was the vice-chair of the Federal Assembly and the chairman of the chamber of deputies, the literary scientist, Milan Šútovec. He accused Dubček of reluctance to respond to the attempted coup in Moscow, indicating that Dubček was on the side of Soviet conservatives. It was exactly the opposite of what happened. Dubček had telephoned Yeltsin from the Tatras when on holiday on the day of the attempt and had immediately sent him a telegram where he clearly stood at his side condemning the attempted coup d'état. Šútovec, dazzled by the support of the Czech right and his vision of the chairmanship of Parliament, began another round of tough attacks on Dubček. When the whole bubble burst, he publicly disowned them, "It may have been unserious, and so I'm sorry. Is there the possibility of taking back everything I said?"

Right-wing politicians even accused Dubček's allegedly fake image of the republic he created as a leftist politician abroad. The desire for revenge had possessed the Czech right so much that it has lost the ability to reason rationally. After the wreck of the Šútovec initiative, it seized on the lustration law, which was supposed to hammer inconvenient, especially left-wing politicians. There was such hysteria about him that even the right-wing President Havel felt it necessary to cool the hot heads of these late-arriving heroes. Dubček was disgusted by these attacks but proudly resisted them. He only voiced astonishment that the attacks came not from those who actually suffered under the communist regime, but mostly from those who had adapted to it and used it. Dubček didn't defend himself, but the beliefs and principles in which he believed. He knew that this dispute wasn't about him, but about the future character of the republic. He was particularly concerned about the lack of sophistication of some political opponents. The Civic Democratic Party (ODS), which had been formed in the Czech Republic on the ruins of Civic Forum, officially asked Dubček to resign as President of the Federal Assembly.

The crown on everything was put on by Pavel Tigrid, who prevented Dubček from speaking at the meeting for a Common State at Václavské náměstí in November 1991 where he was invited by President Havel. Dubček was very hurt that Havel accepted Tigrid's insolent position without a single word. Although Havel sent Dubček a letter of apology in a short time, it didn't improve their relationship. Even before this an ODS deputy, Václav Malý had publicly insulted Dubček at a gathering of hundreds of thousands without embarrassment. The humiliation of Dubček and with him and all decent Slovaks and Czechs was all the more painful as he had prepared an emotional statement on preserving the common state of the Czechs and Slovaks.

"This is not the first time in our public life voices have been raised in a very critical way directly requesting my resignation from the position of the Chairman of the Federal Assembly and putting certain pressures, as before, on the Vice-President of the Federal Assembly Jičínsky and many others to testify on this. And I will tell you sincerely that I am grief-stricken."

The hounding by the Czech and Slovak right of Dubček even had international repercussions. The office of the Federal Police Corps' turned to the German side with a request for a recording of the speeches of President Richard von Weizsäcker during the investigation of a Czechoslovak citizen's declaration regarding the public activity of some Czechoslovak representatives. The German side in its diplomatic note expressed astonishment at such a procedure. President Weizsäcker at the Potsdam conference in May 1992 considered it necessary to condemn publicly the practice of Czechoslovak police authorities, who shamelessly hadn't hesitated to ask him for some of his appearances in order to discredit Alexander Dubček. "Dubček understood the necessity of the reforms in 1968 and now has to be excluded from political life on the basis of the so-called lustration law," the German president said in some anger. It need only be said that at that time the Interior Minister was Ján Langoš.

Later on, Dubček said resolutely to the editor of the German weekly, Spiegel, "For twenty years we were on the occupational, social and personal indices. And now they are expelling us again!" Then he smiled and added with his typical calm, " Well, we've stepped into a war and we'll have to go on fighting. Twenty years ago I was expelled from the Communist Party. I left with this party a long time ago, because I understood that it was unable to reform and democratize itself, it was without a future. I'm close to the ideas and methods of social democracy."

However, people weren't drawn into this tricky and murky political game and didn't support the extremist forces in some political parties and groups. Differences in opinion and attitude led eventually to decay and then to the end of the victorious movements of the Civic Forum and the VPN. The Civic Democratic Party led by Václav Klaus was formed out of the ruins of the Civic Forum, and most members of the VPN established the Movement for Democratic Slovakia (HZDS), headed by Vladimír Mečiar. Political turbulence accelerated Dubček's decision to join those who were closest to his social intuitions and ideals. He had long understood that "socialism

372

of the Communist type is definitely dead. The social system implemented in the Soviet Union, with us and other so-called socialist countries, is without a future. It was just a so-called socialism that had nothing to do with the democratic, free, humane and socially just socialism of the Western type of which the Social Democrats dream."

On 14th March 1992 he became a member of the Social Democratic Party of Slovakia and was elected president after two weeks. "I've completed a great arc. My father had once seceded from social democracy into the Communist Party and after a long, complicated and often thorny journey I've returned from the Communist Party to social democracy."

CHAPTER 44

THE END OF CZECHO-SLOVAKIA

From June 1991 to 1992, the leaders of the Czech and Slovak governments held lengthy negotiations seeking an agreement on the foundations of the decentralized federation, which was preferred by most Czechs and Slovaks. However, in order to build a strong electoral base, Mečiar adopted the theme of nationalism, a topic he hadn't been interested in until then. Through his charismatic way of communicating with the public he gained almost 40% of the votes in Slovakia in June 1992. Dubček's Social-Democratic Party of Slovakia won five seats in the House of Nations, and none in the Slovak National Council. The chairman of the Federal Assembly was the HZDS nominee Michal Kováč. Deputy Alexander Dubček was elected as one of the vice presidents of the Federal Assembly.

On 17th July, 1992, the members of the Slovak National Council approved the "Declaration of the Slovak National Republic on the sovereignty of the Slovak Republic", which became the basis of the sovereign state. On the same day Václav Havel resigned from the position of the President of the Czech and Slovak Federal Republic.

Mečiar and Klaus, the most powerful politicians in their republics, spent several hot summer weeks pretending to negotiate the terms of a state treaty for the federal Czecho-Slovakia. Their meetings were in fact not negotiations as both were clear that their goal was to divide the republic. On 26th

August in Brno, the Czech and Slovak Federal Republic resolved to dissolve on 1st January 1993.

The advocate of Czech-Slovak reciprocity Dubček underwent a calvary of personal and political

attacks, but remained himself. Although he believed in the coexistence of Czechs and Slovaks in

one country, he was primarily a Slovakian patriot and a Democrat. So he was also uneasy about

the forceful manifestations that had begun to appear in Slovak politics.

CHAPTER 45

MYSTERY AT THE 88th KILOMETRE

After the ban on the activities of the Communist Party in Russia following the failure of the anti-reform coup in Moscow in August 1991, the Russian Constitutional Court resumed its negotiations on the constitutionality of a ban on the Communist Party after a break of several weeks. President Yeltsin proposed to suspend the work of the Communist Party of the Russian Federation on the grounds that its leaders organized the August coup. Straight away he issued a decree on the property of the Communist Party, which took property from the Communist party. A deputy of the Russian parliament and advisor to President Yeltsin, Galina Starovojova, requested that the leaders of the Eastern bloc in the seventies and eighties be invited to the court hearing, Czechoslovak leader, Dubček, Polish Prime Minister Jarosziewicz and Afghan President Nadjibullah to testify to the criminal nature of the activity the Communist Party of the Soviet Union in the international field. On 27th July, 1992 Czechoslovak representatives, V.Kural, J.Valent and Ambassador Slánsky, the son of the executed General Secretary of the Communist Party, State Secretary of the Russian Federation G.Barbulis and the representative of the President S.Sachraj, handed over a letter from Václav Havel together with the documents from the Government of the ČSFR Government on the events in 1968. At the same time, they conveyed thanks for the documents provided by President Yeltsin to the Czechoslovak side. Barbulis and Shahraj, who represented Yeltsin at the Constitutional Court hearing, urged Czechoslovak representatives to persuade Dubček to participate. He would have been one of the key witnesses against the

Communist Party, which ruled not only over the vast territory, but also disposed of huge financial resources that many new and old-fashioned leaders in the Soviet Union were entitled to. By deciding to ban the Communist Party, Yeltsin put seventeen million people into a position of guilt persons, members of a banned party, which appealed to the Constitutional Court against this decision. The Soviet newspapers, Moskovski Novosti and Komersant, published information that the top officials of the Communist Party transferred about three hundred billion rubles to Swiss banks at the time its empire collapsed, equivalent to a third of the gross national income of the state. The former treasurer of the party and its last manager committed suicide, documents went missing and not only the files of investigators but some investigators vanished. If the Communist Party had lost this trial, three hundred billion rubles would have been shifted from the Swiss vaults to the incoming Russian rulers.

Alexander Dubček was supposed to be one of those from whom the light could have been shone on this jungle. For a long time, he hesitated to testify, but finally, after negotiating with Kural and Valenta, he decided to travel to Moscow. "I want people to know the truth," he said, and sent a message to Moscow that he'd come. His testimony at the Constitutional Court was due on 5th September, 1992. The trial in Moscow never happened.

The 1st September 1992 was a historic day for the Slovak Republic. The Slovak National Council approved the Constitution of the Slovak Republic in the evening at 22.26. In the morning, shortly after six o'clock, a blue service BMW driven by a 30-year-old driver, Ján Rezník, a trained, professional stuntman, a member of the Federal Ministry of the Interior, led by former dissident Ján Langoš, was in front of Dubček's house. At the time of normalization, Langoš, like Dubček, was ranked by the State Security as NO, nepriateľská osoba (hostile individual). People in this category enjoyed the lowest level of civil and human rights. They worked as couriers or auxiliary workers. While Dubček worked as a mechanical specialist in the West Slovak State forests, the cybernetic technician Langoš was the head of a specialized department of the Institute of Technical Cybernetics of the Slovak Academy of Sciences, which worked closely with a specialized department of the Soviet Academy of Sciences in Celinograde near Moscow. Ján Rezník was one of the participants in the clearing out of state security documents from Tiso's Villa in Trenčín in the spring of 1990. Previously he'd driven other state officials, such as the Federal Deputy Prime Minister, Rudolf Filkus, who soon gave him up as a risky driver. Dubček was assigned a service vehicle in his function as vice-president of the Federal Assembly.

His son, Peter, who had lived with his father after his mother's death in the house himself, saw off his father with Brinzík, the security guard, to the car. Dubček put his briefcase on the backseat on to which some of the materials discussed during a meeting of the Czech and Slovak Social-Democratic Party in Brno had been thrown. In his mind, he returned to previous day's negotiations, which had been very successful. With their Czech partners, they'd agreed that both sides would insist on maintaining a working federation and only the citizens in a referendum could decide on the possible division of the Czech and Slovak Federal Republic. Czech friends even went so far as to promise to pay the Slovak Social Democrats an investment bank loan for the SDSS election campaign.

Rezník politely helped Dubček load the travel bag into the luggage compartment. It hadn't rained in Bratislava for more two months but that morning it had begun drizzle. Dubček played for a while with his favourite German Shepherd, Turo, embraced his son and set off on the trip to Prague for a session of the presidium of the Federal Assembly.

The driver had to grip the steering wheel firmly, as the road was wet and there was a danger of skidding. Although he was in a hurry as the session was starting at nine, he smiled contentedly. He was riding in a BMW 535i, one of the safest cars in the world. The dashboard clock showed a quarter past nine and Rezník, turned on the wipers. Dubček sat in the backseat and read some materials. He didn't know that the fatal eighty-eighty kilometer on the D1 motorway from Prague to Bratislava was approaching. The heavy vehicle was suddenly lifted on a stretch of road where the permitted speed was eighty kilometres, at a speed of about 130 kilometers, flew off the road, swung over onto its roof and landed again on its wheels. The chauffeur and the passenger remained lying on the grass some ten metres away from the vehicle. The clock stopped at 9:25. The briefcase in which Dubček had secret documents and an invitation to the Moscow constitutional hearing of the Constitutional Court was on the grass. The investigators later took the briefcase which has since been lost. Witnesses to the accident immediately summoned the rescue services and the police.

An expert on this type of vehicle, Eberhard Presche of Munich later said that it was impossible that the door could have opened "even if the vehicle collides head on, sideways or spins around a vertical or horizontal axis." The police found a car with an unbreakable windshield and open rear doors and driver's door. As Dubček and the driver were lying ten metres ahead of the car in the direction of the vehicle's motion when the front glass was unbreakable, it was difficult to explain how. Rezník was only slightly injured, Dubček with severe spinal injuries and to his pelvis and chest was transported to the hospital in Humpolec from which he was transported by helicopter to the hospital Homolka at in Prague, although the hospital in Brno, which was equipped with top-of-the-range equipment at the time was only twenty kilometres away. A team of specialists headed by the chief ARO Dr. Milan Ročňo took care of him all the time. At the beginning Dubček communicated with doctors and visitors. Former President Václav Havel and Chairman of the Federal Assembly, Michal Kováč, after meeting him, expressed his condition very optimistically. On the third day, he underwent a several-hour neurological operation in which doctors released a crushed back canal. After temporary stabilization, however, his condition was complicated with neurological and respiratory difficulties. He was basically connected daily to an artificial kidney and respiratory devices. In mid-October, he underwent another operation aimed at decompressing his spinal canal. The crisis deepened as a result of the gradual failure of his vital functions.

The Italian journalist, Victorio Caffeo, a friend of Alexander Dubček, organized help. A helicopter arrived in Prague with experts from Italy who wanted to take him to a top medical facility in Bologna. After four hours of waiting at the airport they were told that Dubček's condition did not allow such a demanding transfer.

On the 4th September, the World Agencies had reported that during the night of 31st August a second witness of the Moscow trial had been murdered in his Warsaw apartment, the former Polish Prime Minister Piotr Jaroszewicz and his wife Alice Solski. A culprit has never until today to been revealed. One of Jaroszewicz's sons admitted that the motive of the murder could have been to get documents that his father never wanted to publish. The third promised witness for the Moscow trial, the Afghan leader, Muhammad Nadjibullah, who successfully zigzagged between pressure from Moscow and a rapport with Afghan traditions, was seized by partisans of the Taliban from asylum in the UN building near the Darulaman royal palace, south of Kabul. They shot him on the Kabul football field, after mutilating his body beyond recognition. It happened on 28th September, 1992.

CHAPTER 46

THANK YOU AND FORGIVE ME

There was silence in Prague's Homolka Hospital. Dubček had closed his eyes, barely breathing through the instruments which were helping him draw his last breaths on this earth unselfishly. A nurse was sitting by his bed. She was beautiful and young. She looked at the man of whom she'd heard from the tales of her parents that he had once tried to bring a little joy into life. In her hands there was a sheaf of letters and telegrams that came to the hospital every day. Patiently and with love she read them to him. "Dear Mr. Dubček! I wish God's blessing on you and your entire family. A huge oak that we have named after you grows in front of our Institute. Dubček's Oak. We have reorganized the park around the oak. We love you. We pray for you, let the good Lord God guide your steps and grant you health. From 150 physically disabled children and 40 sisters in orders, Sister Emilia from the Children's Institute in Osek near Hrabonice."

The nurse saw that he smiled a little. He was dreaming of his granddaughter, Evka, a loyal helper in his small workshop, who was always fascinated watching her grandfather as a craftsman. She was happy when he asked for a hammer or a screwdriver. If he didn't ask her for anything any more, she offered him nothing but a bang-bang. She recognized all the instruments, but the hammer at the Dubčeks was forever a bang-bang.

He dreamed of his first granddaughter. He'd really wanted a boy as his first grandchild, but when Paľo announced that he had become the grandpa of a healthy Zuzka, his joy was unabated. In the garden under the apple tree, he dug out into a circle and poured in sand. He himself picked out a bucket, spades and moulds in the supermarket, Prior, and also added a wooden goods truck. The sandpit became Zuzka's most popular place during a visit to Grandpa. When Paľo called her in, he carefully moistened the sand so that her sand pies would not crumble. The year old Zuzka skillfully handled a shovelful of sand into a sieve, which only let out the finer grains. Little stones remained in the sieve, which Grandpa, sitting in his corduroys in the sandpit, carefully put to the side. To Zuzka it seemed her bucket was filling somewhat slowly, so he inserted a small ball that nearly filled the bucket. In a moment, it was full of sand, and Zuzka shouted with joy as she dug out the ball with her small hand from beneath the sand.

"Ball," he pointed to the rubbery thing.

"Ba, ba," she enthused with her first words.

"At least you could have put some old trousers on, you're all dusty," said Anka, watching her husband, who'd turned into a little boy.

"Babi, that's a grandmother," he pointed to his wife who brought the folding chair and was sitting in it. "Babi," he repeated.

"Babi," said her granddaughter, and she threw herself into the arms of her grandmother.

"Grandpa, that's Grandpa," said Anna pointing at her husband.

"Grandpa," Zuzka pointed her grandfather and ran to him. Dubček stood up and began to throw Zuzka up in the air. The little girl eagerly whooped and laughed out loud.

"Come on, Grandpa will show you something. Aha, a swing," he sat his granddaughter into a chair swing firmly attached to the branch of a cherry tree. Zuzka laughed wildly with every strong push of the swing. The sun shone down through the branches of the apple tree. It was a beautiful day.

Dubček swung his first granddaughter, wondering if he had ever swung any of his sons like this. He didn't know how their boyhood had escaped him in the massive flow of work. Thus he enjoyed his first granddaughter all the more. He turned his face to the sun, sensing every beam. The stresses from the positions he'd held throughout his life were in the past and, despite everything that had happened, he was enjoying life. He was full of strength and energy. They hadn't written him off just yet, Dubček could still do something with his life.

The girl whooped and the grandfather sang a rhythm, "hinta, palinta ... hinta, palinta ... hinta, palinta ... Boom, boom, booom."

The regular rhythm of the swing was echoed the contractions of his heart which left regular tracks on the screen of the device mounted over the bed.

A doctor with an older person came into the room. The man looked at him timidly, his gaze fixed on the sleeping Dubček, his hands trembling. The doctor requested the nurse to leave them for a moment and, before he went out, indicated to the man that he had five minutes. The man nodded, not knowing whether Dubček was asleep or aware of him.

"Šaňo, it's me ... Peter Kulifaj ... your ... friend ... classmate ..." he began quietly. He wanted to tell him so much, but he could not. He fell silent all the time the doctor had left for him. There was no single word left. Either way. "Thank you and forgive me ..." The door opened.

"Mr. Kulifaj ..." the doctor indicated that it was time.

"Forgive me, Šaňko..." Kulifaj's voice shook. He grabbed Dubček's hand and that something singular happened. Dubček, though it was very weak, gave Kulifaj's hand a noticeable squeeze. He couldn't open his eyes, but the squeeze was obvious. There was forgiveness and understanding in him. He forgave now, as he'd forgiven all his life. Without his forgiveness, his life wouldn't have made sense, without forgiveness he couldn't have believed in the good of humankind. Without forgiveness, his life would not have been true.

In the evening Milan, who was in Prague, would come and see him and he'd be with his father every day, along with his brother Peter. Only two guests were allowed to enter the room, so Milan gave up his place to Jožko Brinzík, who had arrived with Peter from Bratislava.

"It is a great wine harvest, but the "burčák" is going, though we've kept some back for you. That's so you don't lie here slacking and get back to your lovely home," joked Jožko. Dubček couldn't talk and just wrote a message on a piece of paper.

"Yes, I'm coming," were his last words.

On Saturday, 7th November, 1992 at 21:20, Alexander Dubček breathed his last.

CHAPTER 47

A DIAMOND DOESN'T ROT IN THE CHEST

On Friday, 13th November, the weather was cold and windy. At Prague's Ruzyně Airport there was a group of about twenty people, including the Chairman of the Federal Assembly, Michal Kováč. By the catafalque with a coffin covered in the Czechoslovak flag, the last bow on Czech territory to a man who'd tried to liberate Czechs and Slovaks from the embrace of totalitarianism. The guard of honour observed a minute's silence in Dubček's honour. There were no speeches. Although the memorial ceremony was funded by the federal government, it was held in Bratislava. Dubček's beloved Pražáks had no chance to bid him farewell, the coffin being driven in the airport through side alleys. When the state anthem finished, those present mostly Dubček's friends from 1968, were confused. Nobody had organized a farewell act. The commander saluted and the honour guard dispersed. Behind it the delegation headed by Kováč also broke up. The rest, his former coworkers in Prague, stood by the coffin at a complete loss. Then the airport staff arrived and asked them to leave the airport area. A group of people there entered the airport building and looked through the glass panels at the abandoned coffin. Nothing happened. Long minutes passed and the coffin still stood there abandoned. Somebody couldn't stand it and exclaimed, "We're silent, and nobody is saying anything. What sort of people are we!"

The airport staff loaded the coffin on to the belt that took it to the aircraft. The youngest son, Milan boarded with the coffin. Odd. He was with his father in Prague in sixty-eight and was with him at that moment. The aircraft started in a moment and ascended in the direction of Bratislava. The coffin, covered with the national flag, stood firmly in the centre, from where the seats had been taken. Milan's head whirled with the images of Dubček's last days. Again and again questions rose up, which no one even after years has ever answered. Why did the doctors treating him behave so unprofessionally? The neurosurgeon informed him that his father wasn't in a condition to be operated on and the next day he learned that his father had been operated on that night. The surgery usually took an hour, the father's lasted four. The operation didn't secure the damaged spinal cord. The surgeon admitted that he had not done the operation before. It emerged that his father's team initially didn't consult with other hospitals and especially with the specialized unit in Brno. He asked the Brno specialists, who arrived by helicopter, to take their father with them, but they could only say that his post-operative condition didn't allow it. The Italian experts have expressed themselves very critically over the level of the first, decisive operation. Milan began to fear that it would come a bad ending with his father. He was with him every day and saw how he gradually lost clarity of mind. His father had begged him to take him out of Homolka and his brothers began to organize transport to Bratislava, but his father had suddenly changed his mind. Milan stared at the pale sky, glowing with endless, loving sunshine.

The 14th November 1992 was frosty in Bratislava. Thousands of citizens came to give a last honour to the deceased at the Slovak National Theater. Patiently, they stood silently for a long time in a line that slowly passed to the catafalque. Slovaks, this small, defiant nation in the midst of Europe, bade farewell to one of their greatest sons. Slowly, the line shuffled to a stop. Those who were at the end didn't manage to pay homage to Dubček even though they had patiently frozen outside until the ceremony ended. In the sombrely decorated National Theatre, the Chairman of the Slovak National Council, Ivan Gašparovič, the Prime Minister Vladimír Mečiar and foreign guests, the German Speaker of Parliament, Rita Süsmuth, Austrian Speaker of Parliament, Heinz Fischer, the President of the Italian Senate, Giovanni Spadolini with a large delegation of Italian senators, President of the Socialist International, Pierre Maura, President of the National Assembly of the Republic of Korea Jyun Kyu Park and many others. The Chairman of the French Socialist Party, Pierre Maura, said over Dubček's coffin, "The world will thank him for the fact that the liberation process began in Eastern European countries, preceded by the Prague Spring of 1968. Alexander Dubček was a hero in sincerity and honesty. He belonged among the greatest because he remained a good man in the hour of truth."

After the farewell ceremony, people stood in front of the theatre and debated. A military truck came to the side entrance of the National Theatre and soldiers in fatigues put the wreaths on the back of the truck and the car moved towards the cemetery in Slávičie valley.

Even though the sky was cloudy all day, the sun peeped through when the funeral began. The funeral ceremony was celebrated by the Bishop General of the Slovak Evangelical Church, Pavel Uhorskai. The Račiansky Cantor of the Church of the Holy Sepulchre sang "To You, O my God ... Even when the cross presses me, I rise to the heights, when the sun falls in the distance, the night over my head, a bed of a few hard rocks ..."

His friend, the writer Ladislav Ťažký, said farewell on behalf of his fellow-countrymen. "You have yet to be laid to rest, the tomb of your wife is not yet dry, nor are our tears and a new tomb has already come. And again to me, as to her, I give a last Godspeed to a friend a dear and precious friend, to whom in his lifetime, especially in recent years, we have not been able to say publicly and loudly, deserved and honest, Thank you. Here, at your grave, my friend Alexander, I announce to the Slovak nation and to the world that the most famous Slovak and a significant Czech-Slovak politician left the world, where the Slovaks have a preserved human, political, national and international golden treasure. This world-renowned and precious treasure is hidden in the impregnable treasuries of our hearts. A mysterious, accidental, tragic mishap wanted us to devalue this treasure, but as it turned out on these sad days, it did not happen. A diamond does not rot in the chest."

The funeral guests slowly dispersed. From the florist's radio at the entrance of the cemetery, came a song. "When I return when I finish my journey, I know, the prettiest corner of the world is there, where my old family home is ..."

Alice Dona, Claude Lemesle

„Le jardinier de Bratislava"

"Cette nuit il a encore gelé
Hier les gosses ont vu un défilé
A Bratislava,
2 avril pas un bourgeon encore
On dirait que les jardins sont morts
A Bratislava

Alexander prend le car de sept heures
Il salue son copain le facteur
D'un "Comment ça va?"
Nulle part il n'y a de sot métier
Et Alexander est jardinier
A Bratislava

Jardinier à Prague en soixante-huit
Il a été, cet homme qui habite
A Bratislava,
Mais d'un grand espoir d'un grand printemps
Bien plus fort que tous les faux sultans
De la Moskova

Puis en août les chars sont arrivés
Les soldats n'ont jamais su rêver
Plus loin que leurs pas,
Ils ont tué Prague et son hirondelle
Mais un jardinier se souvient d'elle
A Bratislava

L'hiver c'est rien, c'est une blague
Le vrai malheur, le seul, c'est quand on a la certitude,
Prague, qu'il n'y aura plus de printemps,
Cette année les roses viendront tard
Comme les chansons sur les guitares
De Bratislava

Alexander parce qu'il a osé
Doit jouer l'arroseur arrosé
A Bratislava,
La doctrine qui lui lie les mains
Ne prendra jamais visage humain
Pourtant il y croit,
Près de la faucille et du marteau
Il rêve d'une fleur sur ton drapeau
Czekoslovaquia!

Cette nuit il va encore geler
Demain il ont prévu un défilé
A Bratislava,
2 avril pas un bourgeon encore
On dirait que l'avenir est mort
A Bratislava

Alexander descend de l'autocar
Y a du foot à la télé ce soir
Et "Allez Dukla!"
Le printemps de Prague est oublié
Et Alexander est jardinier
A Bratislava
Le printemps de Prague est oublié,
Alexander Dubcek est jardinier
A Bratislava"

Alice Dona, Claude Lemesle

THE GARDENER OF BRATISLAVA

That night again it froze solid
Yesterday kids saw a parade
In Bratislava,
April 2nd not yet a single bud
It looks like the gardens are dead
In Bratislava

Alexander takes the tram at seven
Greets his pal the postman
With "How are you?", never routine,
There's no pointless job anywhere
And Alexander is a gardener
In Bratislava

A gardener in Prague in sixty-eight
He was a man late
Of Bratislava,
But a great hope of a greater spring
Than all the false sultans could bring
From the Kremlin

Then in August tanks and soldiers came,
Ordered by those who knew not how to dream,
To make well and truly sure
One swallow didn't make summer
But the gardener remembers
In Bratislava

Winter is nothing, it's a jest
The real bad luck is when we know best,
That in Prague there'll be no more spring,
This year the roses will bloom late
Like songs on guitars played
In Bratislava

Alexander because he was bold
Can only a water sprinkler hold
In Bratislava,
The doctrine that makes him grieve
Will never have a human face
Yet he must believe,
By the sickle and hammer
He dreams of a flower on your banner
Czechoslovakia!

Tonight it will freeze solid
Tomorrow they've planned a parade
In Bratislava,
April 2nd not yet a single bud
It looks like the future is dead
In Bratislava

Alexander gets off the tram
On TV tonight a football game
And "Go Dukla! Go!"
In Prague the spring is quite forgot
And Alexander is a gardener
In Bratislava
In Prague the spring is quite forgot
Alexander Dubcek is a gardener
In Bratislava

Bibliography: Literature referred to for this book

Alexander Dubček, človĕk v politice (1990 – 1992), Hubert Maxa, Kalligram Bratislava, 1998
Alexander Dubček: Od totality k demokracii, Jozef Žatkuliak, Ivan Laluha, Veda Bratislava, 2002
Alexander Dubček, prvý muž československej jari, Slovenský rozhlas Bratislava, 2001
Alexander Dubček, Spomienky, úvahy, komentáre, Ivan Laluha, Garmond Nitra, 2006
Alexander Dubček, život a dielo, Ján Uher, Knižné centrum Žilina, 1999
Antipoučení, Jan Moravec, Naše vojsko, Praha, 1990
Cesty k novembru 1989, Nová práca, Bratislava 2000
Contemporary World History, Jan Palmowski, Oxford University Press, 2004
Daten der Weltgeschichte, G.Hellwig, G.Linne, Orbis Verlag 1989
Dejiny Slovenska, Dušan Kováč, Lidové noviny 1998
Dejiny Slovenska a Slovákov, Milan S.Ďurica, SPN Bratislava, 1995
Dejiny Všezväzovej komunistickej strany (boľševikov), Pravda Bratislava 1949
Dějiny Ruska, Milan Švankmajer a kol. Lidové noviny, 1995
Dubček známy, neznámy, Tereza Michalová, Prospero, 1998
Hovory o Alexandrovi, Tereza Michalová, Prospero Bratislava, 2000
Internacionálna pomoc československého proletariátu národom SSSR, Pavel Pollák, SAV Bratislava, 1961
Internet
Jak pukaly ledy, Michal Horáček, Ex Libris Praha 1990
Komunistický experiment v Rusku 1917 – 1991, Václav Veber, Vydavatelství Roman Míšek, 2001
Komunismus, Richard Pipes, Slovart Bratislava, 2007
Kronika Slovenska, Dušan Kováč a kol, Fortuna Print 1999
Labyrintem revoluc, Jiří Suk, Prostor, 2003
Moskaus Griff nach der Weltmacht, Wjatscheslaw Daschitschew, Mittler Hamburg, 2002
Mráz přichází z Kremlu, Zdeněk Mlynář, Mladá fronta Praha, 1990
Nádej zomiera posledná, Z pamätí, Alexander Dubček, Nová práca Bratislava 1993
Na večné časy, Vladimír Babnič, Vydavateľstvo Spolku slovenských spisovateľov, Bratislava 1998
Národný archív Bratislava
Návraty k prevratu, Vladimír Mináč, NVK International, 1993
Paměti Vasila Biľaka, Agentura Cesty, 1991
Politický profil Alexandra Dubčeka, Tomáš Ferenčák, Trnavská univerzita v Trnave, Trnava 2007
Polojasno, Václav Bartuška, Ex Libris Praha 1990
Pozývací list, Otakar Kořínek, Albert Marenčin, Vydavateľstvo PT, Bratislava 2006
Prag „68", Klaus Kukuk, Das Neue Berlin, Berlin 2008
Predjarie, Londák, Sikora, Londáková, Veda Bratislava, 2002
Prevrat 1989, alebo história sa opakuje? Miroslav Dolejší, Agres Bratislava, 1991
Rok 1968, Stanislav Sikora, SAV, Bratislava 2008
1968, rok, ktorý otriasol svetom", Mark Kurlansky, Slovart 2006
Sedm pražských dnů, Josef Macek a kol. Academia Praha, 1990
Stalin, Edvard Radzinskij, Mladá fronta Praha, 1996
Storočie násilia v sovietskom Rusku, Alexander N.Jakovlev, Slovart Bratislava, 2008
Studená vojna, Gabriel Partos, PTK Echo Bratislava, 1994
Svedectvo o procese, Eugen Löbl, Vydavateľstvo politickej oliteratúry 1968
ŠtB na Slovensku za normalizácie, Ministerstvo spravdlivosti SR, Bratislava 2002
Štruktúry moci na Slovensku 1948 – 1989", Jan Pešek, Róbert Letz, Vydavateľstvo Michala Vaška, Prešov, 2004
Taký bol Ladislav Mňačko, Jozef Leikert, Luna, Bratislava, 2008

The concise Encyklopedia of World History, Rodney Castleden, Parago Book Service London, 1995
Uhrovec, Kolektív, Obec Uhrovec, 2007
Utajovaná pravda o Alexandru Dubčekovi, Antonín Benčík, Ostrov 2001
Václav Havel, Necenzurovaný životopis, Jan Bauer, Cesty, 2003
V čakárni dejín, Imrich Kružliak, SAP Bratislava, 1999
Verejnosť proti násiliu, Občianske fórum, Ingrid Antalová, Nadácia Milana Šimečku, Bratislava 1999
Veterné topánky II, Drahoslav Machala, Vydavateľstvo Matice slovenskej, 2004
Věrní soudruzi, nelítostní kati, Slava Katamidze,Levné knihy Praha, 2008
V chapadlech kremelské chobotnice, Antonín Benčík, Mladá fronta, 2007
Volá Londýn, Jan Masaryk, Lincolns – Prager Ltd, 1945
Vom Götterstreit zum Kampf der Ideologien, Theodor Fuchs,Urachhaus 1987
Vom Zarenreich zur Sowjetmacht, Karl Gustav Ströhm, E.Diederichs Verlag, 1967
Vzostupy a pády, Viliam Plevza, Tatrapress, 1991
Weltgeschichte in einem Blick, Kurt M.Jung, Ullstein 1985
Willy Brandt – Erinnerungen, Spiegel Verlag, 2006
Zločiny komunizmu na občanoch z čiernej listiny, Maroš Smolec, Konfederácia občanov z čiernej listiny, Bratislava, 2006
Zóna nadšenia, Jozef Banáš, Kelion Bratislava, 2008
Zrychlený tep dějin, Vladimír Hanzel, OK Centrum 1991

Selected Sources for further reading

Dean, Robert W. Nationalism and Political Change in Eastern Europe: the Slovak Question and the Czechoslovak Reform MovementDenver: East European Monographs, 1973.
Dubček Alexander, Hope Dies Last: The Autobiography ofAlexander Dubček,Hochmann, Jiři, ed. New York: Kodansha International, 1993.
Gola, Galia, The Czechoslovak Reform MovementCommunism in Crisis, 1962-1968, Cambridge University Press, 1971.
Kirschbaum, Stanislav, A History of Slovakia: The Struggle for Survival, New York: St. Martin's Press, 1995.
Kopanic, Michael J. "Case Closed: Alexander Dubček," Central Europe Review(Vol 2, No 8, 28 February 2000) https://www.pecina.cz/files/www.ce-review.org/00/8/kopanic8.html
Kopanic, Michael J. "He Had a Dream and Offered Hope for the Future: Idealism and Reality, Alexander Dubček, 1921-1992," Almanac of the National Slovak SocietyCVII (1999): 117-121.
Kopanic, Michael J. "The Legacy of Alexander Dubček, 1921-1992," Almanac of the National Slovak Society, CII (1994): 34-35.
Kusin, Vladimir V. The Intellectual Origins of the Prague SpringCambridge: Cambridge University Press, 1971.
Littel, Robert, ed. The Czech Black Book, New York: Praeger, 1969.
Michalová, Tereza, ed., Dubček známy neznamy [Dubček known and unknown], Bratislava: vudavateľstvo Propero, 1998.
Mlynář, Zdeněk, Nightfrost in Prague The End of Humane Socialism, London: C. Hurst, 1980.
Palovic, Zuzana and Bereghazyová, Gabriela, Czechoslovakia Behind the Iron Curtain: A History of Communism, Bratislava: Global Slovakia and New York: Hybrid Global Publishing, 2020.
"Rekonštruované zväzky" [Reconstructed volumes], Ústav pamäti národa [The Nation's Memory Institute], https://www.upn.gov.sk/rekonstrukcia/ (Accessed July 14, 2020).

Shawcross, William, *Dubček*, New York: Simon & Schuster, 1990.

Skilling, H. Gordon, *Czechoslovakia's Interrupted Revolution*, Princeton: Princeton University Press, 1976.

Spiesz, Anton, **Illustrated Slovak History**. eds. Ladislaus J Bolchazy, Dušan Čaplovič, Michael J. Kopanic. Wauconda, IL: Bolchazy Carducci Publishers, 2006.

Stolarik, M. Mark. *The Prague Spring and the Warsaw Pact invasion of Czechoslovakia, 1968 : forty years later*. Mundelein, IL: Bolchazy-Carducci Publishers, 2010.

Suda, Zdeněk, *The Czechoslovak Socialist Republic*. Baltimore: John Hopkins Press, 1969.

Suda, Zdeněk, *Zealots and Rebels: A History of the Communist Party of Czechoslovakia*. Stanford: Hoover Institution Press, 1980.

Sviták, Ivan, *The Czechoslovak Experiment*. New York: Columbia University Press, 1971.

Windsor, Philip, and Roberts, Adam, *Czechoslovakia 1968: Reform, Repression and Resistance*. New York: Columbia University Press, 1969.

Jozef Banáš
STOP DUBČEK!
The Story of a Man who Defied Power
(Documentary Novel)

Jozef Banáš
ZASTAVTE DUBČEKA!

Translated from the Slovak original ZASTAVTE DUBČEKA! (an imprint of IKAR, a.s., 2009) by James Sutherland-Smith

First English Edition Published by Hybrid Global Publishing, New York and co-published by Global Slovakia, Bratislava Slovakia, a.s. in 2020
Printed in the United States of America, or in the United Kingdom when distributed elsewhere

Paperback: 978-1-951943-24-0
Ebook: 978-1-951943-25-7

WWW.GLOBALSLOVAKIA.COM

GLOBAL SLOVAKIA
OUR FUTURE IS GREATER THAN OUR PAST

ALSO BY JOZEF BANÁŠ:

MILAN RASTISLAV ŠTEFÁNIK: A MAN OF IRON WILL

Per aspera ad astra - Through adversity to the stars

Milan Rastislav Štefánik was great not only for the Slovaks, but also for the Czechs and the French. A virtuoso in life and death, a magnificent example of a man who in every act surpassed himself. A man who went to the very limits of his strength to pursue his dream despite pain and adversity. The liberation of the Slovak nation was a work worthy of the measure of this man. His life was a composite of enormous faith, iron will and noble love for his nation.

In everyone there is a will to fly to the stars, but few manage to reach them. Only those whose desire is greatest can achieve this. While those lacking faith perished in the glow of street lamps, Štefánik managed to reach the stars.

SLOVAKIA: THE LEGEND OF THE LINDEN

This book takes you on an emotional journey deep into the Slovak and Slavic inner world. Follow the trail that opens your eyes to the magical realm guarded by the Linden tree and its sacred heart-shaped leaf. It is a code that carries the story of the people born at the crossroads of worlds.

Available on **amazon**

www.globalslovakia.com

THE GREAT RETURN

In the beginning of the 21st century, Europe opened its borders to the countries from behind the Iron Curtain. Since then, over 100 million citizens, including Slovaks gained the freedom to move West without a visa. Now, a decade after the East-West exodus, our pioneers are returning home.

Telling the stories of international Slovaks who left, learned and returned, 58 voices including government, business and society share their views on the transformation of a nation. The 59th voice is that of the author, who reveals a personal tale of loss, lessons and reconnection through a rite of passage shared by millions of people across the planet.

Time-travellers to culture-shifters, Slovakia's lost daughters and sons come home, proving that return is not just a possibility, but an opportunity.

Available on **amazon**

www.globalslovakia.com

CZECHOSLOVAKIA: BEHIND THE IRON CURTAIN

Take a journey into the borderland of the Red Empire, during an ideological battle that saw the world ripped in half. Dare to step into communist Czecho-Slovakia, where the controlled 'East' and the free 'West' converged at their closest.

This is a story of ordinary people caught up in the midst of the 20th century's greatest political experiment. Through tales only told in whispers, glimpse into the everyday reality of those whose entire universe was ruled by the Hammer and Sickle.

The brothers Milan and Stefan Dubček migrate to the USA, where Stefan meets the blue-eyed Pavlina, whom he marries later on. Their son Alexander Dubček is born in 1921, after the newly-weds' return home to Slovakia. The Dubčeks are enthusiastic about the new socialist movement and long to help building the arising socialist society. They decide to move to one of the most neglected areas of the Soviet Union, where the little Sasha (Alexander) meets his future wife Anna. After some time, however, the Dubčeks lose their illusions and return home in search of happiness. Here, Alexander Dubček's story begins – he participates in the Slovak National Uprising against the Nazi occupation, assumes his political career, during which he attempts to establish a 'socialism with a human face', but fails due to the Soviet invasion of Czechoslovakia. The novel reflects his life till his tragic death in a car accident, which still remains unresolved by authorities.

"This novel is a must-read for anybody interested in Czechoslovak history. And for anybody interested in the vividly told story of what shaped and drove one of the greatest heroes of the 20th century."
Prof. Josette Baer, University of Zurich, Switzerland

GLOBAL SLOVAKIA

ISBN 978-1-951943-24-0

9 781951 943240

Printed in the USA
CPSIA information can be obtained
at www.ICGtesting.com
LVHW020015280524
781539LV00046B/1054